VALMIKI R

CW00815805

The inspiring story of Shri
A story that has held India spellbound for millennia
A story of Rama's obedience, of Sita's unending suffering
and of Ravana's lust

VALMIKI RAMAYANA

Abridged and Translated by

Rajendra Tandon

RUPA

Published by
Rupa Publications India Pvt. Ltd 2013
7/16, Ansari Road, Daryaganj
New Delhi 110002

Sales centres:
Allahabad Bengaluru Chennai
Hyderabad Jaipur Kathmandu
Kolkata Mumbai

ISBN: 978-81-291-2421-0

10 9 8 7 6 5 4 3 2 1

The moral right of the author has been asserted.

Typeset in 9.5/12 PalmSprings Regular at SÜRYA, New Delhi

Printed and bound in India by
Replika Press Pvt. Ltd.

Dedicated to my father, Shri Anant Ram
Who shared his name with Shri Ramachandra.
I heard my first Ramayana stories from him at bedtime at a very young age.
My father was, although self-taught, a voracious reader of the epics, the
scriptures, poetry and fiction in Urdu. He was a poet who recited at
local mushairas and mehfils. He was also a great raconteur.

Contents

Preface

'Jai Ramji ki'

That is how they greet you in large parts of India even today. That is how my father greeted everyone else and the others responded in Patiala, the town of my birth.

'Jai Ramji ki'

I was welcomed with this salutation to Rama in Nairobi by Premlal Mahajan in 1974. Most of the Hindu community use this greeting in Kenya, and all over the world. Rama is remembered and his victory hailed with these three words which generate warmth, a fellow feeling and a sense of oneness.

'Jai Ramji ki'

'Victory to Rama'

It started with Valmiki who wrote the story of Rama and his journey, [Rama +'ayana', that is, 'going, advancing'], and named his magnum opus 'Ramayana'. Many other poets have written their own epics, the most famous being Tulsidasa's *Ramacharitamanasa* written in Awadhi Devanagri. Radhe Shyam Kathavachak of Bareilly wrote his own text and used to recite to gatherings of thousands in various towns of India. Several other Ramayanas were written in South India. From Kashmir to Kanyakumari, in every part of India, we read, enact or recite the Ramayana in one version or the other.

As a child, I heard the story of Rama narrated by my father at bedtime. Each session ended with unbearable suspense for what was to follow the next evening. This audio was enhanced by the visuals of Ramleela enacted every year at several places in the town.

As I grew up, I organized our own Ramleela with my companions enacting various roles. I used to direct the play and act as Lakshmana. Each household contributed a little money, and also clothes for making curtains and dressing the actors. Our dialogues were borrowed from the musical Ramayana written in Hindi by Jaswant Singh Tohanvi of Haryana wherein he had even peppered the dialogues with English sentences such as, 'Who comes there,' when Hanuman is challenged by the guards at the entrance of Asoka Vatika in Lanka. The make shift stage was set on a terrace in front of a house in our narrow street. The audience sat all around, more like in Shakespearean theatre. It was an amateur effort repeated for several years. However, everyone enjoyed the tamasha with devotion and expectation. The audience knew the story by heart and shouted for the next episode.

The President of India and the Prime Minister often witness the annual spectacle of Ramleela in Delhi where the actors playing Rama and Sita are honoured and garlanded

At times, I wonder: what shall we do without Rama? Rama permeates our subconscious and our civilization.

It all started with Valmiki.

Why is the Ramayana so popular? Partly it is because of its emotional content. It is a story of suffering of Rama, but more than him, that of Sita. Besides, 'it depicts the duties of relationships, portraying ideal characters like the ideal servant, the ideal brother, the ideal wife and the ideal king.' [*Wikipedia*]. There is a code of conduct for each member of the society in Valmiki's Ramayana that holds true even today, thousands of years after the epic was written. 'Thematically, the book explores themes of human existence and the concept of dharma.' [ibidem]

The sheer number of stories told in the Ramayana is overwhelming. The epic consists of 24,000 shlokas. The writing of this epic in an era when the use of paper was unknown must have been a herculean effort.

'The Ramayana is not just an ordinary story: it contains the teachings of ancient Hindu sages and presents them through allegory in narrative and the interspersion of the philosophical and the devotional. The characters of Rama, Sita, Lakshmana, Bharata, Hanuman and Ravana (the villain of the piece) are all fundamental to the cultural consciousness of India.' [ibidem]

While translating Valmiki's Ramayana I have taken care not to edit/omit any relevant issues and stories. I have designed my own chapters keeping in mind the development of the story line. However, I have tried not to deviate from the original text in whatever has been included. An abridgement necessarily requires editing. I have tried to be faithful to the original as best I could be.

It should also be noted that doubts have often been expressed about the authenticity of the Uttarakandam as a text written by Valmiki. Though at the end of the Yuddhakandam, shlokas 107 and 112 of the 128th chapter mention that this was the conclusion of the adikavya written by Valmiki, in my humble view, the entire Uttarakandam is an interpolation. Its writing lacks the clarity and finesse of the other kandams of the adikavaya. Goswami Tulsidasa chose to omit the events as narrated in this kanda completely in his *Ramacharitamanasa*.

However, the Uttarakandam includes the story of Sita's banishment and the birth of Lava and Kusha. In the present times and versions of the Ramayana story that exist, this has become a part of every Hindu's understanding. Keeping this in mind, I have translated and abridged the relevant chapters for the benefit of the readers.

For the text, I have relied on the Gita Press, Gorakhpur version, thirtieth reprint, Samvat 2063. I express my gratitude to that matchless organization that has rendered a yeoman's service in popularizing our ancient scriptures.

I have accessed the Ramayana paintings from the specified museums and sources. The copyright of these paintings expired long ago. Still, I express my gratitude to the organizations and the persons who are in possession of these paintings and images at present. Wherever possible, I have obtained written consent.

Swarn, my wife has been a constant pillar of support in my effort. I cannot repay her debt.

I thank my daughter Bindu for valuable comments on my translation.

I express my gratitude and appreciation for my editor, Ms. Elina Majumdar who has handled this assignment with professional competence.

I thank Shri R.K. Mehra, Managing Director, Rupa & Co. and the Executive Director, Shri Kapish Mehra for accepting this manuscript for publication. They have supported me for several years by accepting and publishing my manuscripts one after the other.

'Jai Ramji ki', dear readers!

I have tasted the rasa of Shri Rama's name while doing this translation. I hope you do the same while reading it.

RAJENDRA TANDON

श्री रामायण महिमा

श्रुत्वा रामायणमिदं दीर्घमायुश्च विन्दति।
रामस्य विजयं चेमं सर्वमक्लिष्ट कर्मण: ।। युद्धकाण्डं, १२८/१११

Rama's deeds were always without blemish. Listening to the Ramayana that narrates the tale of his victory, a human being attains a long life.

श्रृणोति य इदं काव्यं पुरा वाल्मीकिना कृतम्।
श्रद्धानो जितक्रोधो दुर्गाण्यतितरत्यसौ ।। ११२

This is the original work that Valmiki wrote in ancient times. He, who listens to this narrative with faith and without anger, succeeds in overcoming all obstacles.

समागम्य प्रवासान्ते रमन्ते सह बान्धवै: ।
ऋण्वन्ति य इदं काव्य पुरा वाल्मीकिना कृतं।।
ते प्रार्थितान् वरान् सर्वाण् प्राङ्क्षुवन्तीह राघवान्।। । ११३, ११४

The devotees who listen to this composition of Valmiki, written long ago, return safely to the welcoming arms of their near and dear ones. They rejoice in their reunion. Lord Rama blesses them with whatever they desire.

पूजयंश्च पठंश्चैनमितिहासं पुरातनम्।
सर्व पापै: प्रमुच्येत दीर्घमायुरवाप्नुयात् ।। ११७

Anyone who worships and recites this ancient history is rid of the results of his evil deeds. He lives long.

रामायणमिदं कृतस्नं श्रृण्वत: पठत: सदा।
प्रीयते सततं राम: स हि विष्णु: सनातन: ।। ११९

Shri Rama who is Vishnu incarnate is pleased with a devotee who regularly reads or listens to the Ramayana. The lord holds him dear.

आयुष्यमारोग्यकरं यशस्यं
सौभ्रातृकं बुद्धिकरं शुभं च ।
श्रोतव्यमेतन्नियमेन सद्भि—
राख्यानामोजस्करमृद्धिकामै: ॥ १२५

A reading of this epic bestows longevity, sound health, glory, and a sense of goodwill among brothers. Its reading is auspicious and sharpens the intelligence. Consequently, the noble persons who desire to prosper ought to listen regularly to the recitation of this epic. The Ramayana is a narrative that makes a person enthusiastic and enterprising.

A Critical Appreciation

Written more than three thousand years ago, Valmiki Ramayana continues to be as popular today as it was when written. There is no city in India where the story of Rama, as told by Valmiki, is not enacted annually either like Ramleela in the large Ramleela Maidan in New Delhi or in the public squares of the smaller towns. Rama pervades the Hindu consciousness like no other avatar despite there being a black mark on his conduct for putting Sita through Agni Pareeksha and later her banishment. The source of this reverence and of the stage plays is the Ramayana written by Valmiki. Even the most illiterate man in India knows the story of Rama by heart.

Adikavi, the First Poet

'The sacred literature of India,' writes M. Krishnamachariar in the *History of Classical Sanskrit Literature*, 1937, 'inferior to none in variety or extent, is superior to many in nobility of thought, in sanctity of spirit and in generality of comprehension. In beauty or prolixity, it can vie with any other literature ancient and modern.' Valmiki's contribution to this heritage is unique and unsurpassable.

Valmiki wrote Rama's story in verse form as a breakthrough. The only existent literature of his times was confined to religious hymns, prayers or philosophy, such as the Vedas or the Upanishads. For this reason, he has been called the Adikavi or the first poet, the originator.

The epithet Adikavi is used for the divine Brahma because he first produced and promulgated the Vedas. Among humans, this appellation is used for Valmiki alone because he became the first poet when his grief unconsciously took the form of a verse on seeing a heron killed while mating.

Epic Proportions

Going through the 24,000 shlokas of the Ramayana, one wonders at the sheer magnitude of the task undertaken and at the remarkable imagination of its author. This amazement has been well captured by M. Williams [1819-1899], a professor of Sanskrit and a pioneer in the study of Indian classics, when he wrote in *Indian Wisdom*, 'In India, literature like the whole face of nature is on a gigantic scale. Poetry, born amid the majestic scenery of the Himalayas, and fostered in a climate which inflamed the imaginative powers, developed itself with oriental luxuriance. Although the Hindus like the Greeks, have only two great epic poems [*the Ramayana* and the *Mahabharata*], yet to compare these vast compositions with the *Iliad* and the *Odyssey*, is to compare the Indus and the Ganga, rising in the snows of the world's most colossal ranges, swollen by numerous tributaries, spreading into vast shallows or branching into deep divergent channels, with the streams of Attica or the mountain torrents of Thessaly.'

A Great Literary Achievement

Normally epic poetry deals more with 'external action than internal feelings.' It is an extended narrative poem in elevated or dignified language, celebrating the feats of a legendary or traditional hero. It surpasses the usual or ordinary, particularly in scope or size. 'It is expected to abound in stirring incidents of exaggerated heroic action.' However, Valmiki's Ramayana is more than an epic. Besides being lyrical in parts, his writing is refined, sensuous where need be, rich in detail of the social panorama, and steeped in religious and political learning and ethos. Valmiki's word paintings of landscape and nature's moods are remarkably imaginative. His palette is rich in colours.

Valmiki stands tall as a poet when compared to any poet of any period in any civilization. M. Krishnamachariar writes: 'As a piece of poetic art the Ramayana stands supreme and Valmiki's poetic fancy and imagery have been the standard for imitation. There is no ideal, there is no reality, there is no fancy, there is no sentiment which Valmiki has not depicted and there is no expression which can excel or equal his in grace and eloquence. Cosmogony and theology, folk-lore and tradition, mythology and history, have all formed a part "in the weaving of the mighty web and work of magic drapery evolved by Valmiki."'[Ibid]

Valmiki, the Genius

Valmiki displayed the astonishing qualities of a poet who is a genius as well. His writing combined a mastery of the meter used for his verses along with elaborate characterization, spell binding story-telling, an intimate study of the moods of nature, of *shringara* and *karuna rasas*, a deep understanding of *rajaneeti*, a remarkable power of visualization of battle scenes and a vivid imagination.

Valmiki wrote for human empowerment, for the betterment of mankind and to rid people of lust, anger, cruelty, greed and intolerance. The reprehensible conduct and fate of one character alone in the Ramayana, that of Ravana, is enough to show the consequences of excess, anger, arrogance and lust. Valmiki showed a path of restraint and virtue to mankind.

Valmiki was not just the first poet. He was an example for all the poets who followed. His literary competence, his excellence, has thus been commented upon by M. Williams [ibid]:

'Notwithstanding the wilderness of exaggeration and hyperbole through which the reader of the Indian Epics has occasionally to wander, there are in the whole range of the world's literature few more charming poems than the Ramayana.

'The classical purity, clearness and simplicity of its style, the exquisite touches of the true poetic feeling with which it abounds, its graphic descriptions of heroic incidents and of nature's grandest scenes, the deep acquaintance it displays with the conflicting working and most refined emotions of the human heart, all entitle it to rank among the most beautiful compositions that have appeared at any period and in any country.

Who Was Valmiki?
Valmiki in His Own Words

Little is known of the Adikavi except through what has been mentioned by him in the Ramayana or in the Adhyatma Ramayana. In the Uttarakandam, shlokas 19-20, the sage declares:

'I am the tenth son of Pracheta [Varuna] and I do not recall ever telling a lie. I have performed tapasya for thousands of years.'

In the Ramayana, Valmiki is a sage living in an ashrama on the banks of the Ganga.

A more detailed personal introduction is available in the Adhyatma

Ramayana [Ayodhyakandam, 64-65, chapter 6]. Addressing Shri Rama, the saint describes how, although born as a Brahmin, he had fathered several children from shudra wives.

'Having fallen in with robbers, I became a brigand, bearing constantly a bow and arrows and resembling Yamaraja.'

Valmiki then describes his meeting with seven rishis whom he wanted to rob of their belongings for the benefit of his wives and children. Unruffled, the rishis asked him to go to his wives and children and ask them whether they would share the fruits of his sins. He went home and questioned his wives and children. They told him, 'All the sin is, we believe, only yours. We are willing to share only the immediate fruit of your deeds.'

A disillusioned Valmiki returned to the waiting rishis.

'At the sight of them my soul was purified,' writes Valmiki. 'They were full of compassion. I threw away my bow and other weapons and prostrated at their feet and prayed for being saved from eternal damnation.'

The rishis blessed him with the words: 'Rise, rise. We bless you. Your coming in contact with the pious, the holy, is going to be auspicious. You have returned from the path of evil. We shall certainly help you.

'Concentrate on the syllables *ma, ra* and continue uttering them till we return.'

Valmiki sat and did as directed. Over a period of time, the syllables changed and became *ra, ma,* the name of the lord.

'I meditated with intense concentration and lost all consciousness of things external. I sat rigid and an ant-hill grew around me. At the end of thousands of cycles I was awakened by the rishis. "Come out," they commanded me. I stood up and emerged from the ant-hill like the sun emerging from the morning mist. They addressed me thus:

"Great muni, be thy name Valmiki; your emerging from the ant-hill [valmika] has been to you a second birth."

'Saying this they disappeared.

'Raghava, I have attained the rank of a Brahmin saint by chanting your name in meditation.'

The Beginning

It was the tradition of Sanskrit literature that everything good written by an author was ascribed to the inspiration received from higher beings, quite often Narada or Brahma, the Creator and the first poet. Let us call it divine inspiration. The birth of Ramayana is ascribed to Narada and Brahma in the first two chapters of the Balakandam.

Tapasvi Valmiki asks muni Narada:

'Tell me, O muni, in this world, who stands tall, virtuous, chivalrous, knowledgeable in dharma, ever grateful for an obligation, truthful and firm in his commitments?

'Who is a man of character, a well-wisher of mankind, learned, powerful, and handsome?

'Who has conquered his senses, controlled his mind, overcome his anger, who is glorious, and who does not condemn anyone? Even the devatas fear if he is angry on the battlefield. Maharshi, you alone are capable of knowing such a person. I am curious to know about him.'

A delighted Narada replied,

'He is known as Rama and he was born in the Ikshavaku dynasty. He alone has the rare virtues narrated by you. He has conquered his senses, his anger, and his thought. He is brave beyond words. His patience runs deep as the ocean.

'Rama is wise, has deep knowledge of Niti, and is a terror for his enemies. He speaks softly and sweetly. He is glorious as the sun. His shoulders are muscular and his arms long. His neck is like a conch and he has a full chin. His chest is broad. Rama has a broad forehead and he walks gracefully. His eyes are large. He is of medium height. His body is muscular, and his skin is soft.

'Rama is truthful. He is a protector of his praja and of the righteous. He is pure in thoughts. He is learned in the Vedas and other scriptures. He is a great archer. The public admires him. Men of noble character interact with him as the rivers meet the ocean.

'Blessed with such virtues, Rama is a source of great happiness to Kausalya, his mother. His forbearance is that of the Himalayas and his thoughts are deep as the ocean. Rama is as brave as Vishnu. He looks charming as the moon. He is kalagni when angry. In kshama he is like Prithvi. He is charitable like Kubera and truthful like Dharmaraja.'

Narada narrated the events of Rama's life in brief to Valmiki and asked him to write about Rama. He said,

इदं पवित्रं पापघ्नं पुण्यं वेदैश्च सम्मितम् ।
यह पठेद् रामचरितं सर्वपापैह प्रमुच्यते ।।

'Whoever reads this story of Rama, holy as the Vedas, destroyer of evil and a source of virtue, will be freed of all sins.' [1.98, Balakandam]

Continuing the tradition that an epic, or for that matter any holy book, is born out of divine inspiration, the second chapter in the Balakandam narrates how Valmiki suddenly uttered a metered shloka that would eventually become the basis of the verse structure of the Ramayana.

The Birth of Shloka

As Narada departed, Valmiki and his pupils arrived at the banks of the Tamasa. The bank was free of mud and the water was clean. Valmiki asked his pupil, Bhardwaj to fetch a pail of water from the river along with his upper garment made of bark. Carrying the bark wrap on his arm, the rishi wandered enjoying the natural sights in the large forest. Shortly he noticed a pair of kraunch birds calling and, moving in unison while lovingly touching each other.

Meanwhile, a hunter lurking nearby in search of prey took aim and shot at the male bird. The female of the pair shrieked in horror. Her handsome partner had loved her. His forehead was copper red. At that moment they had been in heat. Her plaintive call moved Valmiki to tears. He felt pity for her. Coming to a conclusion that a sacrilegious act had been committed, the rishi addressed the hunter saying,

मा निषाद प्रतिष्ठां त्वमगमह शाश्वतीह समाथ्श ।
यत् क्रौंचमिथुनादेकमवधीह काममोहितम् ।। १५ ।।

'O hunter, you shall never be at peace with yourself because you have killed one of the mating, innocent birds.'

Valmiki wondered at his own utterance. Analyzing what he had spoken, he told his pupils,

'Moved by sorrow, the sentence I uttered is in four quarters. Each quarter has eight aksharas. It can be tuned to be sung to the accompaniment of a veena. I shall, therefore, write Rama's story in shlokas in the same meter. Not otherwise.'

Brahma's Blessings

Back home, sitting in his cottage, Valmiki's mind was focussed on his composition in the poetic form used by him earlier. At this moment the almighty, effulgent Brahma, the Creator, descended to meet Valmiki in person. An astonished rishi, in full control of his senses, stood up in greeting and bowed his head. He was silent, at a loss for words in the august presence.

Thereafter, Valmiki washed the divine feet, offered arghya and asana to Brahma. He then worshipped the Creator and touched his feet.

Brahma took his seat and asked Valmiki to be comfortable on his asana. However, the rishi's mind was haunted by the cruelty of the hunter who had shot dead an innocent bird. While thus ruminating, he recited to Brahma the same shloka that had escaped his lips in the forest when the bird was killed. He thought of the justification or otherwise of the curse he had uttered on the hunter. Recalling his anger, Valmiki was full of grief.

Brahma gauged Valmiki's thoughts, smiled and said,

'Brahmin, the poetic words you spoke in meter are inspired by me. Have no doubt, therefore. Saraswati resides on your tongue. The determination is mine. The effort will be yours.

रामस्य चरितं कृत्स्नं कुरु त्वमृषिसत्तम ।
धर्मात्मनो भगवतो लोके रामस्य धीमतः ।।३२।।
वृत्तं कथय धीरस्य यथा ते नारदाच्छृतम् ।

'O sage, you should narrate Rama's story in detail. The wise Rama is the most truthful and pious soul in the world. There is none higher than him as a dharmatma. Tell his story as Narada told you.

रहस्यं च प्रकाशं च यद् वृत्तं तस्य धीमतः ।।३३।।
रामस्य सहसौमित्रे राक्षसानां च सर्वशः ।
वैदेह्याश्चैव यद् वृत्तं प्रकाशं यदि वा रहः ।।३४।।
तच्चाप्याप्यविदितं सर्वं विदितं ते भविष्यति ।

'O wise man, whatever is known or hidden about Rama will be revealed to you. This includes the lives of Lakshmana, Sita and the behaviour of the rakshasas.

न ते वागनृता काव्ये काचिदत्र भविष्यति ।।३५।।
कुरु रामयणकथा पुण्यां श्लोकबद्धां मनोरमाम् ।

'In this poem written by you there would be no untruths. Write the holy and pure life of Rama in the form of shlokas. Your writing will be a source of delight to everyone.

यावत स्थास्यन्ति गिरयह सरितश्च महीतले ।।३ ६ ।।
तावद् रामायणकथा लोकेषु प्रचिरिष्यति ।
यावद् रामस्य च कथा त्वत्कृता प्रचिरिष्यति ।।३ ७ ।।
तावदूर्ध्वमधश्च त्वं मल्लोकेषु निवत्स्यति ।

'Till the rivers flow and the mountains stand on this earth, the Ramayana story will be narrated.

'So long as the Ramayana written by you is recited on this earth, you will be immortal and live on this earth or in Swarga as you desire.'

Thus the Ramayana was written with a perfect grammar, appropriate use of adjectives and adverbs, compound words and words that had to be phonetically combined according to the principles laid down by the ancient grammarians. It has a steady and even flow. Its stanzas are mellifluous. Valmiki's sentences are rich in meaning. His writing is immortal.

The Structure

The epic as available today is divided into seven kandas or books:

1. Balakandam
2. Ayodhyakandam
3. Aranyakandam
4. Kishkindhakandam
5. Sundarakandam
6. Yuddhakandam
7. Uttarakandam

The Ramayana is the story of Rama and every event revolves around his life, his struggles, his joys, his sorrows, his battles, his bereavement, and his viraha after his wife's abduction. The other main character is that of Sita in whose absence there would have been no Ramayana, perhaps. The third character, whose presence towers over everyone other than Rama and Sita, is Ravana, the arrogant king of Lanka who wants Sita to surrender to his lust at any cost.

Dashratha's favourite queen Kaikeyee plays a pivotal role in the story because it is her manoeuvring that sends Rama into exile. This in turn leads to a conflict between Rama and Ravana's governors ruling over the Dandakaranya, and consequently ends in Sita's abduction. Thereafter, Hanuman, the great warrior, later a devotee of

Rama, comes on the scene in an unforgettable role. Rama's brother Lakshmana is present throughout the Ramayana as the right hand man of the hero.

Valmiki has sketched these and other characters such as Ravana's queen Mandodari, his brothers Vibhishana and Kumbhakarna, his son Indrajit, and Rama's brother, Bharata, with great depth. They are not mere puppets on a stage. They live and act out of conviction. Their actions, words, and brave deeds are of unforgettable heroes as befits an epic.

A Raconteur Par Excellence

The poet turns out to be a great story-teller. He misses no detail when describing events like the purification of Ahalya [12, Balakandam], transformation of Rajarshi Vishwamitra into a Brahmarshi [13, Balakandam], Kaikeyee's redemption of pledges given by Dashratha [3, Ayodhyakandam], the accidental death of Shrawan Kumar [8, Ayodhyakandam], or the death of Vali at Rama's hands [3, Kishkindhakandam]. All through, Valmiki is a keen observer and narrator of human foibles, greed, emotions, motives, and surroundings. As a story-teller, he is never dull. The dialogues that he has written are full of logic, persuasion, expressions of happiness or sorrow, triumph and achievement. These are suited to the station of each character, to his/her country and surroundings.

Certain other chapters deserve to be mentioned in this context to highlight Valmiki's narrative prowess. The argument and counter-arguments by which Maricha is inveigled into the conspiracy to abduct Sita are the work of a master strategist [6, Aranyakandam]. Maricha dissuades Ravana twice with powerful arguments. Yet in the end he submits to his king's unbending insistence and turns into a golden deer. The story of the golden deer has become a metaphor in India's vocabulary as 'mrigtrishna'.

One can give more instances of absorbing story-telling by Valmiki. The Ramayana is ultimately a story that has not become dated although told millions of times in recitations, in temple sculptures, wall murals, paintings, on choupals, in theatres, in ballet, in comic books, and in cinema. The story of Ramayana with modifications is popular in several countries beyond India, such as Mauritius, Thailand, Bali and Cambodia. In particular, I invite the reader's attention to the chapters on the abduction of Sita [8, Aranyakandam], Setubandhan [6, Yuddhakandam], the wrestling bout between Sugreeva and Ravana [9, Yuddhakandam], the awakening of Kumbhakarna [17, Yuddhakandam], and the battle between Rama and Ravana [32, Yuddhakandam]. The list is endless.

Unparalleled Descriptive Skills: Cities and Harems

A great story-teller has many accomplishments beyond the weaving of events and writing of dialogues. He writes about locations in cities and in nature. He writes of wars, of king's councils and of state policy. He writes of relationships. He has the competence to write on any subject that props his story. One such is architecture.

Valmiki excels in describing the Ayodhya city [1, Balakandam], Lankapuri [2, 3, 4, Sundarakandam], and Ravana's inner chambers and harem [5, Sundarakandam]. His description of Lankapuri, the City of Gold, is visually rich in colour and detail. He compares the city with a stunning woman:

'Vishwakarma had designed Lanka as if he was creating a stunning woman. The protection walls and their pillars were like her thighs. The forests and the limitless ocean were her clothes. Weapons like shataghni and lances were her tresses. The tall buildings looked like pendants in her ears.'

Shringar Rasa

Shringar, the sexual passion or the erotic sentiment is one of the main ingredients of poetry. Valmiki knew of this and the Ramayana is rich in the shringar rasa. In Rishi Atri's ashrama, Anasuyia decks Sita as a bride. Look at the finesse with which a delicate scene has been written.

Ravana addresses Sita as a mendicant before abducting her with the following flattering but erotic words:

'You glow like burnished gold. Dressed in yellow silks, you look like a stream wearing garlands of lotus flowers.

'Sita's soles are red, her feet well formed and soft and her nails have the sheen of copper. Just the act of looking at her feet fires my lust. Looking at the tejasvini Sita who is luminous like a flame rising out of the havana kunda where an ahuti of ghee has just been added, glorious like the sun, at her high nose, her large eyes set in an enchanting face, I have lost control over my desires. Kamadeva, who is unaffected by joy or sorrow, who diminishes his victim's lustre, has enslaved me and has made me restless in mind and body' [4, Yuddhakandam].

Karuna Rasa

The finest of verses in world poetry have been inspired by karuna, that is, compassion, pity or tenderness. 'Our sweetest songs are those that tell of saddest thought,' wrote Percy Byshe Shelley.

The Ramayana is the story of Sita's tragedy. Throughout the unfolding of events Maithili suffers. As a young bride she accompanies Rama into exile. She is abducted by Ravana and is subjected to torture and cruel invectives. On return, she is asked to prove her chastity. What can be worse for a woman than being disbelieved by her husband? Valmiki has handled these situations with compassion.

'To Hanuman, Janaki looked diminished in splendour, a faith discarded, wisdom lost forever, a shattered hope, a future destroyed, a violated royal command, a city burning in a riot, a ritual violated in the course of worship, the Poornima night darkened by an eclipse, or a delicate lotus torn to pieces by a hailstorm. Vaidehi was like an army whose brave commander has been killed on the battlefield, effulgence overcome by darkness, a river with dry bed, a holy altar made impure by the contact of filthy human beings, or an extinguished flame.

Nature

There is hardly any poet in the world who has not been moved by the unfolding panorama of nature in the universe. The Ramayana has an abundance of descriptions of nature in her varied moods. Every time Valmiki writes of nature, he excels. He is at home whether describing the night sky, running streams, thundering cataracts, the trees and birds in the forests or on the banks of lakes. A few examples:

Rama crosses the Ganga and the Yamuna at Prayag and travels to Chitrakoot. [7, Ayodhyakandam.] They are in the territory of the holy Ganga:

'When her waters struck the broad banks,
The waves crackled like her laughter.

The foam on her surface was like her smile,
Pure and white.
At places, her stream ran like braided hair,
All compact,
And at others,
Several whirlpools added to her charm.

On the banks of Ganga,
Glided the raja hansa and sarus birds, shrieking in pleasure.
The chakvas enhanced the beauty of the divine stream.
Over her waters,
Intoxicated birds, singing in joy,
Hovered all the time.

Magnificent trees garlanded her banks.
Her waters nourished blue and pink lotus in abundance.
White water lilies and buds sprouted everywhere.
Like a woman in heat,
Intoxicated with the pollen of flowers, hovered the black bees.'

In chapter 11, Ayodhyakandam, Rama shows Sita around Chitrakoot. He describes the flowers and the trees growing there and the birds inhabiting the place. The frolicking of mankind in the midst of nature is not forgotten.

'Here we see the beds on which lay the merry-making lovers. Lotus leaves make their bed sheets. Leaves of various trees like bhojapatra, punnag, utpal and putrajeevak provide sheets to cover. All around lie scattered lotus flowers for their fragrance and loveliness. The lovers having crushed them underneath [while making love] have discarded garlands of lotus flowers.'

Most of the seasons are written about during Rama's journey searching for Sita. Each chapter is rich in vivid images of nature intertwined with human activity.

Rajaneeti in the Ramayana

Valmiki's Ramayana is a story of kings. Its pages are full of discussion of the policies either adopted by the kings of the age or by what was considered desirable as their conduct. While announcing Rama's anointment as Yuvaraja, King Dashratha has a few words of advice:

'Despite being sure of your qualities, I have a few words of advice to offer for your benefit. You shall be humbler than ever before and restrain your desires. You must abjure the evil consequences of lust or anger. Discover the truth either through your intelligence network or by hearings in open court. Administer justice impartially.

'Take care of the legitimate interests of your ministers, officials, commanders and soldiers. Your subjects' welfare should be your priority. The king who commands a treasury full of wealth, an armoury full of armaments, and who is a master of all that is necessary to run a state, is a source of happiness to his well-wishers just like amrita was to the devatas. A ruler who holds his ministers, commanders and the praja dear to him, commands their sincere loyalty.

'Therefore, my son, control your thoughts and follow the correct practices befitting a ruler.' [2, Ayodhyakandam.]

Ethics, Morality and a Philosophy of Life

The Ramayana is a story of morals and the consequences of immoral behaviour. In Valmiki's' reckoning, virtuous conduct was of paramount importance as a way of living. Rama's qualities of head and heart are brought out in chapter 1, Ayodhyakandam. Writes Valmiki, 'The prince had conquered krodha. His heart overflowed with the milk of human kindness towards the humble and the unfortunate. Rama exercised control over his desires. He was pure in mind and in his behaviour. Following in the footsteps of his ancestors, Rama engaged himself in noble deeds, acts of charity and generosity, and provided shelter to the needy.'

Later, declining Bharata's request for his return to Ayodhya, Rama told him,

'A moment in time never recurs just as the night that has passed shall never again be. Yamuna travels to meet the ocean but does not retrace her journey. Day and night move relentlessly and thus the life span of every living thing is being exhausted all the time. It is like the summer sun sucking the water on the earth dry.

'A river never retraces its path. Similarly, youth, once past its prime, never returns. Life ebbs steadily. Hence, we ought to use our time performing noble deeds.'

When Ravana is dead, Vibhishana initially declines to perform his last rites. Nobody in the family has survived. Rama tells him of his duty to do so even if Ravana's behaviour had been despicable. [34, Yuddhakandam]

'Rakshasaraja, I owe you my victory and I owe you a return of gratitude. Hence, I must advise you of what is correct and what is not.

'This nishachara might have been untruthful and evil. However, on a battlefield he was always glorious, brave and chivalrous. I hear that even Indra and other devatas could not defeat him in war. A mighty warrior, Ravana could make the world weep.

'However, an enmity ought not to last beyond death. Our purpose has been served. Now, he is as much my brother as yours. Hence, you shall perform his last rites and cremate him.

'Dharma demands that you perform his last rites with proper ceremony at the earliest. This will earn you a good name.'

Valmiki's Uniqueness

Think of a hermit sitting in an ashrama thousands of years ago and writing on palm leaves a book as mighty, majestic and exhaustive as the Ramayana. Consider his command of moral values, ethics, and his observation of the daily life of the public whether in Ayodhya or Lanka. Read his chapters on the battles that take place in the forest or in Lanka. The narrative is mesmerizing. The Ramayana as an epic maintains its unity of plot and action from the beginning to its end. The story line flows uninterrupted.

Read Valmiki's Surya Stuti in chapter 31, Yuddhakandam. Valmiki's understanding of the importance of the sun to mankind is amazing.

'Surya is Shishira [natural creator of happiness]; Tapana [source of heat, of energy]; Ahaskara [Creator of the day]; Ravi [to be worshipped by all]; and Agnigarbha [a storehouse of fire].

'Surya is Shankha [a source of bliss. Widespread]; Shishiranashana [alleviates cold]; Vyomanatha [master of the skies]; Tamobhedi [destroyer of darkness]; and Rigyujahsamaparagah [learned in the Rig, Sama and Yajur Vedas.]

'Surya is Ghanavrishti [the harbinger of rains]; Apana Mitra [creator of water]

Hundred of poets have been born after Valmiki. However, not one of them could match his brilliance.

Prologue

Lava and Kusha, the princes born to Sita in exile in the ashrama of the Rishi Valmiki, both had melodious voices. They had a remarkable memory and power of retention. Valmiki had taught them the Vedas and all available knowledge. Recognizing their talent, he made them learn the epic Ramayana in detail, narrated the story of their mother Sita, and of Rama, the king of Ayodhya and their father.

The epic was easy. It could be set to music and sung in vilambit, madhya and drut modes. It was sung while playing the veena, to the beat of percussion instruments. The author had shown great literary merit in the use of shringar, karuna, hasya, raudra, bhayanaka and veer rasas.

As an image multiplies when reflected in mirrors placed opposite each other, the young princes resembled Rama, their father as if they were his twins. They sang the Ramayana in gatherings of sages, rishis, the Brahmins and other devotees. They sang from memory, their eyes shut in deep concentration. Listening to the tale of Sita's suffering, the assembled mahatmas shed tears. Amazed at the fluent rendering, the rishis applauded the young singers. They gifted them a golden pitcher, clothes made of bark, the sacred thread and a deerskin.

One fine day, the princes, admired everywhere for their song, were wandering in the streets of Ayodhya, narrating the story of the King. Bharata, Rama's younger brother, happened to listen to them. He invited them to his palace and welcomed them suitably. Later, presenting them to Rama in the court, he said,

'These handsome young men sing a touching story in heart-warming words. There is an undefined sweetness in their voice. It is a moving tale of sacrifice and chivalry. If you permit, they can be requested to sing for the king.'

Surrounded by his brothers, ministers and other dignitaries, Rama sat on a celestial golden throne. He was not aware of the identity of the two young singers. Yet he felt a warmth towards them. He asked everyone present to listen to the tejaswi young men who reputedly sang an epic composed by Rishi Valmiki in proper ragas and with emotion.

As commanded by the king, Lava and Kusha plucked the strings of their veenas. Their pronunciation and accent was precise and clear-cut. Every listener could understand the import of the words. Listening to them, the audience felt a stirring of joy. They felt uplifted by the refinement and high intent of the narrative.

'These two young men even though they are munis,' observed Rama,' reflect the qualities of princes. They are, of course, dexterous in music. However, at the same time their grammar and intonation is that of the learned. The poem is rich in apt similes, suitable figures of speech, and meaningful thought. Even I feel uplifted in spirit. Therefore, listen carefully to what they say.'

BALAKANDAM

1

The City of Ayodhya and its Residents under Dashratha's Rule

Lava and Kusha plucked at the strings of their veenas and sang:

This great historical epic of Ramayana has been composed to celebrate the glory of the Ikshavaku kings, descendants of Prajapati Manu and of King Sagara. Since times immemorial, they ruled over the entire universe.

We shall recite this epic in full for your delight and enlightenment. Please look for the positive aspects of the story as we narrate.

The City of Ayodhya

Prosperous and happy people inhabited Kosala, the country situated on the banks of the river Saryu. Its capital was Ayodhya, built by Manu in old times. The glorious city was twelve yojana in length and three in breadth. A broad royal avenue ran through the city and led to other cities. A variety of trees had been planted on both sides of the road in order to make it look unique. Every day, water was sprinkled and flowers showered on the roads.

Large gates were erected to protect Ayodhya. The city had several streets. Many artisans lived in it. The city had its share of learned pundits. Flags flew high on the roofs of tall buildings. Hundreds of catapults guarded the city.

Ayodhya had several exclusively female dance troops and actors. Gardens were laid all over. Mango trees abounded. Sal plantations surrounded the city.

Deep moats, difficult to cross, protected the city. It was not easy for an enemy to conquer Ayodhya. Rather, vassals travelled in large numbers to Ayodhya to offer tribute to the King. Vaishya traders visited the city in hordes to sell and buy goods.

Considerable precious stones had been used in the construction of

Ayodhya's palaces. The King had several mansions with inner chambers for confidential negotiations. In the palace, the women had separate living apartments.

Ayodhya stood on even land. The farmers grew superior quality rice in abundance. The ground water was sweet like sugarcane juice.

The city resounded with the music of dundubhi, mridanga, veena and other musical instruments.

Ayodhya was a city of warriors who protected the helpless, and who never pursued an enemy who ran away from the battlefield. They were more powerful than the wild elephants, the roaring lions and fierce boars.

The king, Dashratha ruled over Ayodhya and looked after his subjects like a father. Learned Brahmins who had mastered the Vedas, surrounded him. He was a man of charitable disposition. He was truthful. He protected the rishis and the munis who lived in his kingdom.

Dashratha looked after his subjects with care. He was a far-sighted man. He accumulated all that was useful for the kingdom without greed. His subjects adored him. They, in turn, were largely prosperous and indulged in fair trade practices or productive agriculture. Cows, bullocks, horses, and objects of material wealth were available to them in plenty.

The populace was advised to stay clean, away from pollutants, take frequent baths, maintain good conduct, and refrain from lechery and licentiousness. The society was expected to be of the standard of the maharishis in purity of conduct. It was common to apply sandal paste for beauty and fragrance. People loved to wear earrings, garlands and caps shaped like crowns. Golden armlets were in use and so were necklaces and chains.

The residents of Ayodhya regularly performed yagyas. They did not find fault with each other. They took pride in being educated and learned.

They owned elephants brought from dense jungles and horses from the lands near the river Sindhu.

The King's Administration and the Qualities of the Ministers

Dashratha had eight ministers to advise him in administration, carefully selected out of experienced advisers. Their motto was 'purity of conduct.' They possessed qualities of humility, restraint, dexterity in doing their job, control over their senses, and knowledge of political and religious scriptures. They obeyed the king's command and carried out his orders diligently and faithfully. They did not tell a lie under the influence of kama, krodha, or self-interest.

The ministers were practical in their approach. However, they did not desist from punishing even a son if a punishment was due. On the other hand, an enemy who surrendered was not killed.

The king had spies all over his domain. They kept him up to date on happenings in various parts of the kingdom.

Dashratha's ministers well knew how to settle disputes. They were experts in making treaties and in carrying out negotiations with vassals or other kings.

2

Performance of Ashwamedha Yagya for the Birth of a Son

Dashratha worried that he would not be able to discharge his duty towards his ancestors because so far his queens had not given birth to a son. 'Who will be my successor on this majestic throne? Who will carry on our dynasty?' he thought to himself.

He ordered his ministers, 'Please summon the learned gurus, the venerable purohits and the rishis rich in Vedic studies. I desire to consult them.'

The invited sages advised him to send out a horse for one year to roam freely on the earth to establish his suzerainty, to order the erection of a yagya platform to the north of Saryu and to start ordering the material goods needed for a great ceremony where kings and commoners would assemble.

In the palace, the king advised his queens accordingly. He told them,

'Be ready for consecration for a holy yagya that will be performed in order for us to beget a son.'

The queens were delighted. Their faces glowed like the fresh lotus blooms in vasanta.

Invitation to Rishyashringa

At this point in time, Sumantra, a confidante of the king, who was well versed in economics and finance, advised him of one Rishyashringa, a holy man who was dexterous in performing a yagya for the birth of a son. Narrating the events of the rishi's life, he said, 'It is said that the sage Rishyashringa used to stay in a forest where he kept himself occupied with self-education and the study of the Vedas. Indifferent to sensual pleasures, the rishi never looked at a woman's face.

'Romapada, an illustrious king of Anga desha, unknowingly committed some misdeeds in violation of his dharma. He was advised to invite Rishyashringa to help him to atone for his sins. In order to attract the tapasvi away from his sylvan abode, the king was told to offer him a warm welcome and marry off his pretty daughter Shanta to the recluse.

'Maharaja, it was not easy to persuade the celibate Brahmin to move to the city. Yet the ministers of Anga desha devised a scheme to inveigle the sage. They sent a bunch of flirtatious dancing girls to camp in the forest not far away from the cottage of Rishyashringa.

'The rishi had not cast his eyes on a woman ever. Once he wandered near the camp of the courtesans and was amazed to see women dressed in colourful finery. They were singing melodiously and dancing with abandon. Some of them were quite bewitching and delicate. He liked what he saw. He decided to befriend them. Addressing them, he said,

'I am the son of Vibhandak Muni. I am performing penance in this forest and my name, Rishyashringa, is well known all over. You are so charming. It gives me pleasure to look at you. I consider your arrival to be a blessing. I invite you to my ashrama where I can welcome you suitably.'

At his cottage, the rishi welcomed the attractive women with arghya, washed their feet and offered them fruit and flowers. However, knowing his reputation for celibacy, the city women feared him. To accomplish their assignment, they offered him fruit and flowers in return. While doing so they came close to him, held his hands, and embraced him. Tasting fresh flavours , the rishi realized that he had never tasted such delights in his life, perhaps because he had been staying in a forest.

'Next day, a disturbed Rishyashringa visited the site where he had met the delightful women. They offered to take him along to Anga desha where he was promised an abundant supply of all the fruit and flowers he was used to in the ashrama. The sage readily agreed.

'With the arrival of the Brahmin, Anga desha received heavy showers as a blessing from Indra. The king saw it as an auspicious omen. He welcomed the sage with a bow. He offered him his daughter, Shanta in marriage, an offer the rishi accepted with joy.

'Maharaja,' continued Sumantra, 'now we have to approach Shanta's son, the present king, Rompad, and request him to graciously let his father, Rishyashringa to come to Ayodhya and perform the yagya for the birth of a son in your dynasty. There is none superior to the sage in the knowledge of the Vedas and the rituals required to be completed while performing the Ashwamedha Yagya.'

Ayodhya was decked to receive the royal guest, Rishyashringa. The roads were swept and watered. Incense was lighted. Colourful flags flew in front of every house. Dashratha entered the city with the sage preceded by an orchestra of conches and dundubhis. The large-eyed Shanta was warmly welcomed by the queens into their private chambers. She enjoyed the respectful attention that mighty and handsome Dashratha and his queens bestowed upon her.

Guru Vasishtha Prepares for the Yagya

As Vasanta approached, Dashratha visited Guru Vasishtha at his ashram to request him to come and undertake the preparations for the yagya. The latter readily agreed and said,

'Rajan, in the meantime, issue orders to artisans, architects, deeply religious and learned Brahmins, carpenters, masons, astrologers, actors, dancers and other learned persons to assemble at the site.

'We shall require thousands of bricks. Palaces furnished to provide all comforts are to be built for the kings to stay. We must provide housing for the Brahmins and make arrangements for their meals to be cooked in clean utensils and healthy kitchens.

'Build stables for elephants and horses. Raise cantonments for the soldiers coming from other countries. Sufficient provisions ought to be available for the large gathering. Look after your subjects so that they too are catered to during this period. Nobody should misbehave with another. Please ensure that none is insulted under the influence of anger or lechery.

'A well-fed artisan works competently and sincerely. He must get a fair wage. If that is done, his output will be high and aesthetically satisfying.

'It goes without saying that all the kings and friendly princes will be invited. Send personal invitations to the soft-spoken king of Kashi, the truthful Janaka of Mithila, your father-in-law, the venerable king of Kekaya desha, the warrior king Romapada of Anga desha,

Bhanuman of Kosala, and Praptigya of Magadha who, besides being a warrior is learned in Shastras, and the kings of Sindhu desha and of Saurashtra. Do not forget the kings of various southern countries.'

Dashratha sent his ministers to invite dozens of kings and princes. All of them arrived gladly. They carried presents of precious stones and other gifts suitable for a king.

Officers looking after the arrangements reported satisfactory completion of various facilities. Listening to their reports, Vasishtha remarked,

'Friends, if you give anyone anything, do it with grace and humility. Do not act as if you are obliging him. For certain, charity dispensed with arrogance and loaded with insults destroys the giver.'

With remarkable speed, the Yagya-Mandapa was erected according to the Guru's specifications. It was as if it appeared the moment the king willed it to be. Accompanied by his wives, Dashratha attended the consecration ceremonies.

The Yagya started with the return of the holy steed. Rishyashringa led the team of Brahmins invoking the blessings of Indra with words, melody and intent, learned through years of study. All assembled and those who appeared on the scene whether to participate or just to watch, were served a meal. One could see piles of delicious cooked food near the Yagyashala. The architects, the masons and the menials were well looked after. So were the old, the sick, women and children. Clothes were given to the needy.

The learned Brahmins debated religious texts and their interpretation during intervals and rest periods. Each one tried to show off as being superior to the others. Arguments flew like missiles. All the Brahmins were masters of grammar, and presently celibate. They had taught hundreds of pupils.

To mark the occasion, yupas made of khair, bela and palash were erected. Pillars of baheda and deodar circled them. The eight-sided yupas, smoothly chiselled, were covered with gold plates and cloth. Flowers and sandal were offered in worship. The pillars looked resplendent like the Saptarishis in the sky. Agni was consecrated as a statue resembling a Garuda who had spread his golden wings and had the tail spread out.

Kaushalya, the senior queen ritually worshipped the Ashwamedha horse and touched him with three different swords. She slept next to him for one night.

The king offered his entire country to the priests performing the sacrifice. The latter declined to accept. They said that to govern was the king's prerogative and that they could not protect the country against invaders. They said that they preferred a gift of cows, cash, and gold to the gift of land. The king readily agreed. In turn, the priests handed over all that they received in charity to the sage Rishyashringa and the Guru Vasishtha.

Rishyashringa Performs Putreshti Yagya while the Devatas Approach Vishnu

Reciting mantras from the Atharva Veda, the rishi started the Putreshti yagya meant to please gods to grant the boon of a son to the Yajamana. Several devatas, gandharvas, siddhas and maharishis had gathered to collect their share of the yagya offerings at the site. Looking at Brahma, the Creator, the devatas addressed him in well-chosen words,

'Blessed by you, Ravana, a king of the rakshasas, is harassing us with all his might. We have tolerated him in order not to dishonour your boon. He is jealous of our status. He has challenged even Indra. Surya dare not hurt him with his flares nor Pavana uproot him. Even the ocean has been stunned into immobility. Ravana has frequently abducted the apsaras to satisfy his lust.'

Brahma thought it over. He had so blessed Ravana that the latter would not be killed by a devata, gandharva, yaksha or a rakshasa. He had not included a human being in this list.

At this moment Vishnu, the master of the universe, riding on Garuda, arrived on the scene. He dazzled like the sun casting his brilliant rays on a cloud. He wore yellow raiment and carried a conch, a chakra, a lotus and a mace in his hands. He wore golden bracelets on his upper arms. All the devatas bowed in his presence and prayed for help in overcoming Ravana. They suggested that Vishnu be born as four sons to Dashratha so that as a human being, he could destroy Ravana without violating Brahma's commitment.

Acceding to their prayer, Vishnu assured them that he would do whatever was necessary. He agreed to be born to the queens of Dashratha as four sons.

As the Putreshti yagya continued, a giant-sized man of unparalleled brilliance and strength appeared out of the holy fire. He was wrapped in red, had a dark complexion and his face glowed like fire. He was high as a mountain and walked like a majestic lion. He had the radiance of the sun. In his hands, he carried a large gold dish covered by a silver lid. The dish was full to the brim with celestial kheer. He raised his arms lifting the dish as if it was a beloved being lifted by a lover. Addressing Dashratha, he said,

'Rajan, carrying this kheer from the gods, I arrive with permission from the Prajapatis, to help you to sire several sons. This divine food gives health and prosperity. Distribute it among your capable wives and take a portion yourself. Several sons will be born to you.'

The king placed the gold dish on his head and full of joy went round the divine being in parikrama. He felt happy like a pauper who has chanced upon a treasure. His wives glowed with happiness like the sky illuminated by the soothing rays of the autumn moon.

Dashratha handed over one half portion of the kheer to Kaushalya and one fourth to Sumitra. Of the rest, he gave half to Kaikeyee and the remaining once again to Sumitra after giving it some thought.

Soon after the queens showed signs of pregnancy.

Devatas Take Birth to Assist Vishnu

At Swargaloka Brahma summoned the devatas and said, 'Bhagwan Vishnu keeps his word. He is our well-wisher. In turn, we must assist him to fulfil our mission on earth. I desire that all of you take birth as warriors who can change form as desired, who can fly with the speed of the wind, who are diplomatic, wise, cunning when need be, crafty, invincible, brave like Vishnu, and knowledgeable. Your avatars must know how to use various weapons.

'I have already created Rikshraja Jambavan. He appeared suddenly out of my mouth when I yawned. '

The devatas obeyed the Creator's orders and gave birth to thousands of warriors in various forms. These kings, princes and soldiers were denizens of the forest. They took birth as bears, monkeys and other animals, intellectually sharp and capable of changing form at will.

Vali, the king of monkeys was born to Indra. He had the massive build of a mountain. He had enormous strength. Surya gave birth to Sugreeva. Brihaspati created Tara, who, like his father, was intellectually well endowed and sharp of wit. Vishwakarma gave birth to Nala and Gandhamadana was born to Kubera. Neel was a son born to Agni and Sushena to Varuna.

Pavana, the god of the winds gave birth to Hanuman, the bravest of all and the wisest. His body was hard like solid rock, like diamond. He could fly with the speed of Garuda. He was chivalrous and could change form at will. He could assume a vast form, the size of an elephant or even a mountain.

These warriors were brave like lions. They could hurl mountains at the enemy. They knew how to use a variety of weapons. Besides, they could fight tooth and nail. They had the strength to uproot a tree and fight with it as a weapon. They could create mighty disturbances in the oceans, cross it in a jump. They could pierce the skies, catch hold of the clouds and confront an elephant in musth to stop his movement and place him in chains. They had the capability to fell birds flying in the sky with their roar.

These sons and daughters of the devatas were unlike the monkeys we see around us today. They were unique in attributes and behaviour. They settled on the top of the Rikshawan Mountain and awaited the moment when they could assist Vishnu in the destruction of Ravana. In course of time, they made their presence felt all over the country, on the mountains and near the ocean.

3

Rama is Born

A whole year with its six seasons passed since the completion of the Putreshti Yagya. In the twelfth month on the ninth day of the waxing moon in Chaitra, Kaushalya gave birth to Rama, a child with divine attributes. The universe bowed to the child who was born under the major Gemini stars and the constellation of Cancer. At his birth, the Sun, Mars, Saturn, Jupiter and Venus were in their respective auspicious positions. The moon and Jupiter appeared close-by.

Rama added to the joys of the Ikshavaku dynasty. There was a touch of red in his pupils. His lips were red, his arms long and he had a deep, resonant voice. The child enhanced the lustre of his mother just as Indra had added to that of Aditi, the mother of gods.

Kaikeyee gave birth to Bharata and Sumitra to Lakshmana and Shatrughna. Bharata born under Pushya [Cancri] nakshatra and Meena [Pisces] lagna was a happy-go-lucky child. Sumitra's children were born under Ashlesha [Hydrae] nakshatra and Karka [Cancer] lagna. At this time, Surya was in the ascendant.

Each one of the sons of Dashratha had different qualities. They shone like the four stars of Bhadrapada. [Pegasii and Andromedae]. The Ayodhya city celebrated the birth of the princes with abandon. Food, money and gems were distributed. Acrobats performed their acts to delight the large crowds that had gathered in every square to rejoice. Cows were given in charity to the Brahmins.

Education of the Princes

The young princes were brought up according to the best traditions of the family. They studied the Vedas and learnt archery. They obeyed their mothers and respectfully bowed before their father. They learnt to be discrete, knowledgeable, valorous and far-sighted. They were taught how to behave with humility and dignity.

Rama shone like an unblemished moon. Soon, he learnt how to ride an elephant, a horse and drive a chariot.

4

Rishi Vishwamitra Seeks Help

Once, while Dashratha sat in private audience with his ministers and close relatives discussing marriage of the princes, the palace guards informed him of the arrival of the glorious sage, Vishwamitra.

The king, accompanied by his purohits, joyously welcomed the Maharishi as if Indra was receiving Brahma. Vishwamitra was a man who performed tough penances and this showed on his face which was glowing with inner strength. Dashratha offered him arghya and led him to the courtroom. The rishi enquired about his well-being, about the state of the treasury, about the safety of the kingdom and about the health and happiness of his subjects and near and dear ones. Seating the maharishi on a couch, Dashratha said,

'Your arrival here, Maharishi, is auspicious like nectar being poured into the mouth of a person on death bed, like showers on a parched land, or the pregnancy of a barren woman. What service can I render to you? It will be my pleasure to be of help in your noble tasks.'

The rishi nodded in acknowledgement.

The king continued,

'O sage, your arrival is like a pretty dawn following a dark night, a sunrise when I have had the good fortune to look at you, the crown of the Brahmins. You were known as a Rajarshi in earlier times. Later you attained to the present high station as a Brahmarshi.

'When you are here, I consider my house to have been sanctified as a teertha. I feel as if I have returned blessed from a pilgrimage.

'I shall carry out your command, whatever that be. You are an honoured guest and therefore a devata for this grihastha.'

Listening to these humble outpourings, the glorious Vishwamitra, a man of high virtues, felt immensely happy. He said,

'O lion of a king, none else could have been as generous as you are. Two rakshasas, Maricha and Subahu, educated and strong, are determined to violate my yagya being performed to attain Siddhi. The sacrifice is almost complete. These demons come and pollute the Yagya Mandapa with blood and meat. I believe that your chivalrous son Rama can annihilate these devils and help me complete the yagya. I need your lotus-eyed son only for ten days. Do not say no. Do not worry about his safety.'

Hearing these words, Dashratha fainted and slipped from his throne. Coming to his senses, he said,

'Maharshi, Rama is not even sixteen. How will he fight those mighty asuras? He has not yet learnt the art of using secret weapons in a war. He is my eldest child. I love him the most.

'I am willing to go personally or send my generals to protect your Yagya Mandapa with all their might. However, who are these rakshasas? Which family do they belong to? If I know correctly, some of these demons are invincible.'

Responding to the king's entreaties, Vishwamitra replied,

'Rajan, you might have heard of Ravana, born in the family of the rishi Pulastya. He enjoys the boon of immortality from Brahma. He is a brother of Kubera and sends his minions to harass us. Maricha and Subahu too have been sent by him.'

On hearing the mention of Ravana, Dashratha was stupefied. He said,

'Maharshi, even I cannot face Ravana. My armies will not be able to face him. Maricha and Subahu seem to be the messengers of Yamaraja. I can come and fight one of them to keep my word. However, please spare Rama for the sake of my dynasty.'

Vishwamitra flew into a rage like the fire in a yagya kunda fuelled by excess of ghee. He retorted,

'You are besotted with the love for your child whose reality you are not aware of. You promised to grant my wishes. Your breaking this promise indicates that your dynasty has fallen on evil days. I have no problem with returning empty-handed. Yet, I wish you well.'

The gods were frightened and the earth quaked out of fear when the angry sage uttered his words. Maharshi Vasishtha, who was always at peace with himself, realizing the gravity of the situation, addressed the king thus:

'Rajan, born in the Ikshavaku dynasty as an avatar of Dharma, you must not give up doing your duty. If a man goes back on his promise, he forfeits the credit for any virtue he might have earned in his earlier lives. Please permit Rama to accompany Rishi Vishwamitra. No demon can survive a fight with him.

'Rama and Vishwamitra are embodiments of Dharma, of righteousness. The learning of the sage is unparalleled and makes him superior to anyone else in the world. He has profound knowledge of the use of powerful weapons of war. He has the capacity to forge armaments not yet designed by anyone.

'Moreover, the rishi is omniscient. He is aware of the past and he can anticipate the future. Do not be afraid. Shed your doubts if any and let Rama accompany Vishwamitra.'

The advice of his family guru convinced Dashratha that Rama's departure with Vishwamitra was in his son's best interests.

5

Rama Departs to Assist Rishi Vishwamitra

It was decided that Lakshmana would accompany Rama. Guru Vasishtha performed religious ceremonies to bless them and chanted sacred mantras to consecrate the young princes with charms and magic formulae.

Dashratha breathed deep the fragrance of his son's forehead before handing him over to Vishwamitra for safekeeping and care. A dust-free, life-giving breeze blew at this hour. The devatas blew dundubhis in the sky.

The two princes walked behind the rishi. They carried bows and arrows. The arrows in the quivers, the bows on their shoulders and their foreheads in between presented the image of triple-headed cobras moving in formation, ready to attack. Generous to the core, the two princes walked like Ashwini Kumars staying a step behind Brahma.

Both the princes were elegantly dressed. They had put on leather gloves. Sheathed swords were tied to their waists. They were handsome of limb. While Vishwamitra walked like the all-powerful Mahadeva, the two young princes resembled his sons Kartikeya and Vishakha*.

---

*Kartikeya and Vishakha are the names of the children born, according to legend, when Agni scattered Shiva's semen impregnating Krittikas, the stars in the star cluster, Pleiades. Vishakha also refers to the posture of an archer who takes an aim standing with his feet a span apart. Either ways, Valmiki's simile is powerful and visually powerful. Kartikeya fought on behalf of the devatas to destroy the demons that had been harassing them. The posture of the archer befits the princes carrying bows and arrows. The subtlety of the two images above needs to be appreciated on another count. Rama and Lakshmana are avatars of Vishnu. Brahma and Mahesh are leading them respectively in the two images. While the other two deities of the Trimurti lead, the action lies with Vishnu alone.]

Arriving at the southern banks of the river Saryu, a few kilometres out of Ayodhya, Vishwamitra asked Rama to rinse his mouth with Saryu water and vow to accomplish the task at the earliest. [This was a sacred ritual called aachaman, before doing anything important.]

The rishi further asked the princes to chant the well-known mantras, Balaa and Atibalaa, a chanting that would relieve fatigue, keep out fever and sickness and ensure absolute uniformity in form, posture and bodily strength. He said:

The fountain of these two streams of knowledge is Brahma who treats them as his glorious daughters. I earned them through relentless tapasya. I believe that none other than you deserves to know them better. Hence I am passing on this knowledge to you.'

Rama felt uplifted and purified after the aachaman and a bath. He looked resplendent like the autumn sun radiating light in millions of rays.

Come evening, the two princes and the rishi slept peacefully on the banks of Saryu on beds made of grass unsuitable for the sons of a king.

6

Mahadeva Ashrama and the Death of Tataka

Early next morning, the two princes had a bath, worshipped the gods and recited the elevating Gayatri mantra in praise of the rising Sun. Soon after, they arrived at the confluence of the rivers Saryu and Ganga. An ancient ashrama known as Mahadeva Ashrama was situated at this site. It was inhabited by great ascetics with conscience pure as crystal. At this site, once upon a time Kamadeva's body had been destroyed by Mahadeva when the former disturbed the lord's samadhi in order to attract his attention to the charms of the young Parvati.

The rishi and the princes spent their night as guests of the munis living in the ashrama. The former regaled Rama and Lakshmana with stories from ancient lore. Next morning they crossed the river in a well-appointed boat. Getting off the boat at the southern banks of Ganga, the trio walked through a dense, dark forest resounding with bird sound and the roars of fierce wild animals such as the tigers, boars, and elephants. Sal, Arjuna, Tendu, wood-apple and trees laden with wild berries abounded in the forest.

Narrating the history of the dense jungle, Vishwamitra told Rama:

'A long time ago two prosperous cities were built near this piece of land. Sometime ago, Tataka, a Yakshini, who could change her appearance at will, arrived here. She is the wife of a wise daitya, named Sunda, and the mother of the chivalrous demon, Maricha who is as brave as Indra. The latter is large-bodied with muscular arms, a broad forehead and a wide mouth. The mother and son have been desecrating the two cities as well as the forest. She wanders freely in the forest as if she owns it. I desire that you kill Tataka and rid this area of her terror and that of her son.

'Princes, you need not be concerned that I am asking you to kill a woman. In the line of duty, a king has to take uncomfortable decisions. He must act even if he has to perform a cruel deed or a tainted action. Tataka is evil incarnate, without even a trace of virtue.' Rama replied, 'My father had asked me to unhesitatingly obey you. For the welfare of my country, of the cows and the Brahmins, I am willing to do your bidding, Maharishi.'

Rama made ready his bow and arrows to give Tataka a fight in order to annihilate her. He firmly held the central part of the bow in his fist and pulled at the string to test its tightness. This produced a thundering sound echoing in the four directions which frightened every living being roaming in the forest.

The Yakshini was startled and enraged. Who dare disturb her peace of mind? Walking a super-human gait, she followed the roar of Rama's bow. Her face was twisted with anger and contempt. Her height touched the firmament.

Addressing Lakshmana, Rama said,

'Look brother, Tataka's body is harsh, fierce and frightful. A coward could die of heart failure even if he looks at her once. I hesitate to kill her for she is after all a female. Hence, I shall slice her nose and ears and force her to flee. Striking at her legs and feet, I shall impair her mobility and minimize her strength.'

A fierce fight ensued. Tataka tried to blind the princes with clouds of dust. She showered them with stones. Rama stalled her bombardment of stones with arrows shot from his bow. He sliced both of her hands with the sharp blades of his arrows. A furious Tataka raised a frightening roar. Lakshmana cut her nose and ear lobes.

However, Tataka could change her form at will. She disappeared into the sky and started pelting the princes with rocks.

Vishwamitra advised Rama not to be kind to the cruel woman and speedily finish her off. Rama covered her with arrows as if placing her in a cage. He shot an arrow into her chest and instantly killed her.

The rishi and his protégés spent the night in Tatakavana. The forest came to life as soon as the evil woman was dead. The wild animals became tame. Trees flowered and birds chirped merrily in the early morning.

Vishwamitra Empowers Rama with Celestial Armaments

A pleased Rishi Vishwamitra handed over many powerful and divine missiles and weapons to Rama. These included Danda chakra, Dharma chakra, Kala chakra, Vishnu chakra and the most frightful Aindra chakra. He further gave Rama Indra's thunderbolt, Shiva's Trishul and Brahma's Brahmashira. He handed over to Rama two stunningly built maces besides snares like Dharma pasha, Kala pasha and Varuna pasha. He blessed him with Narayanastra and Agni's favourite Shikhirastra. The rishi handed over to Rama sharp swords made of the finest metal, imparted to him knowledge of how to put the enemy under delusion, and the blinding weapons of the Sun God.

'These weapons are of use to the mightiest of warriors,' said the sage. 'They can be transformed at will and will always obey your commands. '

A humble Rama accepted the rishi's gifts after taking a bath and saying his prayers. The latter imparted to Rama the techniques of their use.

7

Vamana Ashrama and the Destruction of Rakshasas

Leaving the Tatakavana far behind, Rama noticed a salubrious site surrounded by trees, dense as clouds, situated next to a hillock. Herds of deer wandered freely. Birds of diverse colour and plume chirped melodiously.

'Where is your ashrama situated, Maharishi?' asked Rama of Rishi Vishwamitra. 'Where is the site where the yagya you are performing is interrupted by the rakshasas and their heinous activities?'

The rishi replied, 'We have arrived at the Vamana Ashrama where in ancient times Mahatma Vamana sat in penance.

'It was known earlier as Siddhashrama because Vishnu had attained Siddhi here. Later Vishnu took birth as Vamana, as a son to Rishi Kashyapa and his wife Aditi, in order to tame king Bali, son of Virochana and grandson of Bhakta Prahlad. Having defeated Indra and other devatas, Bali was busy performing a great sacrifice. He had to be restrained somehow from completing this sacrifice. Therefore, Vamana arrived at the yagya site as a mendicant and extracted the universe from Bali's control, measuring it in three steps. Bhagwan Vamana spent time in this ashrama. Being a devotee of Vamana, I like to spend time here. Kindly treat this ashrama as much as your home as it is mine.'

Rama and Lakshmana looked like the stars Punarvasu when they entered the ashrama holding Vishwamitra's hands on either side. In between, the sage appeared like the moon on a frost-free night. The inmates of the ashrama accorded them a warm welcome. At the earliest opportunity, Rama asked the rishi to engage himself in performing the yagya so that the demons if any could be enticed to reveal themselves.

For six days and six nights, without a wink of sleep, the princes stood guard at the sacred grounds. The havana kunda was surrounded by Brahma, Vishwamitra and other rishis. They were reciting holy mantras while adding kusha grass, fragrant herbs called samidha and sandalwood to the holy fire. Ghee was poured to feed the flames.

Suddenly, the sky erupted with a fierce and loud roar. The rishis noticed the rakshasas led by Maricha and Subahu running towards the yagya mandapa spreading their maya all around. Reaching the yagya site, the demons showered blood like rain on everyone present.

Rama hit Maricha with a mild Manavastra in his chest. Its impact threw the rakshasa into the sea hundreds of miles away. Rama hit Subahu with Agni astra and killed him instantly. By and by, all the other demons too were eliminated.

Peace prevailed in the Vamana Ashrama once again. Come evening, the rishi sat reciting Sandhya with the princes sitting by his side.

8

Departure for Mithila

Full of joy at having accomplished the arduous task successfully, the two young princes felt contented. Next morning after ablutions and prayers, they approached the illustrious rishi and bowed before him. Politely they asked,

'O mighty sage, we wait for your command. Is there anything else that we can accomplish to please you and your companion rishis?

A few rishis sitting near Vishwamitra responded.

'O jewel among men, we hear that the King Janaka, the ruler of Mithila, is about to perform a holy yagya. All of us desire to attend the ceremony. Both of you can accompany us. Raja Janaka is in possession of a magnificent bow, given to him by Shankara who was pleased at his tapasya. It is a unique weapon, glorious, yet terribly powerful and frightening. The central hold of the bow has been made with exquisite artisanship. Leave aside human beings, even gods and demons cannot string an arrow on this bow. Quite a few brave kings and princes have come to try to bend this bow, but without success.

'Rama, O lion among men, visiting Mithila we shall look at Janaka's prized bow and participate in the marvellous yagya ceremony, the like of which has never been held.

'Raghunandan, Shankara's bow has been consecrated in Janaka's palace like the idol of a god. It is worshipped by offering flowers, fragrance, and burning incense.'

Accompanied by the princes, Rishi Vishwamitra set out towards north into the Himalayan valley. A hundred carts carrying other rishis followed. At sunset, the caravan camped at the banks of the river Shona. Sitting there, Vishwamitra regaled the princes with tales of events from the local folk lore.

At midnight, Vishwamitra told Rama that he had narrated enough stories and that it was time to go to sleep under an open sky resplendent with stars. Said he,

'I do not want that fatigue and lack of sleep make our journey tomorrow uncomfortable.'

Saying this Vishwamitra fell asleep. In sleep, he looked like the magnificent setting sun gone to sleep for the duration of the night.

9

Ganga-avataran and the Birth of Kartikeya

By the next afternoon, the caravan led by Rishi Vishwamitra reached the banks of the Ganga. They were delighted to see king swans and sarus birds merrily floating on her waters. Everyone had a bath in the sacred waters. They prayed to gods and invoked their ancestors. They performed havana and feasted on sweet pudding that tasted like Amrita.

Vishwamitra was a storehouse of knowledge. Sitting among the sages surrounding the Maharishi, Rama asked him,

'Bhagwan, I seek to know how Ganga, flowing through three different routes, runs into the ocean in a convoluted route.'

Vishwamitra replied, 'Himavana the king of mountains, rich in minerals, was married to the charming Mena, daughter of the Meru Mountain. Mena of a delicate build and slim waist, gave birth to two pretty daughters. The elder of these daughters was Ganga and Uma was the younger one.

'Sometime later, the devatas asked Himavana to give away Ganga to them in order to facilitate some sacred tasks. For the welfare of the universe, Himavana gladly gave away Ganga who used to wander freely, purifying the world.

'Uma was a pious child. She sat doing tough penance. She was determined to marry Bhagwan Rudra. The latter, pleased with her determination agreed to marry her and she became a deity worshipped by the entire world [as Parvati, Shiva's consort].

'Now, I will tell you how Ganga became Tripathagamini [that is, the one who has taken three paths]. At first [as a young damsel], she wandered in the skies. Later the Girirajakumari [daughter of Himalaya, the king of Mountains], Ganga descended in the Devaloka as a stream for the gods. Later, in the form of water, she flowed on to earth to purify everyone, wash their sins and then she moved on into the ocean to reach the depths of the earth.'

Rama wanted to know further. He asked, 'Could you please elaborate upon what tasks Ganga performs in her three streams. How does she relate to the Devaloka and the Mrityuloka? '

'I shall start with Uma's tale that leads to Ganga,' replied Vishwamitra. 'Uma had married Shiva. For a long time thereafter, the couple had no child. The devatas were afraid that if a child was born to this divine couple after years of enjoyment, it could be a mighty god. They approached Shiva in order to influence him not to beget a child.

'However, Uma was upset. Rebuking the devatas, she said, 'I married Shiva partly to beget a son. You have thwarted my longing. I curse you that you will become impotent and your wives will be barren.'

'Addressing Prithvi, Uma said, 'You will no longer have one form. You would be exploited by many.'

'Shiva and Parvati moved into the northern Himalayas to meditate.

'However, the devatas needed a commander who could fight on their behalf. But, because of the curse, they could not beget children. Therefore, they approached Brahma for a solution. He told them that if Ganga, Uma's elder sister accepted a part of Shiva's semen from Agni, she would give birth to a chivalrous god.

The devatas asked Agni to pour Shiva's semen into Ganga. Simultaneously, they asked Ganga to join in this effort. She agreed and assumed a divine form. Agni scattered Shiva's divine radiance all around her. Every drop of her being was soaked in Shiva's power.

'However, quite soon Ganga told Agni that she was unable to carry this powerful radiance any longer. She felt singed inside out and found her consciousness slipping. Agni suggested that she deposit her foetus at the back of the Himalayas. She did so. What came out of her womb looked burnished like gold. [After all Ganga was herself a granddaughter of Sumeru, a mountain of gold.] Soon Ganga's foetus was transformed into a child whom Indra and other devatas welcomed. They organized his feeding by the six Krittikas, [the stars in the constellation, Pleiades]. The latter gladly owned the child. They nursed him jointly and proudly called him their son.

'The devatas named the child Kartikeya. It was predicted that he would be immortal and that his fame would spread everywhere. He was also known as Skanda, that is, thrown out like quick silver by Shiva and Parvati. He sucked at the breasts of Krittikas with his six mouths. He grew into a giant commander in a day and defeated all the yavanas who had been harassing the devatas.

'The devatas anointed Kartikeya as their commander-in-chief as a mark of gratitude.'

10

Bhagiratha Brings Ganga to Earth

Continuing his narration of Ganga's arrival on earth, Vishwamitra added, 'Ayodhya was once ruled by Sagara, a childless king. He was a devout and conscientious man. He was married to Keshini, daughter of the king of Vidarbha. She too was a truthful and religious person. Sagara's second wife was Sumati, daughter of Kashyapa and sister of Garuda. Accompanied by both his queens, Sagara went to the Himalayas and meditated on a peak known as Bhriguprashravana. This pleased the Rishi Bhrigu and he blessed them with several children. The sage prophesied that while Keshini would mother one brave son, Sumati would give birth to 60,000 sons.

'In due course, Keshini gave birth to a prince named Asamanja. Sumati gave birth to 60,000 children who soon grew into handsome men.

'The elder son Asamanja was a disgrace to the family. He would playfully drown other children in Saryu. Sagara threw him out. However, Asamanja's son Anshuman was a soft-spoken man and won over each of his grandfather's praja.

'Sagara decided to perform a yagya as prescribed for a king. Rama, remember that he was one of your ancestors.'

'I am listening carefully, Maharshi,' said Rama. 'Describe all the events of that yagya.'

Vishwamitra had a hearty laugh. Rama was anticipating the entire narrative. He continued, 'As was the practice, Sagara sent a horse followed by an army led by his warrior and archer grandson, Anshuman to assert his suzerainty over other kingdoms, far and near. Indra who did not like rivals raising their head waylaid this horse. At the yagya site, the priests declared that unless this horse was traced, the ceremony could not continue.

'Sumati's 60,000 sons came forward to look for the missing horse. As they could not find him on earth, they started digging deep.

'Deep in the womb of the earth, the princes came upon the yagya horse grazing by the side of Bhagwan Kapila who was an incarnation of Vishnu. They were quite incensed and ran to attack the maharishi. They did not know that Indra had deliberately left the horse there and that Kapila muni had nothing to do with its disappearance.

'Maharishi Kapila was annoyed with their behaviour. He looked at them angrily reducing them to a pile of ashes in a moment.

'Missing his sons for long, Sagara asked his chivalrous grandson Anshuman to go and look for his uncles worldwide. 'Worship those who deserve to be worshipped and finish them who obstruct your course', said he. Wandering in pursuit of his mission, Anshuman reached the ashrama of Kapila Rishi where lay his uncles in a pile of ashes.

'As Anshuman was about to sprinkle holy water over the ashes, Garuda, the king of birds and an uncle of the dead princes arrived on the scene and said, 'O prince, O lion among men, your uncles were destroyed for the good of mankind by Mahatma Kapila. Offering ordinary water in their memory would be of no help. Brave man, you should seek the help of Ganga, Himavan's elder daughter, to come down and permit you to use her water for the salvation of your uncles. The moment Ganga, who purifies the universe with her waters, washes away the ashes of your uncles, the dead will go to Swargaloka.

'Garuda asked the prince to take away the yagya horse and complete the sacrifice started by his grandfather.

'The king Sagara was succeeded by Anshuman. His successor was Dileep, a glorious king. King Bhagiratha succeeded Dileep. He undertook the unfinished task of bringing Ganga to earth to wash away the ashes of his ancestors, which were still lying in the Kapila Ashrama. For this purpose, Bhagiratha sat in penance in the Gokarna Teertha. Years passed and Bhagiratha stood with both his arms uplifted, praying to Brahma to bless him with wisdom so that he could persuade Ganga to come down from Swargaloka. He lived the life of a celibate and repeatedly fasted for thirty days at a time.

'Brahma, pleased with Bhagiratha's penance, appeared and told him to ask for any boon. 'Bhagwan,' said Bhagiratha, 'If you are pleased with me, make Ganga come and wash away the ashes of my ancestors. Further, bless me with a child to continue our family. Please bless the Ikshavaku dynasty so that it may prosper forever.'

'Brahma replied, 'O brave Bhagiratha, I grant you all the boons desired by you. However, you have to persuade Bhagwan Shankara to receive Ganga when she descends, for none other can stand the impact of her fall. Otherwise the earth will crack and burst into ravines.' Saying so, Brahma disappeared.

'Bhagiratha now stood in penance on the tip of his toe and prayed to Shankara for one year. Bhagwan Pashupati gave him darshana and said, 'O king, superior among men, I am happy with your penance. I shall certainly help in your effort to bring salvation to your ancestors. I shall receive Ganga, daughter of Himavan, on my head and slowly release her onto the earth.'

'On receiving Shankara's consent, the elder daughter of Himavan, worshipped by the universe, descended from the skies in a fierce torrent onto Shankara's radiant head. She thought that sweeping Shankara with her forceful flow, she would slip into the netherworld. Shiva, the omniscient, knew of Ganga's haughtiness and high opinion of herself. He decided to teach her a lesson by making her disappear as soon as she descended. He received her in his dense tresses and made her a captive as if in a cave. For years, Ganga went on flowing circuitously in Shiva's tresses. She just could not get out.

'Once again Bhagiratha stood in penance. A pleased Shankara let Ganga go in seven streams. Hladini, Pavani and Nalini full of sacred, purifying waters flew in the eastern direction. Suchakshu, Seeta and Mahanadi, the next three purifying streams flew towards the south. The seventh stream followed the chariot of the King Bhagiratha onto the earth.

'The waters of this stream created a stunning uproar on the earth. The fish, the crocodiles and other aquatic animals fell into these waters in large numbers adding charm to the earth on which Ganga flowed. Ganga's charms were admired by the devatas, the siddhas and the rishis sitting in large vimanas and on elephants floating in the sky. Gangavataran was a sight for the gods as well as for the humans who had assembled in large numbers to see the unprecedented miracle. The cloudless sky shone like a thousand suns under the light reflected from the jewels put on by the devatas who were witnessing this spectacle.

'In the waters of Ganga, dolphins, multi-coloured fish and reptiles danced. The sky looked like a rainbow with the light reflected by these animals. Gusts of wind created foam and divided it into many parts suspended high above the surface of water. These billows of foam looked like the snow-white autumn clouds. They resembled large white swans flying in the sky.

'Ganga waters flowed sometimes fast, at other times slow, in meandering streams, fell into narrow gorges and climbed over cliffs. One could see whirlpools where her waters caressed themselves. At other times, she flowed at leisure, at an unhurried pace.

'The earthlings washed themselves of their impurities in the waters of Ganga, waters that had touched Shiva forehead. They used this water for drinking because it was so pure and holy.

'As Ganga followed Bhagiratha, she swept aside a yagya mandapa of a valorous king Jahnu who was busy worshipping. The enraged king swallowed the entire water of Ganga. The devatas in Swargaloka descended and assured Jahnu that Ganga was like his daughter and would be known as such in future. The king mellowed and allowed her to flow from his ears and Ganga came to be known as Jahnavi. Soon after Ganga washed away the ashes of Sagara's sons into the ocean and they joined the devatas in Swargaloka.

11

Samudramanthan

Next morning the princes crossed Ganga in comfortable boats to arrive at the town of Vishala. Here too Vishwamitra continued with narration of ancient events. Said he,

'Rama, in the Sat Yuga the sisters Diti and Aditi gave birth to mighty daityas and devout devatas respectively. Each one of them wanted to be immortal. After great thought, they concluded that if they churned the ocean, they could surely obtain Amrita.

'Having thus made up their mind, the cousins persuaded Vasuki, the king of reptiles and son of Rishi Kashyapa, to be tied as a rope around the Mandarachala Mountain. The latter was used as the churning rod for churning the Ksheerasagara.

'The churning continued for a long time. Meanwhile the multi-headed Vasuki started spewing sprays of poison and bit into the sides of the Mandarachala Mountain with his sharp teeth. His poison singed like fire and formed a ball of rising foam that could drown everyone present. The devatas, the asuras and the human beings present at the site felt the intensity of this fiery poison. They felt as if it would reduce them to ashes in no time.

'Frightened by the reach of the lethal poison, the devatas approached Bhagwan Shankara for succour. The latter agreed to help them. He sipped the entire poison as if it was Amrita and let it stay suspended in his throat.

'The churning continued. However, owing to its weight the mountain being used as the churning stick sank deep into the ocean bed. This time the devatas approached Vishnu for help. Shri Hari assumed the form of a tortoise, lifted the mountain on his back, and went to sleep. Simultaneously, Vishnu stood holding the churner, and continued to churn in order to help the devatas.

'Later, Dhanvantari, the soul of Ayurveda, appeared out of

Ksheerasagara. He carried a stick in one hand and a kamandalu in the other. Apsaras radiating golden light followed him. They were called apsara because they were born of 'ap', which is water. Varuni, daughter of Varuna, the goddess of suraa [liquor], followed. She set out in search of a suitable groom without loss of time. While the daityas declined her advances, the devatas welcomed her into their fold. Having been deprived of Suraa, the demons were called asura, [that is without sura] while Aditi's sons who accepted Suraa came to be known as Sura. The devatas were immensely pleased that Varuni married one of them.

'Thereafter, in succession, Ucchaishshrava, the sublime horse, Kaustubha jewel and then Amrita emerged out of the ocean. A fight ensued between the sons of Aditi and Diti over the possession of the Amrita Kalasha. Bhagwan Vishnu assumed the form of Mohini, a woman of unprecedented beauty and ran away with the Amrita Kalasha. Later he destroyed the daityas who laid a claim to Amrita. Vishnu handed over the Kalasha to Indra and other rishis who, on taking a sip, became immortal.

12

Purification of Ahalya

Travelling forward, Vishwamitra accompanied by Rama and Lakshmana arrived at Janakpuri, capital of Mithila ruled by king Janaka. They decided to stay in an old ashrama, which though well maintained, looked desolate. The rishi, in answer to an inquisitive question by Rama narrated the history of this ashrama.

'In an earlier age this ashrama belonged to Rishi Gautama and looked magnificent. Gautama lived here with his wife Ahalya and was always busy in tapasya.

'Once when Gautama was away, Indra, Shachi's husband, arrived at this ashrama disguised as a muni. Addressing the charming Ahalya, Indra said, 'O lovely woman, a man keen to make love does not wait for a woman's menstrual cycle to be over. I admire your slim waist. I desire to make love to you.

'Ahalya recognized Indra's disguise. Although a woman of noble character, unwisely she yielded to the temptation of having sex with the great Indra. 'Well, Devaraja Indra desires me! Fantastic! I am flattered,' thought she. After their copulation was over, Ahalya addressed Indra and said, 'O king of the devatas, I feel obliged that you made love to me. However, please leave post-haste and protect yourself and me from Gautama's anger.' Indra too expressed his pleasure and assured her of his return incognito. He tried to make a hurried exit but could not escape being noticed by the great muni who was returning after his ablutions and was carrying havana samagri. He was wet having just taken a bath. His body glowed like a flame. Indra shivered at the sight of the muni.

'The rishi immediately guessed what had transpired. Confronting Indra he said, 'You appear to have lost your discretion. Assuming my form in disguise, you have committed adultery. I curse you to be impotent.'

'That very moment, Sahasraksha Indra's testicles dropped to the ground.

'Gautama now cursed his wife. Said he,

'O harlot, for thousands of years you shall lie in a heap of ashes. Air alone will be your diet. You will be confined to this ashrama, completely out of touch with humankind. When Rama, son of Dashratha visits this ashrama, he will resurrect you. When he accepts the hospitality of this place and you look after him, you will become pure and purged of greed and attachment. Then, you can happily come and join me.'

'Saying so, Gautama Rishi, the great ascetic, departed from this ashrama and left for the Himalayas.'

'Rama,' said Vishwamitra, 'please come into Gautama's ashrama and rid Ahalya of her husband's curse. '

Even though she glowed in her beauty, Ahalya lay invisible in a heap of ashes. The Creator had taken great care in shaping her limbs. She was like a flame surrounded by soot. She resembled a full moon obliterated by dense clouds and a hailstorm. She was like a ray of the sun lost during its journey into the ocean.

As soon as she saw Rama, Ahalya regained her visible form. Her curse was instantly terminated. Everyone could see her.

Rama and Lakshmana bowed and touched Ahalya's feet. She too, remembering her husband's admonition and words, received the two princes with ceremony. She washed their feet, offered them arghya, and offered them seats.

The ceremonies being over, Ahalya joined her husband who had suddenly appeared in the ashrama. He too worshipped Rama as an atithi.

Rama and Lakshmana accompanied by Rishi Vishwamitra now moved into Mithila.

13

Transformation of Rajarshi Vishwamitra into a Brahmarshi

The following narrative is attributed to King Janaka's purohit Shatananda, son of Ahalya and Rishi Gautama. He welcomed Vishwamitra, Rama and Lakshmana on behalf of the king and made them comfortable.

'Rama, you are being protected by Kushikanandana, Rishi Vishwamitra, who had performed arduous tapasya. He is the son of King Gaadhi and had ruled as a king for hundreds of years. Once upon a time, leading a vast army over land, rivers and mountains, he arrived at the ashrama of Maharishi Vasishtha. The ashrama was rich in flowering plants, creepers, and large trees. Different types of animals freely wandered. At any given point of time, several tapasvis performing tough penance lived in the ashrama. A few of them lived merely on water and air, while others subsisted on fruit alone. They had conquered disease and exercised control over their senses. The Vasishtha Ashrama looked like Brahmaloka where the munis were ever performing yagya with the holy fires lit.

'While Vishwamitra humbly bowed before Vasishtha, the latter welcomed him in the manner suitable for a king and offered him arghya and fruit. The sage enquired of the king about his praja, his policies as a king and his victory over his enemies. 'I trust,' said Vasishtha, 'that your treasury is full, that you take care of your people in order to keep them happy, that you look after your servants and employees so that they are well-paid and well-fed.

'Vasishtha insisted that Vishwamitra spend some time in his ashrama. He said he wanted to look after his entourage and forces like his own people. For this purpose, the sage sent for his sacred cow of mottled skin, a cow that could fulfil any wish of the sage. Addressing her Vasishtha said,

'Kamadhenu, we have to look after our guests like never before. Arrange for delicious meals, succulent fruit, nourishing grains, sugarcane, honey, fruit juices, grape juice, and spices. Please get sweets and puddings of many varieties cooked. Make sure that there is plenty of milk, curd, pulses and ghee.'

'In thousands of silver plates, Vasishtha served mouth-watering meals to Vishwamitra's companions. The king was amazed. His greed for possession got the better of him and he told his host:

'I shall present you with a hundred thousand cows in exchange of this spotted Kamadhenu. As a king, I am entitled to any valuable property and this cow is one such. She is mine as a matter of right.'

'Vasishtha replied, 'Nareshwara, I shall not exchange this cow even for a million other cows or for that matter for any other object in the universe. As a man's reputation cannot be parted from his person, this cow cannot be taken away from me. My entire life, yagya, swaha, worship and many other activities of the ashrama are organized around Kamadhenu. She is all that I have.'

'This refusal angered the king no end. Angrily he replied,

'I shall give you 14,000 elephants with golden carriages. Their necklaces and goads too will be of gold. I shall give you 800 chariots burnished in gold. I shall further add a crore of spotted cows. Please take whatever precious stones you wish but hand over this cow to me.'

'Vasishtha declined saying,

'No sir. I cannot comply with your wishes. Kamadhenu is my jewel, my life, my wealth. She is all that I have. I shall not part with her.'

'A great battle ensued. Vishwamitra's forces destroyed the property of the ashrama. However, Kamadhenu created warriors who overcame the king's forces. Vishwamitra was humbled like an ocean whose waves subside after stormy weather. He felt like a defanged cobra. He lost lustre like the sun in eclipse.

'Vishwamitra did not easily give up. He did tough penance to please lord Shankara. The latter blessed him with divine missiles and weapons. He returned to destroy the ashrama of Vasishtha once again. However, he was no match for Vasishtha who had dharma on his side. The latter using his Brahma danda destroyed all the divine weapons that the king hurled at him. The guru was invincible in his fury. Rishis and devatas descended from Swargaloka to pacify Vasishtha.

'Vishwamitra realized that unless he could be a Brahmarshi, he would always be inferior to Vasishtha. He was known as Rajarshi. He wanted to be a Brahmarshi and be accepted as a Brahmin. Once again, he started a penance in the Himalayas. He created the southern Saptarishis and other constellations. He wanted to create a Swargaloka, parallel to the one ruled by Indra.

Indra Sends Menaka to Divert Vishwamitra from His Penance

'Vishwamitra's unending cycle of tapasya worried Indra that the king might succeed in dethroning him. He asked Menaka, one of the celestial beauties to descend and win over the tapasvi king's affections. She came to Pushkara Teertha where Vishwamitra was sitting in meditation. As she prepared for a bath, her body glistened like lightning. The rishi found her irresistible. He invited her to come over to his ashrama and live with him.

'Kamadeva has conquered me, O beauty. Come and oblige me,' said Vishwamitra.

'Menaka readily agreed. She lived with him for ten years. The Rishi's penance was thus successfully interrupted by Indra.

'However, Vishwamitra was not one to give up easily. He started his penance again. He stood with both his arms raised and without any support for years.

'Indra once again tried to disturb the king's penance. This time he sent Rambha, another dazzling celestial beauty to entice the tapasvi king. Afraid of the Rajarshi, she descended hesitatingly in the month of Vaishakha when the koel was singing its melodious song. Nascent soft leaves had appeared on the trees and myriad flowers were blooming. Indra had promised all help and sent Kamadeva to assist her in enticing the tapasvi.

'However, this time Vishwamitra saw through Indra's game plan. He suspected the motive behind Rambha's melodious singing, cooing of the koel and of flowers blooming in such abandon. Cursing he said, 'O unfortunate one, I have been doing penance to conquer lust and anger. You have come to disrupt my tapasya. You will turn into a stone till Brahma's son, Vasishtha comes and provides you release from my curse.'

'In the meantime, Indra and Kamadeva had disappeared from the scene.

'Vishwamitra repented his anger and lustful thoughts. Thought he, 'Krodha has once again interrupted my tapasya. My mind is not at peace. I determine that henceforth I shall never be angry nor give in to lustful thoughts. I shall stay silent till I succeed.'

'The Rajarshi started his penance again. He continued observing silence and controlled his breathing.

'At one stage, the rishi stopped breathing as part of his penance. This most difficult part of his tapasya made him glow like fire and stunned the devatas and other rishis. The rishi's forehead began to emit smoke, which filled the air. The devatas ran to Brahma requesting him to assuage Vishwamitra and bring normalcy to the universe. They prayed,

'Bhagwan, Vishwamitra's radiance will annihilate everyone. Please grant him whatever he desires, even the sovereignty of Swargaloka. Help, O father, help.'

'Brahma appeared in person where Vishwamitra was at his penance and sweetly said,

'Brahmarshi, I bless you. You have attained the status of a Brahmin through your tough penance. I grant you long life. You are free to travel anywhere like the gods of wind. I guarantee your welfare. You will always be happy and blessed.'

'Vishwamitra bowed in the presence of Brahma and greeted all the devatas and rishis accompanying the father of the world. Humbly he said,

'With your blessings I have been granted the status of a Brahmin and a long life. I request the four Vedas to accept me as such. Further, Brahmaputra Vasishtha should acknowledge this fact. His acceptance will be my fulfilment.'

'Vasishtha obliged by reaching the spot where the Rajarshi was sitting in penance. The Rajarshi worshipped Vasishtha and asked for his blessings.

14

Rama Bends the Divine Bow

Raja Janaka warmly received Rishi Vishwamitra and the two young princes in the yagya mandapa with arghya and flowers. He offered them suitable seats and introduced the Maharshi to other sages assembled there. With folded hands, the king addressed the Maharshi and said,

'May you be blessed, O great muni. Who is the father of these two young princes who look chivalrous like gods and carry heavy arms with ease? They walk an elephant's graceful walk. Yet, they are like a lion or a bull. They are charming like lotuses in full bloom. Carrying swords, bows and quivers full of arrows, they outdo Ashwini Kumars in majesty and glory. They seem to have just gained adulthood. What purpose brings them here? '

Vishwamitra, full of limitless self-confidence replied, 'Rajan, these princes are the sons of the King Dashratha of Ayodhya.' He then narrated all the events since their departure from Ayodhya.

The Story of Shankara's Bow

Next day, Janaka, the devout king, sent for the Maharshi and the two princes and enquired what service he could render to them.

Vishwamitra, never at a loss for words, replied, 'The sons of Dashratha are chivalrous princes. They desire to see Shankara's bow that is in your family's possession. Casting a glance at the bow, they will be more than satisfied and then return to Ayodhya.'

At this, Janaka narrated the circumstances under which the mighty bow had come into the possession of his family.

'This bow was handled by Shankara when he was destroying the yagya being performed by his father-in-law, Daksha Prajapati for the latter had humiliated the mighty god. He wanted to behead all those present who had joined in insulting him. However, he forgave them and handed over the bow to the devatas who in turn gave it to my ancestor, Devaraat, son of the king Nimi. It has come to my possession as a family heirloom.

'One fine day, I was ploughing to level the soil for the yagya ceremonies. Miraculously, in one of the furrows ripped by the blade, a girl child appeared. I named her Sita after the sharp line drawn by the plough. With time this daughter of mine, born of the earth, grew into a charming maiden.

'I determined that Sita would be married to a warrior who could bend the sacred bow and shoot an arrow. This shall be her price. Unless such a strong and dexterous man appears she, the ayonija, shall stay unmarried.

'Several kings and princes have come and tried to mount an arrow on Shankara's bow. Each one has failed. None could even lift the bow from its sacred mount.

'I shall certainly display the holy bow to Rama and Lakshmana. Munishrestha, this bow shines like the sun. If Rama can string it, I shall happily offer him the hand of my ayonija daughter, Sita.'

Janaka ordered his officers to bring the sacred bow, adorned with garlands and scented with sandal. The bow had been lying in a heavy casket made of metal. Five thousand hefty warriors had to pull the chariot on which they placed the casket, lifting it with great difficulty.

Addressing them Janaka said,

'Maharshi, the holy bow of Bhagwan Shankara has been brought ceremoniously. None has been able to move it or lift it to date. The young princes may look at it and try to handle it as a warrior might.'

Rama Takes Up the Challenge

At Maharshi Vishwamitra's instance, Rama opened the trunk that contained Shankara's bow. He spoke,

'I shall make an effort to lift this mighty, divine bow. I shall then try to put a string on it if I can.'

The muni nodded in agreement.

With the Maharishi's permission, Rama, the scion of Raghu's dynasty and an upholder of Dharma, miraculously lifted the bow, holding its central curve in his palm. In a moment he had stringed it. The assembled crowd looked at him in amazement.

However, the moment Rama stretched the string to his ear to place an arrow on the bow the sacred dhanusha broke into two with a sound like that of a hailstorm. The earth shook as if there was an earthquake. It sounded as if a volcano had erupted. Quite a few bystanders fainted with fright at the noise.

Coming to his senses, Janaka who always spoke in measured tones, addressed Rishi Vishwamitra,

'Bhagwan, I have seen the valour of the son of Dashratha. To lift, bend and stretch a string on Shankara's bow is an amazing feat. I never thought that it was possible. My daughter, Sita, will wed Shri Rama and spread the name of my family everywhere.

'My determination to place a condition on my daughter's marriage has paid off. I had made her Veerya-shulka. I love Sita more than my life. In all humility, I offer her to Shri Rama. I am deputing my ministers to go to Ayodhya in super-fast chariots and invite king Dashratha to come to Mithila for the wedding.'

15

Rama Weds Sita

In Ayodhya, Janaka's messengers were ushered into the presence of king Dashratha. Hands folded, bowing with humility, speaking politely, they said,

'Maharaja, Mithilapati Janaka, with Agni as witness, has, in words full of affection and warmth, enquired of your well-being and the well-being of your Gurus, purohits and ministers.

'Further, with the consent of the Rishi Vishwamitra, he has sent a message. He says,

'I had fixed chivalry as the price of my daughter while choosing her bride-groom. Several kings, valorous and proud came and tried to move the sacred bow of Shankara inherited by me from my ancestors. Each one of them failed and returned empty-handed.

'Your son who arrived with Maharishi Vishwamitra by chance, has, in the presence of hundreds of spectators, chivalrously lifted and broken this holy weapon into two. He has thus won the hand of my daughter, Sita.

'I invite you with your Gurus, purohits and near and dear ones to come to Mithila and bless the union of your son with my daughter. Your arrival here would be a source of immense joy to both of your sons.'

Next morning Dashratha ordered Sumantra, one of his confidantes, to prepare for the marriage party to depart. The treasurers carrying precious stones and gold coins were to lead the group, under sufficient protection. A part of the armed forces was to accompany them. Guru Vasishtha, rishis Vamadeva, Jabali, Kashyapa and Markandeya joined the marriage party, riding decorated chariots and on pedigree horses.

The marriage party arrived at Mithila in four days. Janaka received them outside his capital and warmly embraced Dashratha.

'I welcome you, Raghunandan Dashratha,' said Janaka.

'It is my good fortune that you agreed to come at my request. You will soon come face to face with your glorious sons who have earned name and fame by displaying unparalleled bravery. All the obstacles in my path have disappeared. The warriors of Raghu's dynasty are unique in chivalry. Associating with your Vansha, my family feels honoured.

'Tomorrow morning, O king, at the conclusion of my yagya, please come over and perform the auspicious marriage ceremony of Shri Rama and my beloved daughter, Sita.'

Dashratha, learned in speech and graceful in manner, replied,

'Maharaja, you are learned in Dharma. I have heard that the right of acceptance is subject to the convenience of the giver. Therefore, we shall follow your dictates and do your bidding.'

This humble and honourable statement by the king of Ayodhya took Raja Janaka by surprise. He considered himself blessed in making this alliance of the two families.

Both the princes arrived on the scene and touched their father's feet. The father was delighted to meet them after a long time.

Next day, during an assembly of the kings and maharishis, Vasishtha narrated the entire genealogy of Dashratha's family. Janaka's purohit followed suit. This was an accepted ritual so that the two families that came together in a matrimonial alliance could be sure of each other.

Later, introducing his younger brother Kushadhwaja, Janaka said, 'He is my younger brother and like me he has two daughters.

'I offer my elder daughter Sita for Shri Rama and my younger daughter, Urmila for Shri Lakshmana. I am offering these two daughters without any compulsion, with joy and in good faith. I repeat my offer three times to confirm it.'

It was decided to perform the marriage ceremony after three days when the stars of Poorva Falguni and Uttar Falguni, [various stars of the constellation Leo], would be in the ascendant. Dashratha gave cows, gold, oil seeds and grains in charity while praying for the welfare of his two sons.

At this stage, Vishwamitra and Vasishtha suggested that, in order to bring the illustrious families closer, Kushadhwaja's daughters could be married to Bharata and Shatrughna. Everyone happily agreed to this proposal. After all, the four princes of Ayodhya were handsome, radiant like the Lokapalas and brave like the devatas.

To celebrate the occasion and for the good fortune of his sons, Dashratha gave away thousands of cows in charity. Gold caps covered the horns of these animals. Their calves accompanied them. Milk vessels made of bronze were given away to each recipient of a cow.

The Wedding Reception

On the auspicious day of the wedding, everyone got up early. After ablutions, king Dashratha arrived, preceded by the rishis, at the Yagyashala of king Janaka. Rama, accompanied by his brothers, followed them in Vijaya Muhoorta. The princes were decked as bridegrooms. Maharishi Vasishtha approached Janaka and ceremoniously asked for permission for the marriage party to enter the consecrated space. He said,

'Charity and righteousness go together only if the one who makes the gift and the one who accepts it come together in good faith. Hence, you may extend them a formal invitation so that you can perform the kanyadan as a matter of your dharma.

Janaka replied, 'Munishrestha, no guards stand here to bar the Maharaja's entry. He need not wait for my orders. Coming into his own house, he does not need any permission. The auspicious ceremonies for the wedding of my daughters have started. The brides stand near the yagya vedi [altar] and radiate light like the flames of fire. I too am present here, waiting your convenience. Please start the marriage ceremony and complete it without any interruption and obstruction.'

The Wedding Ceremony

Under the large canopy erected for the wedding, Janaka set up an altar as per ritual that was decorated on all sides with flowers and garlands and was fragrant with incense. Many other articles like golden utensils, pitchers painted with barley sprout motifs, earthen bowls in which barley sheaves were sprouting, stands with burning incense, ablution pots made of conches, utensils full of puffed rice, and plates full of wet rice, were arranged in a beautiful way.

Maharishi Vasishtha spread mats made of kusha grass around the havana kunda and, chanting mantras, ignited the sacred fire.

Janaka led Sita dressed in bridal finery and made her sit facing Rama near Agni. Addressing the prince, he said,

'Raghunandan, may god bless you! I offer you my daughter, Sita as your partner to lead a life according to Dharma. Please hold her hand in yours and accept her as your wife. She will be a devoted wife, will bring good luck, and will always be your shadow.'

Saying this, Janaka poured sankalpa water, made holy with mantras, into Rama's palm. He repeated the ceremony with Lakshmana and placed Urmila's hand in the hand of the prince. Bharata and Mandavi, Shatrughna and Shrutakeerti were united likewise.

As directed by Vasishtha, the four newly-weds walked in parikrama around the holy fire, the altar, king Dashratha, the rishis and munis assembled there. This completed the marriage ceremony.

The skies showered flowers and the devatas played divine instruments to celebrate the weddings. Large groups of apsaras danced in glee and the gandharvas sang melodious songs.

Janaka gifted his and his brother's daughters hundreds of cows, carpets, and clothes made of silk and cotton. He gave away decorated elephants, horses and chariots besides foot soldiers, maids and companions. The brides were given gold and silver coins, ornaments made of gold and coral, pearl necklaces and bracelets.

16

Enter Parashurama, the Spoilsport

King Dashratha set out on the return journey to Ayodhya accompanied by his princes, their brides, and the rishis. Armed soldiers protected them.

All of a sudden, the marriage party heard birds making frightened sounds. The wild deer ran on their right side A ferocious dust storm overtook the travellers. The winds blew hard, uprooting several trees. The earth shook as if there was an earthquake. Clouds of dust hid the sun. The entourage lost the sense of direction. Several soldiers fainted. Layers of dust covered the entire marriage party.

Looking up, Dashratha noticed the arrival of Parashurama, son of the rishi Jamadagni and a descendant of Maharishi Bhrigu. He was reputed to have brought hundreds of kings to their knees. He looked ferocious with long unkempt tresses, invincible like the Kailas Mountain and destructive like the fires of doom. He carried a halo that heightened his brilliance. He carried an axe on his shoulder and in his hands, he carried a mammoth, radiant bow. Vasishtha and other Brahmarshis worried whether Parashurama had come to destroy the Kshatriyas again, this time, Dashratha and his sons, and their forces. Despite this apprehension, Vasishtha and the rishis went ahead and welcomed Parashurama with arghya and polite words.

Parashurama and Rama, Face to Face

Parashurama acknowledged Vasishtha's welcome but moved forward to stand face to face with Ramachandra. Addressing the prince, he said, 'O chivalrous Rama, I have heard of your bravery in breaking Shankara's dhanusha. Your deed is amazing. However, it is a matter of concern for me. I have, therefore, brought another bow on which you can exercise your muscles. I ask you to stretch a string on this dhanusha and prove your mettle. After you have tried your best on my bow, I shall invite you to a duel worthy of your strength and heroism.'

Parashurama's words frightened Dashratha who addressed the Brahmin thus:

'O Brahman, you are an asset to Bhrigu's family that is a repository of vast knowledge and famous for their determination. You are a great tapasvi in your own right and a Brahmagyani.

'I heard that you had decided to follow the path of dharma and be busy in tapasya in your ashrama at Mahendra Mountain. How then have you arrived at this moment of joy in our life?'

Parashurama ignored the king. Continuing his address to Rama, he said,

'Rama, these two bows were the best ever made in the world. The universe looked at them with awe. Vishwakarma personally made these mighty and sturdy bows. With one of them Shankara fought the battle of Tripurasura. You broke that one into two. The other one has come to me via Bhagwan Vishnu.

'I was compelled to destroy the Kshatriyas because they had killed my father, Jamadagni who was meditating defenceless. I have come here after I learnt of the destruction of Shiva's bow.

'I challenge you to lift my bow and mount an arrow on its taut string. That is your dharma as a Kshatriya. If you are successful, I shall challenge you to a duel.'

Rama had so far kept quiet out of regard for his father. However, overcoming his restraint at this point, he addressed Parashurama and said,

'Bhrigunandana, I have heard of the extent to which you have massacred the Kshatriyas in order to avenge the killing of your father.

'Following my dharma as a Kshatriya, I have not interrupted you, for you are a revered Brahmin. On the other hand, you are humiliating me, calling me a coward, incompetent and lacking in chivalry. It is time I showed you my might and your place.'

Without wasting any further words or time, Rama snatched Parashurama's bow and arrow which had at one time belonged to Vishnu. He lifted the bow, stretched its string and placed an arrow at its centre. Rebuking Parashurama, Rama said,

'As a Brahmin, you deserve to be worshipped by me. Therefore, I cannot let go of this arrow with your body as its target. I propose that

I destroy your capabilities to travel unhindered anywhere. As an alternative, I can destroy the celestial lands that you have earned by your tapasya. This arrow, blessed by Vishnu, cannot go waste.'

Looking at Rama pulling at the bowstring with an arrow pointed towards Parashurama, the latter lost his nerve. Feeling humble in the presence of the prince, [who was an avatar of Vishnu], the Brahmin said,

'I beg you not to destroy my powers to roam freely over the earth. With a speed as fast as that of the mind, I shall move over to the Mahendra Mountain. You may destroy the lands which I have conquered. The fact that you could bend this bow proves that you are the indestructible Deveshwara Vishnu come down to earth who had killed Madhu, the demon. Rama, I wish you well. My defeat at your hands is not a matter of shame for me. I have been vanquished by none other than Hari, the master of the Universe.'

As Parashurama departed, the gloom and darkness that had enveloped the world disappeared.

17

Arrival in Ayodhya

As soon as Parashurama departed, Dashratha embraced Rama with both arms and smelled his forehead in a blessing. The marriage party set out for Ayodhya where the entire town had been bedecked for receiving the princes and their brides.

On the roads of Ayodhya, water had been sprinkled to settle dust and reduce heat. Flowers were scattered at every nook and corner. The citizens were standing to offer garlands and other auspicious objects to the newly married couples. They were overjoyed at the turn of events. Leading citizens and Brahmins welcomed Maharaja Dashratha and other members of the marriage party outside the city.

Riding their royal chariots, the Maharaja, the princes and their wives entered the king's palace that was magnificent as the Himalayas, with its roof touching the sky. The residents of the palace and the queens, Kaushalya, Sumitra and Kaikeyee, accorded a warm welcome to Dashratha.

Among the queens, Kaikeyee, slim of waist, the youngest wife and mother of Bharata, was extremely charming.

After a few days Bharata and Shatrughna left Ayodhya to visit Bharata's maternal grandfather. Rama and Lakshmana busied themselves with the care of their god-like father. They also looked after the citizens and the welfare of the public on behalf of the king. The people of the kingdom were more than pleased with Rama's cultured behaviour. He was flawless in character and was humble and polite towards everyone, whether high or low.

Sita was deeply in love with Rama. So was Rama deeply fond of her. Both had given their hearts to each other. Living together, many seasons of joy passed to their delight.

Sita loved Rama and Rama alone. Rama too never craved for another woman. Sita stayed by his side like Lakshmi enhancing Vishnu's glorious majesty.

AYODHYAKANDAM

1

Dashratha Decides upon a Successor

While Bharata and Shatrughna had gone to spend some time with their maternal grandfather, Dashratha missed them greatly. He was growing old now, and his sons were his wealth and very dear to him. Yet, Rama was dearer to him because of the way his mind, body and spirit were balanced. What was unknown to others was that Rama was an avatar of Vishnu, incarnated to annihilate the impetuous and mighty Ravana who with his evil deeds harassed the devatas in Indra's Swargaloka. Vishnu had himself descended on the earth as Rama at the pleading of the devatas. Rama's unparalleled effulgence made his mother Kaushalya as glorious as Aditi had become because of her son Indra.

Qualities of Rama

Rama was chivalrous and handsome to look at, a disposition deeply complemented by his words of assurance to everyone and maintaining poise even in the face of harsh circumstances and people. At such a tender age, he had controlled his anger. He understood the essence of Dharma, Artha and Kama as well.

The possessor of a remarkable memory, he remembered every good deed done to him, while he ignored a hundred offensive misdeeds of others. Rama found time to engage in discussions with men of wisdom, those who excelled in learning, who were senior in age and those of impeccable character.

Rama was wise for his age. He was a good host and always tried to say a few pleasant words to a visitor. Though very capable in using weapons, he never boasted of his strength and dexterity. He never told a lie and received love from his people equal to his love for them.

Rama's heart overflowed with kindness towards the humble and the unfortunate. He exercised control over his desires and thus, was pure in his thoughts and behaviour. With such a strong hold over his senses, Rama never felt inclined to commit a wrong, prohibited or evil deed. Like Guru Brihaspati himself, he could argue well in favour of justice and a fair approach towards men and matters.

Rama was completely devoted to his gurus and seniors, unhindered in his actions by either laziness or passion. He looked at the world not with attachment but with unwavering intellect. Learned in the shastras, Rama studied the principles of economics, of how to earn and treasure wealth without straining the resources of the people. He understood the principles of expenditure management as laid down in the ancient treatises.

In terms of his physical abilities, along with his skill with weaponry, Rama had learnt the art of horse-riding. He was trained to tame elephants, to engage them in sports and to ride them. He learnt how to lead an army and how to engage an enemy. In terms of arts, he excelled in the art of writing drama in Sanskrit, Prakrit and other languages. He also took part in sports, learnt music, played on musical instruments and knew how to paint.

Thus, in wisdom Rama was like Brihaspati and in valour like Indra, Shachi's husband. Keeping all these qualities in mind, Dashratha considered the possibility of anointing him as the crown prince to succeed him. He wanted to decide upon this crucial matter in his lifetime to avoid any battle for succession later.

To this end, Dashratha called the leaders of various communities from cities that formed essential parts of his kingdom, kings who owed loyalty to him, and his ministers, for consultation. In his desire to fulfil his duty at the earliest, Dashratha did not extend invitations to Janaka and his father-in-law, the king of Kaikeya.

Dashratha Proposes Rama's Coronation to the Assembled Audience

The mighty king, in a voice as sonorous as that of thundering clouds, explained his proposal to the assembled nobility. He said, 'You are well aware how my ancestors have taken care of this kingdom, as if it was their child. Till now, I too have followed in their footsteps and protected the people with all my might. But now I am growing old and the time is ripe for me to fulfil my last duty towards the kingdom.

With your approval and the consent of the Brahmins gathered here, I desire to hand over the reins of the kingdom to my son, Rama.

'He is skilled and accomplished in all that a deserving prince needs. He is pure in mind, body and soul. I propose to anoint him as the future king tomorrow, when the constellation Cancer is in the ascendant. I am sure that Rama would turn out to be a benevolent and worthy king for his people and kingdom.

'If my proposal meets with your approval, grant me this request. If not, I seek your guidance to proceed in the matter. An advice from an impartial mediator is always welcome.'

The gathering of the kings and citizens approved of Dashratha's proposal whole-heartedly and unanimously.

The Brahmins, commanders, and city chieftains consulted with each other and addressed the king thus:

'We are keen to see Rama, the scion of the Raghuvansha, majestically riding an elephant under a white canopy. He is truthful and a man of principles. He has maintained a fine balance between dharma and artha. He delights the praja like the moon. He is by temperament forgiving, like Prithvi. He has the wisdom of Brihaspati and the valour of Indra.

'Rama is aware of the duty cast upon him by dharma. He has a remarkable character himself and does not seek to find faults in others. He offers solace to the oppressed, gives assurances to the needy, is soft-spoken, does not forget an obligation, is gentle by temperament and is of a stable disposition.

'Rama has the potential to defend the entire universe. With his virtues, the prince looks brilliant like the sun spreading his rays. Your praja, O King, wants to see Rama succeed you as the king of Ayodhya. They pray for him and wish him many victories along with a long life. The people of Ayodhya, irrespective of age, have prayed to gods that Rama be anointed as the Yuvaraja.

'O king of kings, we wish and pray that you anoint Rama, who glows with the complexion of a blue lotus and is capable of annihilating his enemies, whoever they may be, as the Yuvaraja to succeed you, as soon as possible.'

2

Ayodhya Prepares for
Rama's Rajyabhisheka

Everyone present in the king's assembly touched their forehead with palms folded like lotus buds. They whole-heartedly approved of Dashratha's proposal.

The king asked Vasishtha and his pupils to gather the necessary material for performing the ceremony in the sacred month of Chaitra marked by pleasant weather and fresh blooms in gardens owing to the arrival of Vasanta.

The Maharshi asked his assistants, 'Hurry and gather the material goods for the worship of the gods, such as golden utensils, herbs, garlands of white flowers, puffed rice, honey and ghee in separate containers. Arrange for new clothes, chariots, different types of weapons, and armies to parade on the occasion. We require elephants with majestic and auspicious attributes, a white canopy, and one hundred golden pitchers glistening like flames in a fire. We need a bull with gilded horns, and a lion's skin. Everything must reach the king's Yagyashala before sunrise.

'Further, decorate all the doors in the city and the gates of the palace with garlands. Prepare for a feast using milk, curd, and ghee. The food should be sufficient for hundreds of Brahmins who will attend the ceremony and chant the sacred mantras.

'Put colourful flags on high poles all across the city. Sprinkle water on the roads to settle the dust. The men who can play on musical instruments and the women who can dance must be present in suitable finery at the inner entrance of the palace.'

At this stage, Dashratha's confidante Sumantra was asked to bring the prince to the assembly. He soon returned with Rama riding a glistening chariot. Nearing the court, Rama alighted from the chariot and walked with the majesty of an elephant. In the king's presence, the prince bowed in salutation with folded hands. Rama's presence attracted everyone's attention and caught even his father's eye.

Dashratha held his son's hands as he bowed down to him in greeting and warmly embraced him. The king beckoned his son to sit by his side on a golden throne studded with precious stones. Seated there, Rama looked resplendent in his glory like that of the Meru Mountain under a cloudless sky.

Dashratha Lays Down the Rules of Kingship for Rama

Addressing the prince, the king said, 'Rama, you were born to my senior queen, Kaushalya, and you have qualities superior to mine. Not only are you the dearest to me, but your attributes have endeared you to our people as well. Tomorrow I shall anoint you as the Yuvaraja of the kingdom.

'Despite being sure of your qualities and abilities, I would like to offer a few words of advice for your benefit. These will enable you to be humbler than ever before and restrain your desires to administer justice impartially.

'Take care of the legitimate interests of your ministers, officials, commanders and soldiers. Your subjects' welfare should be your priority. The king who commands a treasury full of wealth, an armoury full of armaments, and who is a master of all that is necessary to run a state, is a source of happiness to his well-wishers just like Amrita was to the devatas. The ruler who holds his ministers, commanders and praja dear to him, commands their sincere loyalty. Therefore, my son, control your thoughts and follow the correct practices befitting a ruler.'

Bowing to his father, Rama left for his apartments. However, even after this happy event, Dashratha was restless. He recalled Rama within a short time and asking him to enter the inner chambers, addressed him once again.

'I am too old to continue to be the ruler. I am anointing you as my successor because all my subjects desire me to do so.

'At night, I have frightening dreams. It makes me think my end is not far. You must be anointed before anything untoward happens to me or I change my mind. Human beings are unstable by nature in taking their decisions.

'Go back and fast with your wife. Sleep on a bed made of kusha grass and abstain from physical contact with her tonight. I fear unforeseen obstructions in the course of performing this good deed. I desire that your anointment takes place before Bharata returns from his maternal uncle's house.

'I have no doubt that Bharata is a balanced person and that his conduct is that of a man who lives by principles of truth. He has conquered his desires. He is kind, gentle, dutiful, and he has a high regard for you. However, in my view, anyone can try to influence the way he thinks at any time.'

Rama heard his father's words in silence and departed for his mother's chambers. Kaushalya was engrossed in prayers for the well-being of her family, accompanied by Lakshmana, his mother Sumitra and Sita.

Kaushalya, who had waited for this day for a long time, shed tears of joy and embraced Rama. In a voice overwhelmed with emotions, she said,

'Rama, my son, may you live long! May there be no obstructions in your path!' Listening to his mother's blessings, Rama touched her feet and addressed Lakshmana who was standing nearby thus:

'Brother, you are my conscience. You will assist me in looking after this kingdom. I want you to enjoy the fruit of this elevation in equal measure.'

Rama now moved over to his own chambers that had been painted white like spotless clouds. Soon after his arrival, Vasishtha came to see him. Rama personally received the sage and with great humility, uttered a few words of welcome to the Guru. The latter repeated the advice that had been offered by Dashratha that Rama and Sita should ritually fast until the next day.

Rama's mansion echoed with the joyous voices of numerous men and women. It looked pleasing to the eyes like a pond full of lotus flowers in full bloom, abuzz with delirious birds singing melodiously. Colourful flags were hoisted in the lawns and gardens attached to the mansions and the lanes throughout the city were swept and sprinkled with water.

As Maharshi Vasishtha departed, Rama bathed and started the ritual fast in the company of his beautiful wife. With a strong control over their senses, partaking a little of the yagya prasad, maintaining total silence, and concentrating their thoughts on Shri Narayana Deva, Rama and Sita lay down to sleep on kusha mats in the Vishnu temple.

Rama woke up with the first rays of the sun and listening to lilting prayers sung by the court singers, sat in meditation for his morning prayers.

Rejoicing in Ayodhya

The entire city and its people were wide awake in the early hours of the morning. The traders had opened their shops early, as in festive times, to sell goods. Dancers performed on the street corners while singers sang songs to the sheer delight of listeners. The people, gathered in homes and at the town squares, animatedly talked of Rama's abhishek. The streets decorated with flowers and incense sticks lighted at various places bathed the city in sweet fragrances. With roaring hordes assembled to witness the rajyabhisheka, Ayodhya resembled Indrapuri.

3

Kaikeyee Asks the King to Redeem His Pledge

Manthara Turns the Tables

While the city rejoiced in festive celebrations, Kaikeyee's chamber resounded with Manthara's voice. Addressing the queen who was lying in her bed, Manthara said,

'O fool, wake up! An unprecedented misfortune is about to befall you. You lie totally unaware of the events unfolding in the court. Your beloved king has always professed absolute devotion to you and pretended that he would hand over the reins of his kingdom to you or your son. You have been boasting of his fidelity. Wake up and see how like a stream running dry in summer, your good fortune has been destabilized and is on the verge of disappearing.'

Manthara was a maid who had accompanied Kaikeyee, Dashratha's third wife and a favourite, when she had come to Ayodhya after marriage. She was a hunchback and was the queen's confidante. Standing on the roof of Kaikeyee's palace late in the evening, she noticed Ayodhya being decorated for some sort of celebration. She noticed the Brahmin priests chanting with joy and musicians playing on diverse instruments. She heard the loud echo of Veda recitations and saw elephants and horses being dressed in finery. Further, she noticed Rama's nurse standing on the roof of Kaushalya's palace, dressed in yellow silk and looking cheerful.

On enquiry, Rama's nurse informed Manthara of the intended rajyabhisheka of Shri Rama. It is then that, hurt to the core on hearing this news, the hunchback rushed to the chambers of her mistress and addressed her in a loud voice. She continued,

'You lie with your eyes closed in your chambers and the city is getting ready for your loss. Tomorrow, the king will anoint Rama as his successor. I feel hurt and sorry for you and Bharata. For me, it is like burning in the fire of hell, of fear and apprehension. Your husband talks of dharma, of truth and duty. But see, he is a crook! He has been outwardly polite to you but wicked at heart. You trust him like an innocent fool. He makes love to you but is doing everything to oblige Kaushalya. He has deliberately sent Bharata away. In your son's absence, he wants to anoint Rama as Yuvaraja tomorrow morning. Wake up, O woman. If this happens, you will be devastated beyond repair.'

But Kaikeyee was pleased at the king's intention to anoint Rama. Handing over a precious ornament as a reward to Manthara for being the harbinger of such good tidings, the beauteous queen said,

'I do not differentiate between Rama and Bharata. I am delighted at hearing of Rama's intended anointment.'

Manthara was not going to give up so easily. She retorted, 'You appear to be happy at this sad news. I warn you to protect your interests and your son's before it is too late.

'You do not differentiate between Rama and Bharata but remember, a stepson is the enemy of his stepmother. If Rama gets the kingdom, he will become strong and powerful enough to uproot both of you, his potential rivals. In Lakshmana, he has a devoted and brave follower.

'I shiver at the thought of how Rama, who is skilled in every aspect of politics, will treat Bharata. You will be a maid to Kaushalya when her son becomes the king. You will not be able to live this insult, my queen.

'Bharata will stand in the court as a lowly courtier. Rama will not treat him as his equal because he is a rival. That is the way of the world.

'The king has deliberately planned to hand the kingdom over to Rama in Bharat's absence. I suggest that Rama be banished from the kingdom and Bharata be appointed as the king's successor. Think over what I am saying, O my queen.'

Kaikeyee tried to overrule Manthara's hysteric lamentation and alleviate her fears, but to no avail. Her insecurities as a mother and the fear of losing the place of the favourite queen of the king hindered her rationality. Ultimately, she came round and asked Manthara how to go about achieving Rama's banishment and installation of Bharata as the king of Ayodhya.

The Encashment of Two Boons

Manthara was ready with an answer. She said, 'You had accompanied your husband in the battle against the rakshasas where he assisted Indra. He was critically wounded in that operation and had lost consciousness in the middle of the battlefield. Acting as his charioteer at that critical moment, you drove him to safety, away from the battlefield. At that time, the king had granted you two favours, which you had not redeemed then. The time has come when you can encash those two boons and ask that Bharata be made his successor and Rama be exiled immediately into Dandakaranya for fourteen years. During Rama's absence, Bharata will inculcate the goodwill of the masses and firmly establish his rule.

'My queen, I suggest you now change into dirty, worn-out clothes and roll on bare earth in the Kopabhavana, the chamber meant for showing your anger. When the king arrives, do not talk to him. Nay, do not even look at him, nor acknowledge his presence. Weep loudly, cry and roll on the earth. You have been his favourite; if he sees you in the dishevelled state, he won't be able to refuse your request.

'He will try to placate you with jewels, pearls, gold and precious goods. Do not yield to anything. Remind him of his promise of two boons. Tell him that he has to prove his devotion to truth and commitment. Once you have firmed his will, ask him to anoint Bharata tomorrow and simultaneously banish Rama for fourteen years. The second request is the most important; Rama must be removed from the kingdom to enable the people to accept Bharata as their ruler. It is only in his absence that Bharata can consolidate his hold on the masses and the kingdom.'

Arguing thus, Manthara made the undesirable seem desirable to Kaikeyee. In her twisted mind, the queen marvelled at Manthara's wisdom and said,

'You have talked about my interest most wisely. I shall not over-rule your advice. If it was not for you, the king would have succeeded in his devious plan. I could never have seen through his game.

'When Bharata has been anointed as the Yuvaraja and Rama has departed for the forest, I shall dress your hump in strings of pure gold. I shall make sure your body glows with sandalwood and your forehead gleams with a tilaka of gold. Dressed thus, you will walk like a Devangana.'

An elated Manthara advised the queen not to waste any more time as Rama's anointment had to be forestalled under any circumstances. Kaikeyee was advised to take off her jewels and royal dress, put on rags, and roll in the dust of the floor of the Kopabhavana.'

A determined Kaikeyee declared to Manthara,

'I am least interested in valuable clothes, pearls and ornaments. I shall end my life if Rama is made the Yuvaraja. If the king does not agree to his immediate banishment, I shall give up soft beds, garlands of flowers, sandal paste, betel leaves, royal meals and all other riches and comforts.'

Addressing Manthara thus and having fallen for the hunchback's words completely, Kaikeyee changed into rags and lay on bare earth in a lonely, dark, unfurnished room. She looked like the dark sky, devoid of stars. She rolled on the floor in grief as if struck by a poisonous arrow. She inhaled and exhaled hot air in long breaths like a serpent. Exhausted, she soon fell asleep.

Kaikeyee Humbles the Lusty King

Following his routine, Dashratha walked from his court into Kaikeyee's lavish palace while going into the inner chambers. The place resounded with noises made by peacocks, herons, royal swans and parrots. There were picture galleries all around. Champaka and asoka trees provided foliage and fragrance. Several maids moved about awaiting orders. The palace was full of artefacts made of ivory, gold and silver. The fragrance of sumptuous meals being cooked in the kitchen heightened the pleasure of the king.

However, while the king longed for Kaikeyee's young body, she was not in the chamber. Her luxurious bed was unoccupied.

This was the first instance of Kaikeyee's absence at the time of her husband's arrival. Dashratha was concerned and enquired about her whereabouts and was informed of her lying angry and forlorn in the Kopabhavana.

Dashratha was an old man while Kaikeyee was at the bloom of her youth. While he was pure at heart, she had planned an evil design. On the bare floor of the Kopabhavana, the queen lay like a creeper sliced at the root, heartbroken like a Devangana fallen from the skies.

Like a massive elephant lovingly caressing his mate who, having been pierced by the arrow of a hunter, lies supine, the lustful king lovingly tried to lift his wife into his arms. He was afraid of her rejection as much as of her words. Fondling her, he addressed her in a loving voice,

'I cannot imagine that you are angry with me. Have you been insulted by anyone? Has anyone denounced you? Kalyani, why do you hurt me by rolling in dust on the ground? Your beauty shakes my resolve whenever I look at you. Tell me if you are sick for I have at my command several competent physicians. They will look after you.

'Devi, do not weep. Do not starve your body. I am willing to lay down my life for you.

'My beloved, tell me whatever you desire. I swear by all the good deeds that I have done that I shall carry out your wishes.

'I rule the entire earth where the sun shines. I am the suzerain of the prosperous Dravida, Sindhu-Sauvira, Saurashtra, the Dakshina Bharata, Anga Desha, Magadha, Matsya, Kashi and Kausala. Take any of their wealth, grain, animals, horses, cows, goats and sheep. Why do you suffer like this?

'Get up, O Kaikeyee, and tell me what bothers you. I shall overcome the cause of your fear.'

Listening to the king's assurances, Kaikeyee decided to drive her evil intentions home to him. While the old man was lusting after her youth, she addressed him in a harsh voice:

'Deva, nobody has insulted me or humiliated me. However, I want you to fulfil a desire of mine. If you agree to abide by me, say so and make a firm commitment. I shall reveal my intent thereafter.'

The doting king who desperately wanted her, lifted her head and placed it in his lap. He said, 'Barring Rama, I love you more than any other human being. I swear by Rama that I shall satisfy your desire, whatever that be. You have no reason to doubt my word. Do not underestimate my love for you.'

Being satisfied that the king was under her sway completely, Kaikeyee expressed her intentions, holding Indra and all other gods as witnesses. Her words were as frightening as the very presence of Yamaraja, the god of death.

'Be a witness O gods, the Sun, the Moon and all others, that the truthful, glorious king, the upholder of dharma, a man of pious conduct, Maharaja Dashratha has made a promise to grant my wishes.'

Addressing the king, she continued thus:

'Rajan, remember how once upon a time, working hard through the night, I had saved your life on the battlefield. At that moment, you had granted me two boons, which I kept in your safe custody to be used at the opportune moment. O mighty king, today I seek the fulfilment of the same promises. You had granted the boons yourself and if you fail me, I shall kill myself.

'Whatever preparations you have made for the anointment of Rama must be diverted to anoint our son, Bharata instead.

'Secondly, banish the gentle Rama to Dandakaranya. Dressed in bark and deerskin like a tapasvi, he must leave before sunrise. Please so arrange his departure that I can witness his leaving this city.

'You are the king of kings, as you say. Be truthful to your promise and safeguard the nobility and illustrious name of your lineage and ancestors. The tapasvis advise us that truth is the highest virtue and that truth alone looks after us in the other world.'

4

Rama is Banished to Dandakaranya–1

Dashratha Pleads for Compassion

Dashratha could not comprehend Kaikeyee's words and seemed oblivious to what was happening around him. He wondered if it was a daydream or an illusion. Did it foretell an impending catastrophe? He swooned at the thought of Kaikeyee's words and regained consciousness at the thought of Rama. When he opened his eyes and saw Kaikeyee, he was deeply disturbed. He was frightened of her like a fawn at the sight of a lion. Sitting on the bare floor, Dashratha breathed heavily, and felt like a poisonous snake stilled into inaction by a mantra. Rebuking Kaikeyee with all his might, he said, 'O heartless and villainous woman, you are out to destroy this noble family. O evil incarnate, what harm have Rama and I done to you? Rama has always treated you like his mother. I have been enamoured of his great qualities since he was born. What is his fault that I should renounce him at your instance?

'This universe might survive without the sun but I cannot survive without Rama. It is my request to you: give up your insistence of his exile. I accede to your first request to anoint Bharata as the Yuvaraja. However, your second demand is unacceptable. It will destroy the Ikshavaku dynasty.

'I have always noticed that Rama takes greater care of you than Bharata. He is obedient to the elders and cares for the people. The prince is virtuous to the core and his thoughts are centred in truth, charity, tapasya, detachment, friendship, purity, simplicity, learning, and care of the gurus. Why do you want to harm Rama? Why?

'Kaikeyee, I am an old man nearing his death. Do not hasten my death by taking Rama away from me. I am willing to offer you all that I have; I request for your kindness with folded hands. Do not ask for Rama to be banished.'

Blackmail in the Name of Truth and High Moral Principles

Not worried of her husband losing consciousness over and over again, without bothering to pay any attention to the king's entreaties, not reconsidering or yielding on her demands, Kaikeyee spoke to Dashratha in words full of anger:

'Rajan, your words suggest that you want to renege your promises. In that case, you will not be able to face anyone as a righteous king. You will bring dishonour to your ancestors if you go back on your word. The king Shaibya had offered a piece of his own body to settle the dispute between an eagle and a pigeon. You too should keep in mind the reputation of your ancestors before going back on your word.

'However, I can see that you appear to have given up your pursuit of dharma for the love of your son. Right or wrong, whatever promises you have made must be fulfilled. If you anoint Rama, I shall consume poison and end my life. Nothing short of Rama's going to Dandakaranya will satisfy me.'

Dashratha was silent for a moment in the face of such determination. He fell to the ground like a tree that has been axed. Crying 'Hey Rama', he wept like a man who has lost all reasons to live. He continued to plead with Kaikeyee to reconsider her condition of banishing Rama, but to no avail. In trying to convince Kaikeyee, he said,

'Give up your evil designs, O vicious woman. Bharata is not going to accept this decision. I shall have no reason to survive if Rama goes to Dandakaranya leaving Sita behind to lament her fate. You will certainly be a widow soon after. I do not foresee the loss of fame of my forefathers, but all those who are noble will criticize me for surrendering to this lust.

'I feel like a child that catches hold of a snake while playing, without realising the consequences. In my passionate embraces, when I made love to you, I never realized that you will be the cause of my death one day. People will call me a fool, a man who had no control over his senses. If Rama goes into exile, the people of the city will not see me as a benevolent king; by taking their prince away from them I will surely sow seeds of hatred towards myself and Bharata.

'How will my son Rama, used to the comforts of a palace, walk barefoot in a forest and live a pauper's life? He rides elephants and travels in chariots; how will he survive in a pathless forest?

'Giving up his silken robes, how will Rama put on the bark of a tree? The best of chefs prepare his meals here every day; how would berries and wild fruit satisfy him?

'You are a blot on the Kaikeya dynasty. Whether you wallow in the muck of hatred, or reduce yourself to ashes; whether you poison yourself or be swallowed by earth splitting at a seam, I will not accede to your second demand. It will cause irreparable damage, take all of us to our end, not just me, but the entire kingdom.

'You are like a shining dagger that seems attractive owing to its lustre but kills nonetheless. I realize that all your sweet words for me and my sons are now exposed as poison; I also see that you are not my well-wisher any more. Despite all this, I cringe at your feet and ask for your kindness.'

Dashratha tried to prostrate himself in front of Kaikeyee, the one who had transgressed every limit of propriety. However, she had moved away and the king fell on the ground unconscious.

Kaikeyee did not give up her demand. She spurned every plea of her husband and repeatedly admonished him as the time of sunrise approached.

'Truth is Brahman, the Ultimate Reality. Dharma rests on truth and truth is to be found in the immortal Vedas. It is by relying on truth that one can improve their after-life. Maharaja, if you are truthful, you will have to keep your word and fulfil your promise. You will have to banish Rama and anoint Bharata.'

Dashratha felt like a bullock between the wheels of a chariot, helpless and carrying more burden than he could bear. Kaikeyee saw how Dashratha kept losing consciousness and his ability to take action, so she took matters into her hands and sent for Rama.

Entering Kaikeyee's chambers, Rama saw his father lying distraught and crest-fallen. The king could hardly speak. As the prince bowed to his father and the stepmother, Dashratha's eyes brimmed with tears. He muttered, 'Rama', and fell silent.

'Why is my father sad?' Rama wondered. Addressing Kaikeyee, he said,

'Is my father angry with me? Have I, unintentionally, committed an offence? Mother, why do you not plead with him on my behalf? I see the world because of him and would not ever hurt him.

'Devi, have you by any chance done anything against his wishes? Why is he upset?'

The shameless and stubborn Kaikeyee replied,

'Maharaja is neither angry nor in pain. He is unable to express the tussle between his mind and heart lest he hurts you. Nonetheless, you must obey and fulfil his promises to me.

'He promised to fulfil two of my wishes, whatever they may be and whenever I want them, and is now making futile efforts to not grant them to me. Rama, truth is the bedrock of dharma. You will have to act so that the Maharaja does not violate the sacred boundaries of truth and dharma out of love and affection for you. If you promise to carry out his commands, I shall repeat my requests.'

Rama replied, 'Fie on you, O Devi! You need not have such apprehensions about me. I will follow my father's command till the very end. He is my guru, father and well-wisher, I shall do his bidding. Tell me what he wishes me to do and I promise to fulfil every word of it.'

Kaikeyee, who had deserted the path of right conduct in her will to get Bharata anointed as crown prince, spoke in sorrowful tones, 'During a battle between the Devatas and the Asuras, the enemies' arrows had pierced your father. I rescued him and he offered me two boons. Raghava, I have asked him to make good that promise tonight. I want Bharata to be made the Yuvaraja and you to be exiled to Dandakaranya. If you want your father to be the guardian of truth, you will have to fulfil his commitment. It would mean giving up your ambition to be the Yuvaraja, taking on garments of bark and going to the forest for fourteen years. In the forest, you will have to live the life of a hermit without any help from the palace.

'Just because of this insignificant request, your father is reluctant to grant me my wishes and is unable to utter these words to you. In sorrow and fear, he is unable to make eye contact with you. You should obey his orders and help him stay truthful.'

Rama was least upset. He replied, 'Mother, do not worry. I shall obey the Maharaja's command and travel to the forest dressed in bark and live like a hermit. I wonder why has my father not told me this himself? Unhesitatingly, I shall do his bidding. Even if you would have asked me to do the same instead of father, I would have gladly given up the kingdom and wealth to Bharata.

'I request you to assure the king on my behalf; he does not have to feel miserable on my account. Why is the master of the earth shedding tears? It is unworthy and unbecoming of a king to be drawn into a web of emotions thus, and dharma has to be followed. You may arrange to send a few swift horses to fetch Bharata to Ayodhya; I will prepare to leave the capital forthwith.

A delighted Kaikeyee responded, 'You are right. I shall arrange to send for Bharata immediately. Meanwhile you must not delay your departure for which you appear to be keen. Your father is merely hesitant to speak to you of his intentions. Unless you depart for the forest, he will neither fulfil his responsibilities towards Bharata, nor be in a state of mind to go about daily rituals.'

Hearing his stepmother speaking thus, Rama lifted his father in his arms, and made him comfortable on a bed. Rama was keen to depart for Dandakaranya. Ignoring Kaikeyee's harsh words, he said,

'Devi, I have no desire to live on this earth as a slave to materialistic attractions. I too believe in truth like our rishis. I am prepared to lay down my life for the sake of my father. I believe that there is no higher duty than to obey one's father and to serve him. Even though my father has not commanded me in his own words, I shall go into exile for fourteen years at your bidding. I wish that you had asked me directly; I would have obeyed you without hesitation and father would not have been in this state of misery and anguish.'

Ignoring the mounds of goods collected for his coronation, Rama left for his mother's chambers. He carried with him the effulgence of immortals. The loss of an earthly kingdom mattered little to him. Eager to move into a forest as per his father's promise, Rama was happy to give the responsibility of the kingdom to Bharata instead. His thoughts were away from any feeling of loss. Like a mahatma who is beyond worldly attachments, Rama felt neither sorrow nor deprivation.

Rama forbade the use of a canopy over his head while walking, forbade the fanning by the attendant and did not use the chariot in which he had travelled to Kaikeyee's apartments. Rather, he turned away from his well-wishers, attendants and walked alone to Kaushalya's chambers to convey the unhappy tidings. He was in complete control of his senses and mind and had overcome any sense of loss or sorrow.

5

Rama is Banished to Dandakaranya–2

Rama Bids Farewell to Kaushalya

All this while in Kaikeyee's chambers Dashratha hid his face in the sheets of her bed and wept out of shame. It was out of his doing that his beloved son Rama would now have to live the harsh life of a hermit in a forest.

On the other hand, Rama entered Kaushalya's chambers. He saw his mother performing auspicious ceremonies in anticipation of her son being named the Yuvaraja. Rama bowed at her feet, she lifted him and embraced him warmly.

As Kaushalya asked Rama to sit near her and offered him some food, the prince said in all humility,

'Mother, you appear to be unaware of the misfortune that has befallen us. I no longer need the sumptuous feast offered by you to me. I have been exiled to Dandakaranya for fourteen years where I shall sit on a kusha mat. Renouncing the royal comforts and splendour, I shall live a secluded hermit's life surviving on fruit, vegetables and roots.

'The Maharaja has decided to anoint Bharata as the Yuvaraja while I go to live in a forest.'

Kaushalya fell to the ground like the branch of a mighty tree suddenly axed. It was some moments later that she collected herself and addressed her son thus:

'Raghunandan, had you not taken birth, I would have suffered the deprivation of a barren woman. Today's suffering is more acute. My wish that the pain that I endured all these years be removed, has not been answered. I have never enjoyed the privileges of being the senior queen of a ruling prince. I have lived in the hope that I shall see better times when my son ascends the throne. Your going into the forest will cause me immense pain and the co-wives will treat me with disrespect and speak harsh words.

'My husband always had a special place for Kaikeyee and I never enjoyed that place. If you go now, I will be deprived of your love too, my son. How will I now stand her bitter words, her uncontrollable anger and harsh behaviour?

'My beloved son, why did I not die with grief at the mere thought of being away from you! I shall accompany you to the forest like a cow following her calf.'

Lakshmana Revolts

Lakshmana was silently listening to this exchange between the mother and the son. Bowing to the sorrowing queen, he said,

'I am unable to appreciate the idea of Rama's going into exile while he was about to be named the Yuvaraja. A woman has misled the Maharaja and he has thereby lost his discretion. He is aged and seems to be a slave to his senses. A man loses his wisdom when Kamadeva enslaves him and when a woman like Kaikeyee is goading him in his acts.

'I see no reason for which Raghunath should be exiled from Ayodhya. He has committed no offence for which he is being punished. The king has lost his wisdom and forgets that his promise to his wife should not hold importance in the affairs of the state.

'Dear brother, at this point of time, no one is aware of the decision to banish you to Dandakaranya. Please take control of the state with my assistance. I shall annihilate anyone who challenges your might.

'Even a guru or an elder has to be challenged and punished if he arrogantly ignores the tenets of dharma, duty, and righteousness. Our father, under Kaikeyee's influence, is behaving like a child, oblivious to the good of his people and kingdom. I shall put him to death, if need be, and restore order and dharma in the matters of the state.'

Kaushalya too advised Rama to stay put and act according to dharma. She asserted that she was as important to him as his father was, and that she was ordering him to defy the king, ascend the throne and serve his aged mother.

Rama Lays Down the Rules of Obedience and Non-attachment

However, no argument deterred Rama, who was prepared to obey his father's command and leave the palace and kingdom. Placing his head at the feet of Kaushalya, he said,

'I am unable to disobey my father. Bless me so that I can go to the forest as directed and fulfil my duty of a son. I am not laying down any new principle of dharma. None can accuse a son who obeys his father, of violating the principles of duty.

'Lakshmana, I am aware of your affection for me. I acknowledge your chivalry, forbearance and glory. My mother is unhappy with the situation because she is unable to appreciate my truthful and peaceful intentions as also the king's promise to the other queen. I cannot defy the fact that dharma overrides all other considerations in this universe. Dharma is the supreme bedrock of truth. My father's word is supreme because that too is founded in dharma.

'Lakshmana, we must not act shallow. Your tough stand is not desirable. Respect my decision. The Maharaja is not only our father, but also our guru, our king. His being senior in age and wisdom are reasons enough for me to obey his commands, irrespective of what they may be. I am prepared to obey his orders whether issued in anger, out of lust or happiness. For my mother, he is her husband, her religion and the justification for her existence.

'It is my destiny to live as a hermit all these years. The reversal of the decision to make me the Yuvaraja is an act ordained by a higher power. Whatever cannot be explained, in joy or sorrow, in fear or anger, in gain or loss, creation or destruction, can be attributed to Destiny.

'It is this understanding of the eternal wisdom that has stabilized my mind. I am not in the least annoyed by this obstacle to my anointment. For me being a ruler or living in exile makes no difference to my understanding of the world. Rather, I find that going to live in a forest is the real awakening.'

Lakshmana was not convinced by Rama's words. He raised his eyebrows in anger, looked at his brother and breathing hard like an angry cobra, addressed his brother:

'Brother, your belief that if you disobey your father, the praja will no longer believe in your capacity to rule because you have defied the king, is misplaced. Your laying the blame of this command on destiny is not correct. You call Daiva an all-powerful entity, which is but a helpless exclamation.'

As tears of helplessness flooded Lakshamana, he addressed his brother,

'Why do you not condemn those two sinners? They are cheating everyone. You can still choose to take action like a prince by not following their commands; rather than blame destiny which is an act of cowards and weaklings.

'Today the people of Ayodhya will see who is mightier, destiny or a man's valour. Today I shall vanquish Daiva and make sure that nobody can stop your abhishek, my brother, not all the human beings in the world, or the devatas guarding the directions, and least of all our father.

'Our tradition guides the king to retire to the forest in old age after handing down the kingdom to his most able son; let the king and his queen who have devised the scheme to send you into exile go and live there. I shall reduce Kaikeyee's hopes to anoint Bharata to ashes. I am prepared to defend your kingdom like the shore keeping the ocean water within its limits.

'My sword will not stay sheathed and my arrows will not be used to make a hedge; these weapons are meant to destroy my enemies, even if they be my own kinsmen going off the path of dharma. My arms are covered with sandal paste, and ornaments, but will not hesitate to display unmatched chivalry against those who want to obstruct your abhishek.'

Rama assuaged Lakshmana with words of entreaty and consolation and wiped his tears. He said, 'my dear brother, I am steadfast in obeying my father's orders. That alone is the path of those devoted to truth and dharma.'

Kaushalya was deeply grieved and bemoaned the future years imagining her separation from her beloved son. As she insisted to accompany Rama to the forest, Rama did not lose himself to anger or grief and consoled her saying,

'Kaikeyee has misled the king who grieves at the thought of my going into the forest. If you too go away with me, he will certainly die. It is cruel on the part of a wife to give up on her husband. It is only befitting for you as a queen to stay here and serve him as long as he lives.'

With tearful eyes, Kaushalya replied,

'My son, you are right. As you go ahead to fulfil your father's commands, I shall stay here and wait for your safe return. I will wait to hear your assuring, sweet words.'

Sita's Resolve to Accompany Rama

Rama had another responsibility to fulfil before he could leave for Dandakaranya. From his mother's place, he headed straight for his own apartments where Sita was waiting for the future king. The place was brimming with well-wishers full of joy and anticipation of a celebration. The profusely decorated place lit up as Rama entered, though his head was bowed down. Looking at her husband and reading the sorrow in his eyes, she trembled out of fear of the unknown. She said,

'A canopy with a hundred tassels, white as the rising foam in the sea, no longer covers your fair face, O Rama. Neither are there attendants surrounding you, nor melodious minstrels, masters of song and music and the people of Ayodhya singing auspicious paeans in your praise. Where is the Pushparatha decorated with golden artefacts, with four steeds that run with the speed of lightning in harness? O my dear warrior prince, where are the massive, glorious elephants large as a mountain covered by clouds, that walk ahead of you in a procession?

'Why do you look sullen and gloomy when all the preparations for your abhishek are complete? Your face has lost its lustre. It is unprecedented.'

Rama replied,

'My revered father has decided to exile me to a forest today.'

Having narrated the entire sequence of events, Rama said,

'On my way to an uninhabited forest I have come to bid you farewell. You should stay here and take care of mother. Also, Bharata will be returning to Ayodhya soon; be kind to him and do not hold him in disregard because of these events. Never praise me in the presence of Bharata; those in power cannot stand another's appreciation. I ask you for forbearance.

'As he will be the king of the dynasty, you must obey Bharata's commands. While I depart to live in a forest, you, my wife, will continue living here looking after your mother-in-law and father-in-law.'

Sita was upset at hearing such words and replied angrily,

'I fear that you talk thus because you consider me shallow. Your words do not befit a warrior, Aryaputra. A mother, father, brother, son or a daughter-in-law, all live their lives according to their own deeds. However, it is the wife who shares her husband's fortunes, regardless of whether they be good or bad. Thus with you, I too have been permitted to go and live in a forest.

'For a woman, in this world or the other, her husband alone offers protection and shelter. Neither her father, nor son, nor anyone else including her own body truly support her.

'If you are going into an inaccessible forest, I shall walk ahead of you clearing the hedges and crushing the thorny bushes.

'I have committed neither a sin nor an offence that you leave me behind. For a woman, it is more important to share her husband's lot than to enjoy comforts and luxuries. I would request you not to advise me on this further as I shall rest my decision on the basis of instructions and conduct that I have learnt from my parents.

'Living a celibate life in the fragrant forest, I shall be as happy as I was in my father's house. I shall always walk ahead of you. I shall be satisfied with whatever food is available in the forest and shall not hesitate to give up all material comforts. My wise husband, I am keen to wander and look at hills, mountains and ponds in your company. I desire to gaze at the pools where the lotus blooms, where the royal swans glide and where the herons relax on the banks.

'I am totally devoted to you and you alone. I have never considered the misfortune of being separated from you. I will surely perish if I have to live without you for all this while. Hence, do not decline my request that I may accompany you. I shall not be a burden.'

Ram tried to dissuade Sita with various arguments. He told her of the wild animals and rivers that cannot be forded. He talked of paths difficult to walk upon and the harsh life that a forest will offer to them.

'At the end of the day,' said Rama, 'a tired person has to lie down on a bed of dry leaves. He has often to starve because there is nothing to eat. A dweller in the forest cannot hope to be physically comfortable.'

However, Sita did not agree with Rama's suggestion that she stay in Ayodhya. Though a bit scared, yet with her eyes full of tears, she retorted, 'My father, the king of Videha and of Mithila, could never have imagined when he accepted you as a son-in-law, that although you seem to be a brave man, at heart you are so weak. It will hurt me when in your absence the people will say that Rama, brilliant like the sun, proved to be a coward. Is it out of fear that you want me, your wife, to stay back? Raghunandan, while you are above reproach, I too have never desired another man. I have lived with you since I was very young. Now you cannot hand over your devoted wife to another person for sustenance.

'You are free to live like a slave to Bharata, if you so desire. However, I shall be where you are. I do not consider it a hardship to walk with you on the rough paths in the jungle. For me it will be as comfortable as taking a stroll in a garden, or lolling in a luxurious bed. The tall hedge grass, the thorny bushes and the reeds will feel like a touch of cotton or deer-skin when I walk with you. The dust settled on my body by wild winds will be like sandal paste. I shall eat whatever fruit is available in the season. I shall never think of my father's palace, O Rama.

'My world is where you are, not within these palace walls. I am determined to accompany you into the forest, and request you to joyously accept it as my decision.'

Sita lost consciousness owing to her being aggrieved beyond measure. Rama had no choice but to let her accompany him. As she swooned, he took hold of her in his soothing arms and embraced her. Lovingly he told her,

'How can I leave you behind when you were born to accompany me to the forest? O daughter of Janaka, you are so pretty. Following my ancestors who spent a lifetime of love and dharma in the company of their wives, I shall spend my time with you. I am duty bound to obey my father.

'Sita! I shall let you accompany me and take care of your comfort. You should donate whatever gold, wealth or precious clothes you possess to the Brahmins and the needy, to your maids and servants. We shall depart as hermits to the forest immediately.'

6

Rama is Banished to Dandakaranya–3

Lakshmana arrived on the scene and wept when he heard the conversation between Rama and Sita. Bending, he caught hold of Rama's feet and said,

'Now that you have made up your mind to move to the forest, regardless of the fear of wild animals and the harsh life of a hermit ahead of you, I have decided to accompany you and guard you, walking ahead with a bow and arrow in hand. I shall be there to protect you when you enjoy the natural beauty of the forest, and there to guard you when you need protection from the wilderness. In your absence I do not even wish to go to Swargaloka, to be immortal or to rule the earth. I wish to be with you.'

Rama advised his younger brother to stay behind and look after Kaushalya and Sumitra but the latter did not agree. Ultimately, Rama gave in and asked Lakshmana to go and ask for his mother's permission.

All three of them distributed their wealth to the Brahmins, their staff and the needy. They gave off all their riches—cows, gold coins, silver utensils, and precious stones—with the speed of a cloud irrigating parched fields during a cloudburst.

The Farewell

To bid farewell to the king, Sita, Rama and Lakshmana went to Kaikeyee's chambers. As the word about Rama going into exile had spread among the people of Ayodhya, their path was stopped by many. The rich stood sullen on the rooftops of their mansions, the poor crowded the streets to have a last look at the princes and the adorable Sita. They appreciated how Rama had upheld the finest traditions of dharma to honour his father's words but were grieved at the separation.

The onlooking women could not help but wonder how much Sita's body, made for perfumes, and her limbs meant to be adorned with colourful motifs and red sandal paste, would suffer.The scorching heat of the summer, the rains and the winter cold in Dandakaranya would tarnish her glow. They could not understand what Dashratha had done under an evil influence, and found it unjustified.

Some of the men could be heard talking,

'Taking our wives and children along, let us accompany Rama to the forest. We shall leave nothing useable behind. Let Kaikeyee rule a wilderness where there is famine, and where deserted homes with crumbling walls, broken utensils and barrenness be her only company.

'We shall convert the forest where Rama goes into a city while Ayodhya will be reduced to a lifeless, barren city. We shall lead a happy life wherever Rama lives.'

Dashratha was inconsolable in his grief and looked like the sun eclipsed by Rahu. He was in a disturbed state of mind and was constantly chanting Rama's name. Addressing him, Sumantra said,

'The princes seek your permission to visit you before leaving for the forest, my king! Have a long look at Rama before he goes away for fourteen years.'

Dashratha stood up, looked at the princes and fell unconscious again. Everyone present wailed as if the king had given up his will to live. As he revived, Rama sought his permission to leave for the forest.

'Maharaja, obeying your orders, I am leaving for Dandakaranya. Kindly allow Lakshmana and Sita to accompany me. May you rule over this earth for a thousand years. I am not interested in being the king. After fourteen years I hope to return to the city.'

A weeping Dashratha replied,

'You go in peace for everyone's well being. I pray that your path be without obstructions and free of harm.

'My son, Raghunandan, you are an embodiment of truth and a devout person. I have come to understand your selflessness in the past few moments and feel like a man devoid of a reason to live. I also know that once you have resolved to go, there is nothing that can change your mind. However, not as the king but as the father, I request you to delay your departure for a day so that I can look at your face tomorrow also.

'I will not survive separation from you, Rama. However, this woman Kaikeyee is dangerous and in the name of fulfilling my boons, she has cheated me and taken away my reason to live. You ought to be the king not only by virtue of being the eldest, but also because of your wisdom.'

Replied Rama, 'Father, I have given up this kingdom, the people and my kin along with all else. Kindly hand it over to dear Bharata. I cannot change my decision, O father who granted the favours to Kaikeyee. Do not shed tears of remorse or guilt. The ocean does not get disturbed with the tumultuous currents flowing into it; bound by propriety, it does not break its shores. You too should not be upset. I am not desirous of being a ruler, of enjoyment, of Swarga. My only desire is to maintain your honour.

'I request you to allow us to dwell in the forest and not try to reach us.'

Looking at the king lying in stupor, Sumantra could not help reprimanding Kaikeyee. Said he,

'You have destroyed the dynasty and you will be the end of the king, Maharani. As one who has deserted her husband, you are not beyond doing anything evil. No Brahmin will serve in your kingdom founded on such impropriety. The people of Ayodhya will never see Bharata as their ruler as against Rama.'

Kaikeyee was unmoved by this rhetoric. Rather, she helped Rama, Lakshmana and Sita change into coverings made of bark and deerskin to ready them for departure.

Kaushalya took Sita into her arms, embraced her, smelled her forehead in blessing and said,

'Daughter, the women who, although respected and honoured by their husbands all along, do not stand by them in times of distress, are known as untruthful, evil and cruel.

'On the contrary, a woman of noble conduct looks at her husband and venerates him like god. She stays within the bounds of truth, exemplary character, laws laid by the scriptures and the restraints imposed by family values. My son Rama, your husband, therefore, deserves your respect. He is like a god to you, whatever be his circumstances, whether he is a king or a pauper.'

Sita replied, 'Mother, I am unlike the wives who are disloyal to their husbands and full of untruth. I cannot deviate from my loyalty to my husband just as the moon's lustre never deserts him. As a veena cannot be played without strings, or a chariot cannot move without wheels, a woman cannot be happy in the absence of her husband even if she is the mother to a hundred sons.

'A woman receives solace from her husband, her brother and her son. However, the husband is a source of unlimited ananda in this world and the next. How then can a woman ignore him? Please rest assured about your son; I shall be devoted to him in every circumstance.'

Rama, accompanied by Sita and Lakshmana, left for the forest in a chariot driven by Sumantra, the king's faithful charioteer. A wailing king and a moaning crowd followed their departure. None of the houses had any auspicious fire lit, no meals were cooked. The sky was heavily overcast and clouds were scattered by powerful winds just like the waters of the ocean in high tide. All the cardinal directions were disturbed in the enveloping darkness, as if echoing the loss that Ayodhya and its people witnessed. The men were lost in thoughts of the kingdom's fate and the womenfolk were sorrowing for Rama as if their own son or brother had gone into exile.

Dashratha seemed to have lost his sight in Rama's absence. He seemed to have grown old overnight and kept swooning at the mere thought of separation from Rama.

7

The Journey to Chitrakoot

Having crossed the boundary of his father's kingdom, Rama looked towards Ayodhya and said,

'Ayodhya,
The most magnificent of cities,
Nurtured for hundreds of years by
The Kakutstha kings,
I seek your permission and of
All the gods who protect you,
To go to the forest.'

Addressing his subjects, he said,
'My countrymen, you have been kind to me. You have suffered enough for my sake. It is time for you to get back to your daily chores.'

Arrival at the Banks of the Ganga

With delight, Rama looked at the divine,
Tripathagamini Ganga,
Her cool waters flowing free of weeds.
On her bewitching banks lived many a rishi
Meditating in peace.

Enhancing the grandeur of the holy Ganga,
Salubrious ashramas dotted her banks.
Enchanting apsaras descended from the heavens
For a joyous dip [and playful water games.]
On her banks, even the devatas had planted gardens
In hundreds for their pleasure.

After all,
She looked after their sports even in Swarga where
They knew her as Devapadmini.

When her waters struck the broad banks,
The waves crackled like her laughter.
The foam on her surface was like her smile,
Pure and white.
At places, her stream ran like braided hair,
All compact,
And at others,
Several whirlpools added to her charm.

At places,
The Ganga waters were quiet and deep.
At others, she flowed in a torrent,
Producing the sonorous sound of a mridanga, and
Sometimes a frightening sound, like a thunderbolt.

Where the devatas bathe,
In her placid waters, floated the blue lotus.
On her edges, one saw sand mounds,
And here and there,
Large islands of sand shining as crystal.

On the banks of Ganga,
Glided the rajahansa and sarus birds, shrieking in pleasure.
The chakvas enhanced the beauty of the divine stream.
Over her waters,
Intoxicated birds, singing in joy,
Hovered all the time.

Magnificent trees garlanded her banks.
Her waters nourished blue and pink lotuses in abundance.
White water lilies and buds sprouted everywhere.
Like a woman in heat,
Intoxicated with the pollen of flowers, hovered the black bees.

Ganga purified piles of filth. Yet,
Her waters looked transparent like crystal.
The jungles on her banks
Were full of elephants in heat,
Noisy wild beasts and animals used in Indra's procession.

Surrounded by flowers, fruit, and glistening nascent leaves,
Hovering birds and gliding swans,
Ganga sparkled like a damsel.
Having flowed from Vishnu's feet,
How could she ever be impure?
No sin could pollute her waters.
From all that was evil,
Ganga provided salvation.

Arriving at the banks of celestial Ganga, Rama decided to halt for the night. A local tribal chieftain, Nishadaraja Guha, arrived to offer assistance, meals and all other comforts fit for a prince. He brought cooked meals, desserts, fruit juices, and pickles besides beds and a large feed of grass and gram for the horses. Looking at these welcome offerings, and out of humility, Rama said,

'We are grateful to you for your welcome and care. We are delighted to meet an old friend. However, I ask you to take back all that you have lovingly brought. Under my present circumstances, I can neither accept, nor use goods brought by others.

'We now subsist on fruit and vegetables gathered in the forest. We wear bark and deerskin. However, whatever you have brought for the horses, can be offered to them.'

Rama and Sita spent the night on a bed of grass while Lakshmana stood guard.

Waking up to the sweet cooing of the koel, Rama arranged to cross the river early next morning. He advised Sumantra to return and take care of his father who was now, for certain, a broken man, a man consumed by sorrow. For Bharata, Rama had a message:

'Please treat all your mothers with the same respect and affection that you would display to our father. Kaushalya and Sumitra are as much a mother to you as Kaikeyee.'

Arrival at Prayag

The trio crossed the Ganga in a wooden boat and arrived at Prayag, the confluence of Ganga and Yamuna. Early morning, addressing Lakshmana, Rama said,

'Look, near Prayag, smoke is rising like Agni's ensign. It ought to be the ashrama of Rishi Bhardwaj. Further, this site appears to be the confluence of the two divine rivers because one hears the sound of clashing currents.'

Rama, Lakshmana and Sita visited the Bhardwaj Ashrama and sought the rishi's blessings. The latter requested that they stay at his ashrama for the duration of their exile. However, Rama declined saying,

'Respected Rishivar, the residents of Ayodhya are not far away from this place. If I live here, they will visit me frequently and disturb your penance and peace. Hence, we must stay away in a solitary forest.'

Muni Bhardwaj replied,

'I suggest that you go to stay in Chitrakoot, a hill situated at a distance of ten kos from here, which, over centuries, has been blessed by several maharshis residing and meditating there. The forest there is fragrant like the Gandhamadana Mountain, and is inhabited by long-tailed langurs, monkeys and bears. Several fruits, roots and vegetables grow on its slopes and it is home to beautiful peacocks, elephants, deer, the melodious koel and several natural marvels. Waterfalls, caves and the Mandakini River beautify the hill. It is the most suitable place for you to spend your exile in.'

Rishi Bhardwaj provided them exact directions to reach Chitrakoot. They crossed the Yamuna river on a boat made with wooden planks.

Sita was delighted to walk through the scenic forest. Repeatedly, she enquired about the names of plants, creepers laden with flowers and trees growing on both sides of the path. Yamuna's golden sands, trumpeting sarus birds and gliding royal swans were a source of immense delight to her. Having crossed the river, they spent a night in the open on the shore of the Yamuna.

Arrival at the Rishi Valmiki Ashrama at Chitrakoot

Rama woke up a little before sunrise and awakening Lakshmana, he said,

'Sumitrakumar, listen to the sweet song of the birds, of parrots and cuckoos. It is time to depart for our destination.'

Having slept well, Lakshmana and Sita felt refreshed. They had a bath in the cool Yamuna waters, prayed, and set out for Chitrakoot. Pointing out the glory of the forest to Sita, Rama said,

'O princess of Videha, look at the palash blooming aflame in vasanta. The trees appear to have put on garlands of their own flowers. With masses of reddish brown flowers bunched together on their branches, they seem to be on fire.

'Look at the nut plants and the wood-apple trees bending low with the weight of their fruit and flowers. It is evident that not many people visit this forest and we shall not run short of the bounties of nature.

'Lakshmana, do you see the fascinating honey-combs enriched by the bees with honey and bending low with their weight? Each one is full of seers of honey. This section of the forest is spellbinding to look at, with showers of flowers having laid down a carpet of blossoms and the birds chirping noisily.

'It seems we have reached our destination and should set up a cottage on land that is flat and is surrounded by several trees.'

Soon thereafter, Rama, Sita and Lakshmana arrived at the ashrama of Rishi Valmiki. Lakshmana gathered wood for building a cottage for their stay. He felled branches of several trees and readied a cottage with wood and dry fronds. Wooden beams and doors supported the pretty cottage. He assembled the roof with such dexterity that the rainwater would not drip inside. He made the walls so thick that even the wild mountain winds could not penetrate it.

They took a bath in the sacred waters and chanted the Gayatri Mantra.

Having offered worship to the devatas, Rama, pure at heart, entered the cottage with his wife and brother. He set up small alcoves for the worship of gods like Vishnu and Ganesha.

8

Dasharatha Suffers Pangs of Conscience

Sumantra, the charioteer returned to Ayodhya and found his king in delirium. Dashratha lost consciousness frequently and even when in his senses, he bemoaned his actions. Kaushalya looked after her aged husband patiently and tried to reassure him of Rama's love for him.

Repeatedly, Dashratha expressed his grief and regret at his following Kaikeyee's dictate. He lamented,

'Unfortunately I did not consult even my wise ministers over this issue. Blinded by lust and attachment, I committed an atrocious act at the instance of an evil woman. Sumantra, Destiny has willed that this event annihilate our family.'

Addressing Kaushalya, the king moaned,

'My dear wife, I know I will never come out of this ocean of sorrow that I have created for myself in the absence of Rama. As I flutter to find my wings, Kaikeyee seems to be the wild fire who has destroyed our family and kingdom. This sea of grief is the source for the unending flow of my tears. The two boons I had granted to Kaikeyee are the ocean shores and the banishment of Rama appears to be as unending as the vastness of its waters.

'I want to see Rama and Lakshmana, and I cannot. This is the fruit of my evil deeds.'

Saying this, the king fainted again.

When Dashratha came to his senses again after a while, he narrated certain events, known only to him till now, to Kaushalya who sat by his side.

Shrawan Kumar and His Blind Parents

'Kalyani, a man reaps the fruit of his deeds, virtuous or sinful. Only an idiot does not think of the consequences of his intended acts.

'I was known as a great archer. I could shoot an arrow to follow any source of sound. I was so enamoured of my fame as an archer who could pierce an invisible source of sound, I did not realize that this expertise could lead to something frightful.

'I was yet to marry you and I was still a yuvaraja. The rains had set in and I felt charged with passion. The sky was overcast with dark, water-bearing clouds, alleviating the summer heat.

'The elephants, submerged in ponds and enjoying the sheets of rain, were in musth. The clear waters of mountain cataracts, washing the rock minerals, were coloured red or ochre by the time they reached the ground level. Their waters flowed sinuously like gliding snakes.

'In this joyful rainy season, I rode a chariot to the banks of Saryu in order to hunt. I was young and excited, drunk with pride as an ace archer. I was determined to kill a troublesome buffalo, or an elephant in musth, or a tiger.

'It was dark all around when I heard a sound like a pitcher being immersed in water. I was unable to see anything but I understood this sound to be that of an elephant sucking water through its trunk. Excited that I had a fierce animal to shoot and disregarding the darkness that engulfed me before sunrise, I shot an arrow. As soon as my arrow hit its target, I heard the wail of a human being. Falling to the ground, the victim cried in agony,

"Who shot at me, a helpless, innocent hermit that came to the lonely shore of the river to fetch a pail of water at night? What harm have I caused anyone? Who benefits from my death?'

"My hunter will be considered as sinful as a pupil hankering after his guru's wife. My death does not upset me as much as the inconvenience it would cause my aged parents. The hunter has killed the three of us with one shot."

'I reached my victim lying on the Saryu bank, his hair dishevelled and his body smeared with mud and blood. His pitcher lay waterless. His piercing eyes burnt through my body. Looking at me, he said, "With one arrow you have pierced my core and killed my aged parents. They are blind and weak. They are thirsty and are waiting for me to fetch water. Kindly go and tell them of my death."

'Requesting me to pull out the venomous arrow that had led to this end, the young man continued, "I was born to a Vaishya father and a Shudra mother."

'He could not go beyond these words. The poison of the arrowhead was racing through his veins and his eyes were losing their lustre and focus. Soon thereafter, he breathed his last in my hands.

'I filled the pitcher with fresh, clean water and carried it to his parents who were waiting nearby. They looked like helpless birds whose feathers had been cut off mercilessly. They had been talking of their son. Hearing my footsteps, they asked, "son, what delayed you so long? We are thirsty; hand over the water. My son, you are our eyes, why are you so quiet? Say something."

'I stammered out of fear and explained the situation to them.

'I am a Kshatriya and my name is Dashratha. I have committed a condemnable sin under a wrong impression.

'I told them how in an instance of mistaken identity I had caused the death of their son. I accepted my fault and asked for forgiveness.

'They moaned their loss and asked me to carry them to the spot where the body of their son was lying. All along, they wailed and cried. Cursing me the old man said,

"Rajan, you will undergo torture similar to the one we are undergoing at present. You too shall die pining for your son."

The Death of Dashratha

'Kaushalya, I recollect their words and am sure I too will die pining for my Rama. I can no longer see you; hold my hand.

'Like the fierce sun drying a small patch of water, the absence of Rama whom none on this the earth can equal in virtue, is sucking life out of my body.

'Kaushalya, it appears that I am no longer in control of my body, that I am getting detached from my senses. I am losing consciousness.

'I can no longer see. Tapasvini Sumitra, I am departing from this world.

'O Kaikeyee, the evil incarnate, heartless and vile, you have destroyed my family.'

With these words, Dashratha breathed his last.

9

Bharata Declines to be the King

The attendants found no pulse on Dashratha's, nor could they feel his heart beat. His body lay cold and rigid. As his death was confirmed, a loud wail arose in the palace.

To preserve the body until cremation, it was immersed in a cauldron of oil. Ayodhya had lost its lustre with the death of the king. It was like the sky where the stars did not shine and the sun did not rise.

The Importance of a King

The assembly of the wise discussed the next appropriate step in the absence of any of the princes in the city. Talking of the importance of a ruler in a kingdom, they said,

'Without a king the kingdom will be destroyed. In a state without a ruler, the rich are unable to safeguard their wealth and the farmers cannot sleep fearlessly. The traders no longer travel to sell their wares in faraway lands.'

Another learned man added,

'People live in fear when there is no king. There is no satisfactory settlement of disputes. Armies lack proper command and the learned cannot explain scriptures. No longer do the devotees gather in the temples to worship and offer flowers and fruits to the devatas.

'In the absence of a king, subjects cannot lay claim to any property as their own. There is complete anarchy. In a kingless state the non-believers in Varna-ashrama have a free run.

'Just as the human conscience looks after man's well-being, a king is the guardian of truth and dharma in his kingdom. A king is an incarnation of truth, of righteousness. He is the mother and the father to his subjects and he is the head of their family. A king, because of his noble character, transcends Indra, Varuna, Kubera and even Yamaraja, encapsulating within him all the virtues, such as preservation, noble conduct, wealth and justice, respectively. In the absence of a king the world would be enveloped by darkness and anarchy.'

The assembly decided to send messengers to fetch Bharata from his maternal grandfather's house in the north beyond Panchaladesh. The messenger was directed not to inform the prince about the king's death and the exile of Shri Rama.

Bharata Has an Ominous Dream

Sleeping luxuriously in his grandfather's palace, Bharata had an ominous and frightful dream. His friends tried to divert him with poetry, music and jokes but to no avail. When asked the reason for his unhappiness, he said,

'I saw a pale and lustreless King Dashratha, my father, in my dream. His hair was dishevelled. He slipped from a hilltop into a filthy pit full of cow dung and urine.

'I saw him drinking the filth and laughing. He walked out of the cesspool and had a meal of oilseeds and rice. Once again, he fell down and was given an oil massage, submerged into a pool of oil. He continued floating in the pool with his head bent downwards.

'I saw Maharaja Dashratha sitting on a throne of metal painted black. He had put on black robes and was being attacked by women of reddish brown complexion. I saw him with a garland of red flowers around his neck, a red mark on his forehead, being driven in a chariot pulled by donkeys, heading south. A woman dressed in red, laughing like a rakshasi, was pulling at him.

'My dream is ominous and I fear some misfortune has befallen the family. It can be anyone, my father, one of the mothers or one of my brothers. I am upset, disturbed and worried. I am unable to understand anything. I see no reason to fear; yet, I am afraid.'

Bharata Enters a Desolate Ayodhya

Replete with gifts of horses, chariots and pedigree dogs, Bharata set out on his return journey. He crossed the rivers Sutlej, Saraswati, Yamuna and Ganga on his route. He spent seven days and seven nights before he reached Ayodhya.

Looking at the desolate city, Bharata, surprised, spoke to his charioteer,

'Dotted with gardens, the celebrated Ayodhya does not present a happy prospect. Lovingly tendered by Rajarshi Dashratha, this city once resounded with the Vedic chants of Brahmins, and looked ' luminous with large mansions of the rich traders. Today it resembles a mound of pale earth.

'I do not hear the echoes of its denizens rejoicing. I notice its gardens bereft of the loving couples. Ayodhya looks and feels like a jungle but without the musical notes of the birds. The bees do not hum and the koel does not coo.

'This state of affairs disturbs me about the fate of my near and dear ones. I see bad omens all around. They foretell tragic events.

'Why have I been called in unseemly haste? All around, I see ominous signs of the destruction of a kingdom. I notice that the householders have not swept their homes, nor do I see auspicious fires in their houses. It seems that Lakshmi has deserted these houses and has left Ayodhya barren.

'The temples are deserted, the idols are not decked in flowers. There are no devotees around the temple complexes and even the birds perched on the temple ledges are silent and gloomy. So are the men and women in the streets. Why?'

Bitter Confrontation

Looking at her son returning home, Kaikeyee was delighted. She sprang from her gilded chair to embrace Bharata. No sooner had the usual courtesies been exchanged, the prince asked his mother,

'How is it that your bed decked in gold is deserted? I do not find the usual rejoicing around the palace and cannot see father as well. Where is he, I wish to pay obeisance to him.'

Kaikeyee was ignorant of all the misfortune that had befallen her and her kin, and in her desire to see her son hastily anointed the king, she tried to convey the sad tidings as pleasantly as possible.

'Dear son, your father, Maharaja Dashratha was a mahatma, a glorious and a pious king. He always sheltered the truthful and stood by his dharma. Sharing the fate of all those who are born, he has departed for the other world.'

Moaning his father's death, Bharata fell to the ground. He wailed aloud and wept. He cried,

'With my father lying on it, this sumptuous bed used to glow like the sky resplendent with the autumn moon. In the absence of the wise Maharaja, his bed looks desolate and eclipsed.'

Bharata lay on the floor like a tree trunk felled by an axe. Kaikeyee lifted him in her arms and consoled him saying,

'Rajan! O glorious prince! Stand up. Truthful men like you, honoured by the assembly of the wise, do not mourn in sorrow.

'O my wise son, just like the illumination that never vanishes from the sphere of the sun, your wisdom is unshakeable. You will make a charitable and devout king.'

However, Bharata was neither consoled, nor diverted. He said,

'I travelled full of joy at the thought that my father would anoint Rama as the Yuvaraja. Reaching here, I find that quite the reverse has happened. What was the cause of my father's untimely demise? Blessed are my brothers, Rama and Lakshmana, in that they were here to perform the last rites of our father.

'What were my father's last instructions for me?'

Kaikeyee could no longer hide the facts. She replied,

'The first among the wise, your father breathed his last wailing: 'Ha Rama, Ha Sita, Ha Lakshmana.'

'Like an elephant rendered helpless when chained, your father, in the throes of death, uttered the following last words,

'They will be blessed who would watch Rama and the warrior Lakshmana returning accompanied by Sita.'

A surprised Bharata shot back,

'Mother, where has the devout Rama, a source of immense joy to the residents of Ayodhya, gone? Is he accompanied by Sita and Lakshmana?'

Kaikeyee cleverly replied in sweet words,

'Rama dressed in bark, accompanied by Sita, has departed for Dandakaranya. Lakshmana gives him company.'

'Mother,' said Bharata, 'Did Rama deprive a Brahmin of his wealth? Did he murder an innocent rich or poor man? What crime had he committed that he has been exiled to the forest?'

Replied Kaikeyee,

'Rama has not committed any crime. On coming to know that Rama was being elevated as the Yuvaraja, I asked your father to honour two commitments he had made me a long time ago. I asked that you be crowned as the Yuvaraja and also that Rama be exiled for fourteen years. Being the truthful man that he was, your father agreed to my demands. He banished Rama and later unable to bear his absence, he breathed his last.

'O devout son, knowing your duty, ascend the throne. I have done this for your benefit alone. Do not grieve, be patient. This city and this kingdom are all yours. You have no rivals to challenge you.

'Seek advice from the guru Vasishtha and perform the last rites of your father. Ask them to organize your coronation immediately thereafter.'

'What shall I do with this kingdom?' wailed Bharata. 'I have lost my father to death, and am separated from an elder brother who is more like a father to me. You took away both of them from me. Your asking me to ascend the throne is rubbing salt on my wounds.

'You arrived as the night of doom to destroy this family. In marrying you my father chose to sleep on a bed of live coals. Selfishly, you killed my father. Why did you commit this heinous act? You show no signs of repentance.

'Rama is like a lion, so is Lakshmana. What made you think I could protect this kingdom without them? This burden is too much for me to carry, just as a calf cannot substitute mighty bulls.

'It has been our family tradition that the eldest son succeeds the father as king. The younger brothers work obediently under him in the interest of the state.

'O evil mother, I shall never bow to your wishes. You have created an unfortunate situation that could have led to my death if I were not contemplating on ways to bring them back to the kingdom. Without any further loss of time, I am proceeding to meet the sinless Rama, beloved of the populace, and ask him to come back. I shall spend my years in the service of Shri Ramachandra.'

Bharata's rebuke sounded like the roar of a lion in a Mandarachala cave and silenced Kaikeyee in her attempts to persuade him.

10

Bharata Decides to Visit Rama in Chitrakoot

Having given vent to his anger on his mother, Bharata visited Kaushalya to express his regrets. When Kaushalya saw him approaching her, she was reminded of all the pain that had been caused to her kin on account of his mother. She was furious and looking at Bharata with fiery eyes, she said,

'Son, your dream of being king is now fulfilled. You coveted the kingdom and conspired with your cruel mother to have Rama out of your way thus. Now that Rama is banished, you can rule unchallenged.'

A grieving Bharata assured her of his innocence and asked for forgiveness. He said,

'Mother, I knew nothing of the happenings in Ayodhya. I am innocent and I am willing to suffer for any sin that I may have committed.'

As he broke down, grieving for having caused such misfortune to the family unknowingly, Kaushalya realized that he was not to be blamed for the events and the way they had shaped up. Lifting the broken prince in her arms, Kaushalya blessed him and said,

'I was afraid that you have given up the path of dharma. But your words have assured me that fortunately you are on the right track. You are truthful and will surely go to the land of the pure.'

The Last Rites of Dashratha

Dashratha had not yet been cremated because of the absence of the sons from the kingdom. Vasishtha and other gurus had preserved the body in oil and now prepared for the cremation. The body was washed and dressed in befitting clothes. It was placed on a plank covered in tapestry inlaid with precious stones. Soon after, the king's lifeless body was carried to the cremation ground. The officers of the kingdom scattered silver and gold coins over the palanquin carrying the body.

A pier was erected with sandalwood and deodar logs in the cremation ground. Incense sticks were placed around the dead body and rites were performed. The queens went around the king's body in ritual parikrama after which the body was set on fire using holy yagya tinder.

Bharata Declines the Throne

At the end of the mourning period of thirteen days, the ministers and officers of the state assembled and stood in front of Bharata with hands folded in prayer. They said,

'Our king has departed and Rama has been banished to Dandakaranya. The kingdom has no master to rule. As decided by the late Maharaja, you are now our king. We, the residents of Ayodhya, the rich and the poor, wait for you to be anointed as the king.'

Bharata responded,

'O wise ministers, you ought not to speak thus. Shri Ramachandra is the eldest prince and none can take his place. I am prepared to go and fetch him; if the word of our dead father stops him, I shall propose to spend the fourteen years in exile in his place.

'In no way shall Kaikeyee's scheme succeed.

'Please order the builders, engineers, gardeners and masons to lay new and even roads so that the Ayodhya armies can travel to where Rama is and bring him back with pomp and show.'

Like the high tides of an ocean on a full moon day, a horde of artisans and engineers set out to carry these orders out with great speed and dexterity. The paths were cleared of wild bush, pits were filled and roads levelled and laid with stone. Flowering trees were planted on both sides to provide shade. Reservoirs were built in which water from small streams was collected. The road ran on the shores of the Ganga of which the waters were full of fish, ensuring that cool water and food be available to the hordes of travellers who follow the prince.

The next morning began with the palace musicians playing and beating drums with golden sticks to awaken the king as was the custom. But Bharata asked them to discontinue the routine as he did not see himself as the king.

Even sage Vasishtha desired that Bharata be crowned as the king of Ayodhya as it was the wish of the late king Dashratha. The prince turned down this proposal too. He said,

'How can a son of Dashratha assume kingship ignoring the rights of the first-born son? This kingdom as well as my person is a property of Shri Ramachandra by right and by tradition. I shall go to the forest to request my elder brother to return. If I do not succeed, I shall stay in the forest at his service.'

Bharata's Journey to Chitrakoot

The caravan that travelled to fetch Rama included men from all sections of society, whether Brahmins, Kshatriyas, Vaishyas or Shudras. Men and women of all trades and classes, keen to see their beloved prince Rama followed Bharata's forces. On the banks of the Ganga, Guha, the king of the boatsmen, welcomed the prince. The latter arranged for their meals and other comforts and informed them of the route Rama had taken across the Ganga.

Praising Bharata, Guha said, 'I do not see a devout person equal to you in the universe. Your desire to give up the kingdom is unprecedented.'

However, no words of high praise pleased Bharata. The anguish of having been parted from Rama gnawed at the innards of Bharata, already shrivelled by sorrow at the demise of his father.

Across the river Ganga, Bharata entered the hermitage of Rishi Bhardwaj. After formally welcoming him, the rishi addressed Bharata,

'You are now the king of Ayodhya with all the riches at your disposal. What made you undertake this harsh journey into the forest? I have no faith in your honesty and words of guilt. For me, you have hurt your innocent brother and I will not give you any opportunity to harm Rama, Sita and Lakshmana, now living in peace like hermits in the forest.'

Bharata apologized for what had happened and explained how his mother had contrived things in his absence, without his knowledge. He requested the rishi to tell him of the whereabouts of Shri Ramachandra.

Muni Bhardwaj's initial scepticism was washed away with Bharata's tears and he forgave Bharata. He assured him of all help in tracing the whereabouts of Rama. Through his divine powers, the rishi made lavish arrangements for food and other comforts of the hordes accompanying the prince. Next morning, the rishi indicated to Bharata the route to Chitrakoot, a hill situated about eighty miles from Prayag.

Approaching Chitrakoot, Bharata asked his forces to halt far from the hill so that Rama did not misunderstand the purpose of his visit. Since he was travelling with the armies like an ocean sweeping large tracts of land in high tide, he did not want Rama to misunderstand his intentions.

After looking around for some time, Bharata's warriors reported sighting smoke rising from near a grove of trees, which was a confirmation of human habitation. The prince asked them to wait at the spot where they were. He wanted to approach Rama all by himself.

11

Rama Shows Sita Around Chitrakoot

Like Devaraja Indra showing his wife Shachi the mountain sights, Rama took Sita around Chitrakoot, explaining to her the sights and sounds of the trees and birds. He tried to provide her with some diversion. They had been living here for a few days as hermits. Rama had come to like the sylvan surroundings.

Initiating a conversation, Rama said,

'Although I have been deprived of a kingdom and removed from the company of my well-wishers, I forget my sorrow when I cast a glance at this pretty mountain.

The Mountain, its Trees and Flowers

'Kalyani, look at this mountain. What a variety of birds fly around here singing in low, sweet tones! Its peaks reflecting the colours of minerals, kiss the sky. They glow with various hues, silver at times, red at others; the glow seems to be like that of yellow topaz, rubies, emeralds, amethyst or sapphire at times. As the peaks are touched by rays of the sun, some of the peaks shine like crystal, while others look like the ketaki flowers.

'This mountain is home to a large variety of birds, deer, tigers, leopards and bears. The wild animals have given up their ferocity and live here in peace and tranquillity. They are an asset to Chitrakoot.

'Notice the variety of trees that grow on the slopes of the mountain: mango, jamun, wood apple, priyala, kathala, amla, neem, mahua, berries, kadamba, pomegranates, and several others. On the waterside, willows grow tall.

'Cataracts falling from the mountain peaks, water gushing out of land in tiny streams here and there, make the mountain look like an elephant whose temples are overflowing with musth. The mountain peaks excite kama in human beings, bringing them joy.

'The breeze is rich in intoxicating scent of varied flowers; how can it not excite man. O devoted Sita, even if I have to spend several years here in your company and with Lakshmana beside us, I have no hesitation in doing so. My exile will not hurt me.

'My dear, the exile has benefitted me two-fold. Firstly, I have paid the debt of dutiful obedience to my father. Secondly, my brother Bharata stands to gain by my departure.

'O princess from Videha, does this mountain full of trees, flowers, plants, animals and birds that delight my senses and mind, make you happy?

'O my queen, Manu, my ancestor, and other prominent Rajarshis have described the life in a forest as being akin to imbibing Amrita. They say that death after a life in the lap of nature is most desirable because it leads to the highest form of salvation.

'The forest is teeming with champa and malati plants; these seem to be beds on which lay the merry-making lovers. Lotus leaves make their bed sheets. Leaves of various trees like bhojapatra, punnag, utpal and putrajeevak provide for sheets to cover. All around lie lotus flowers crushed under the lovers making love.

'Rich in fruit, water, and roots, Chitrakoot makes Indra's Nalini and Kubera's Alakapuri look inferior. We shall happily spend the fourteen years of exile at this place.'

Living in the Lap of Nature, Even Ayodhya Can Be Forgotten

Moving ahead with his beloved at his side, Rama approached the banks of the sacred and pleasant looking Mandakini. Addressing the princess with a slim waist, the lotus-eyed prince said,

'Mandakini's splendour is multiplied by the gliding flamingos and the sarus birds fluttering around. Trees bearing fruits and flowers exude fragrance, giving my heart immense happiness. Even the water on the banks, dirtied by deer and other animals, delights my heart.

'My dear, you can see the rishis dressed in bark or deer skin, with knotted hair on their heads, taking a bath in Mandakini. These hermits are performing tough penance. See, they are now raising their arms upwards to offer a prayer and salute the rising sun.

'If you look carefully, you will see at places the running water is crystal clear and at others sand dunes have formed. Many siddhas are taking a bath at several points and Mandakini currents carry mounds of flowers swept by the breeze from the banks into the running water.

'Because I can see you all the time while staying on this riverbank, my stay here is happier than it was in Ayodhya.

'My passionate Sita, you should enter the river and take a bath; you can indulge in sport with the river water and these flowers to your heart's content. Look at the dwellers of the forest as if they are the residents of Ayodhya and at Mandakini as if it were Saryu. It gives me joy to enjoy the bounties of nature with you and Lakshmana here. I neither desire nor think of returning to Ayodhya. I do not crave for that kingdom.

12

Bharata Milap:
Rama Declines to Return to Ayodhya

The movement of the Ayodhya army upset the life of the forest surrounding Chitrakoot. Frightened by the tumultuous noise, even the elephant herds ran helter-skelter. The sky grew dull with the dust raised by the horses' hoofs. Noticing this commotion, Rama asked Lakshmana to investigate the cause of the disturbance.

Lakshmana climbed a shala tree to be able to look into the distance. Looking northwards, he noticed an army consisting of foot soldiers, elephants, horses and chariots. Coming down, he asked Rama to extinguish the fire in the hearth, send Sita into a cave for safety and get ready for a fight. He surmised that Bharata had advanced in full strength to annihilate both of them so that he could rule unchallenged.

Rama pacified Lakshmana and said,

'If the enthusiastic Bharata has arrived here in person, the sword, the bow and arrows need not create a barrier between us. I have no use for the tainted kingdom. Wealth, acquired by killing one's friends and relatives, is like poisoned food. It must be discarded. I do not seek it under any circumstances.

'Bharata comes to meet us out of love and affection. He has never misbehaved with you, nor has he given you any reason to be angry. Then why are you afraid of him today? How can a brother think of killing a brother who is dearer to him than his life? If you continue to doubt Bharata's intentions and talk harshly, I shall ask Bharata to hand over the throne to you.'

Bharata Comes Face to Face with Rama

Moving in the direction of the smoke rising from Shri Rama's cottage, Bharata noticed the thatched hut under a grove. He also noticed how there were a number of markers on the trees for guiding the way to the hut, which he assumed Lakshmana to have done. All this helped Bharata in reaching Rama's cottage.

The parnakutir was thatched with leaves of shala, tala and ashwakarna trees. Soft kusha grass had been scattered around the yagyashala. An altar had been built for worship. Inside, powerful bows with gilded grips were arranged like rainbows. Quivers full of arrows lay tastefully against the cottage walls, shining like the rays of the sun. Two swords sheathed in golden scabbards and shields with round golden patches could also be seen. On the altar, a fire was burning in the havana kunda.

Rama dressed in bark and black buckskin sat in the cottage. His hair was twirled into a knot like that of a sadhu. Rama, the master of the universe, a devout and chivalrous prince sat like the eternal Brahma on a seat made of kusha grass. His shoulders were broad like that of a lion. His arms were long and his eyes were like an opening lotus bud.

Bharata wept at the sight of his revered brother living in such circumstances. In an almost inaudible voice, he called him, 'Arya' and cried in silence. He bowed at Rama's feet. The latter lifted his younger brother and enveloped him in a warm embrace.

Rama Expounds on the Duties of a King

Affectionately smelling Bharata's forehead, Rama asked him, 'Brother, father would not have let you come to the forest alone, and seeing you here in this condition fills my heart with fear. Is father out of his grief? Is the kingdom safe?

'Are our mothers happy? What about the revered guru Vasishtha? I hope that you get good advice to run the government.

'I hope that you consult the right people on important issues and that your parleys and decisions are not leaked to the public. I am sure that important projects that have far-reaching consequences are not delayed.

'A king surrounded by a thousand fools does not get sound and timely advice. However, even one competent minister can assist him in amassing wealth in his treasury. Surely, you have appointed persons suitable for jobs at different levels of competence. Appoint such ministers as do not accept bribes, are free of deceit, and are descendants of trusted ministers

'Are your commanders brave, expert in warfare and dexterous in the use of arms? Do they and their soldiers get sufficient wages and on time?

'Are your ambassadors to other kingdoms your own countrymen, learned, expert in diplomacy and capable of correctly communicating the king's message?

'Brother, I am sure that you keep company of the wise and the learned, and keep non-believers away.

'Is Ayodhya well-protected? Are the forests where elephants roam and multiply, safeguarded?

'Do your employees keep a respectable distance from you or shun your contact altogether? You have to adopt a golden mean. That alone ensures a successful government.

'Are your forts well-stocked with grain, armaments, water, machines, and artisans? Are there enough well-armed soldiers to protect them?

'Does your expenditure exceed your revenues? Do you make sure that your treasury does not enrich the undeserving?

'I trust that unjust punishments are not thoughtlessly meted to those who are innocent and pure in mind, heart and conduct even by judges learned in scriptures and law.

'Do your ministers administer fair and impartial justice to the rich and the poor litigants without consideration of the status of the rich man? Tears that flow from the eyes of the innocents have the power to destroy a partial and unjust king, his descendants and his wealth.

'Do you honour the aged, the young and the physicians with innate kindness and sweet words? Are you generous to them?

'In your regime, I hope, wealth does not override and harm dharma, nor is the latter misused to oppress the wealthy.

'A king must believe in god. He should be truthful. He ought not to be lazy, indolent, and given to losing control over his temper. He must exercise control over his five senses. He must not think over policy matters all by himself. A decision once taken must be implemented immediately. He ought not to consult fools in matters of state. Consultations in matters of policy must be kept confidential.'

Rama Declines Bharata's Request

In answer to Rama's query as to why Bharata had come to Chitrakoot dressed like a hermit in bark and black buckskin, Bharata responded:

'Our valorous father expired as a result of having committed a foul deed. My mother did not get a kingdom. Rather, she became a widow. She has committed an evil deed in destroying the prestige of our family for which even gods will not forgive her.

'Your subjects and our widowed mothers have come to meet you. Raghuvira, you have always honoured others. Being the eldest, you alone have the right to rule the kingdom. Acting justly, according to dharma, and keeping in mind the welfare of your people and kin, you must return and be the king. That alone will please all of us.

'I am your brother and your servant. I bow at your feet along with all the ministers accompanying me. '

Rama reiterated his conviction. He said, 'How can a devout and conscientious man born in a family of repute, disobey his father's command? I never found fault with you. However, you must not condemn your mother.

'Our father was fully empowered to command his wives and us, his sons. He could justifiably choose anyone as his successor and he had the legal right to order me into exile. The news of my father's demise is sad, but this is a part of one's life and must not be mourned.

'The end result of all acquisition is destruction. A union invariably ends in separation and every living being ultimately dies. A man meets his end because he is subject to old age and death.

'Further, Bharata, you must bestow as much respect on your mother as you did on our father. You too cannot ignore his command. I believe that the command of my father that I live in exile for fourteen years is binding on me and that it is for my well-being. I shall not disobey him even if I become immortal by doing so.'

However, Bharata was not the one to give up so soon. Continuing his argument for his brother's return, he said,

'Brother, our father fulfilled his promise to my mother and handed over the kingdom to her, which she handed over to me. Today I offer you the unchallenged kingship of Ayodhya. Come, nourish and rule your kingdom.'

The wise and patient Rama replied, 'Brother, it is the will of god that can do anything, not a human's. We are slaves to Kala that playfully moves us around.

'A moment in time never recurs just as the night that has passed shall never be. Day and night move relentlessly and thus the life span of every living being is being exhausted.

'Bharata, it is time to think of your own interest and not fret about the fate of others. Each one of us awaits death, a goal that steadily draws near.

'Death follows us like a shadow, however long be our journey. Ultimately, it overtakes us. Neither can we run away from it, nor hide the effect of its approach on us, i.e. old age.

'Everyone rejoices when the sun rises and sees the sun set with every passing day. Seldom do they realise that these are just milestones in the journey of life and mark the end of another day in the life-span meant for a person.

'Like two pieces of wood floating in an ocean coming together and parting company after some time, woman, son, family and wealth come together and go their separate ways in the course of time. This is unavoidable.

No human being can override the appointed time of birth or death. None can anticipate it. Therefore, even the one who repeatedly grieves for the departed cannot postpone his own demise.

'A river never retraces its path. Similarly, youth, once past its prime, never returns. Life ebbs steadily and we ought to use our time performing noble deeds.

'Our father was a devout person who followed his dharma. He has, therefore, gone to Swargaloka. We do not have to mourn his death.

'A wise and patient person must not grieve, mourn or wail under any circumstances. Take control of your emotions, dear brother. Go and stay in Ayodhya as commanded by our father.'

'I cannot compete with you in knowledge of dharma, my brother,' said Bharata. 'You know the mystery of life and death and, therefore, grief cannot approach you.

'I was away when my mother, nursing evil thoughts, committed the heinous crime of asking for your exile. Forgive me for what she has done.

'There is a saying that approaching death, human beings lose their balance and fall under delusion. Raja Dashratha's acting so cruelly towards you has proved the truth of this saying.

'You have argued that you would prefer to be a truthful and

obedient son of our father. How then can you support the illegality of what he committed?

'How can exile co-exist with your duty as a Kshatriya? Instead of looking after your praja, you have taken it upon yourself to live like a hermit. You must not act in such a contradictory manner.

'How can I, younger to you in age and wisdom, be a king when you are alive? I have neither talent nor virtue. Without your guidance, I shall not be able to take care of the people.

'Kindly return to Ayodhya and be an unchallenged ruler. If you do this, you will wipe out the stain on my mother's reputation and redeem our father from calumny.

'If you ignore my submission, I too shall stay with you in the forest.'

Assuaging a grieving Bharata, Rama politely told him,

'O devout brother, for my sake you should settle the debt our father owed your mother. Save him from the fires of hell and in the bargain enhance the joy of your mother.

'My brave brother, soon I, accompanied by Lakshmana and Sita, shall move into Dandakaranya. You will be the king of the people in Ayodhya and I will live here in the forest. Let us follow our respective dharma with joy.

'Bharata, I pray that the royal canopy that outshines the sun may provide you with shade. I too shall by and by take shelter under the canopy of the dense, shady trees in the forest.

'Let all the four of us honour and safeguard the word of our father. You ought not to be dejected, my brother.'

Bharata Decides to Act as Regent

After much thought and persuasion, Bharata agreed to return to Ayodhya without Rama. In a tremulous voice, he submitted,

'I cannot take care of the kingdom all by myself. I cannot please the residents of Ayodhya who love and adore you.

'Arya, I place these golden sandals at your feet. Please touch them with your toes. These will then look after the welfare of the world.'

The glorious Rama put on the sandals and then handed them over to Bharata. Bowing to the sandals, the latter said,

'Raghunandan, dressed in bark, loose robes and with my hair braided like a hermit's, I shall live outside the city waiting for your return. I shall subsist on vegetables and fruit. The care of the country will lie on these sandals. If you do not return on the first day at the end of the fourteen years of exile, I shall end my life by entering a smouldering fire.'

Rama embraced his younger brother and said,

'I wish that you look after your mother Kaikeyee as much as other queens. You have to give your word that you will not ever be angry with her.'

With tears in his eyes, Rama bade farewell to Bharata and Shatrughna. The three queens, till now nurturing a hope of Rama's return, were grief-struck and sobbed uncontrollably. Rama bowed to them and returned to his cottage.

13

Bharata Returns to Ayodhya

Ayodhya in Desolation

Ayodhya seemed dead with portals shut and owls holding sway over the once alive city when Bharata returned with Rama's sandals. The city lay helpless with the demise of their king.

Ayodhya looked emaciated like the mountain stream whose waters have been sucked by a burning sun, from where the birds, unable to bear the heat, have flown, and where the fish and the crocodiles have dived deep to avoid the fierce heat.

Ayodhya looked defeated like an army that has lost a war, whose armour has fallen on the ground, whose horses, elephants, chariots and flags have scattered and whose warriors have been slaughtered.

In the absence of Rama and others, Ayodhya had lost its lustre like a necklace of lotus pink, soft and glistening precious stones that has been broken into smithereens.

The grieving traders had lost any urge to do business. Very few shops were open to carry on trade. The city looked dull with the usual hustle bustle missing from pathways and markets.

Looking around and observing the pain of the city and its people, Bharata commented to Sumantra,

'It is painful not to hear the sonorous music of yore in Ayodhya. The spring flowers do not spread fragrance around nor can I smell the purifying scent of sandal or various other incenses. Chariots do not clatter, the horses do not neigh, and the elephants in musth do not trumpet.

'With Shri Rama's departure, the young are disheartened. They do not apply sandal paste or use fragrant aloe. There are neither festivities nor festivals. With my brother's departure the glory of our city has vanished.'

Bharata went in a procession to Nandi gram, an ashrama situated on the outskirts of Ayodhya. Once there, he consecrated Rama's sandals and asked a canopy to be unfurled over them. He declared that he had established Ram Rajya and that he would rule as Rama's representative, for and on behalf of his elder brother. Bharata started living in Nandi gram as a hermit, dressed in bark and matted his braids. The ministers under his guidance carried on the administration.

14

Rishi Atri's Ashrama

Disturbed by the commotion caused by the visit of Bharata and his forces, several hermits left Chitrakoot for other destinations where they could live and worship in peace.

After spending some time at Chitrakoot, even Rama decided to move into a dense forest to continue his exile. His first halt was the famed ashrama of Rishi Atri and his wife, Anasuyia who was reputed to have overcome the effects of a long draught by producing roots and fruit and getting water to flood Mandakini by virtue of a tough penance.

Sita approached Anasuyia and bowed to her. The old hermit was not as active now owing to her old age. Her hair was white and she had tremors in her limbs like a plantain tree shaking in a strong wind.

Anasuyia appreciated the fact that Sita had accompanied Rama to the forest, knowing fully well that a tough life would greet her. Advising the princess further, she said,

'I appreciate your devotion to dharma and that you are keeping company of your husband even in his exile. Women who stay with their husbands in rough times as well, attain to higher levels. A husband is like a devata for his noble wife, his greatest well-wisher. He is a source of happiness to her in this world and beyond like the indestructible fruit of one's own tapasya.

'Women who order their husbands around, those who are lustful all the time, invariably go astray. They indulge in foul deeds and desert the path of dharma.'

Thanking the sage, Sita narrated the story of her birth and marriage to Sati Anasuyia. She said,

'I believe that for a woman her husband is her guru. Even if my husband were not of a noble character, I would have faithfully followed him and served him. However, Shri Raghunath is a man of great stature and noble character. He is kind to everyone and has conquered his senses. He is a man of deep affection. He is virtuous and more like a parent to me. For me, to follow in his footsteps and be at his service is easy.'

Anasuyia affectionately took Sita in her arms and blessed her. It was evening and the sun was setting in the west. Said the elder woman,

'The glorious sun has set and an auspicious night has descended. The birds that had flown off to pick their food throughout the day have returned to their nests and we hear their chirping. The munis wearing wet bark are coming back with pitchers full of water. Rishi Atri's havana is over and smoke, blue like a pigeon's neck, is rising from the dying fire. One cannot fathom the directions because even the faraway trees, although bereft of leaves, are enveloped in darkness. The night animals like owls are wandering while the ashrama deer are resting near the holy havana mandapa.

'Sita, the night sky is laden with sparkling stars. The moon rises swathed in moonlight; it is time for you to go and serve your husband. However, before you leave, do your shringar in my presence. I have a supply of splendid clothes and ornaments and shall be delighted if you put them on and beautify yourself.'

Sita put on the finery in order to please the Sanyasin. She bowed at Anasuyia's feet and went over to be with Shri Rama. The latter was delighted to see Sita looking like a bride once again.

Next morning Rama accompanied by Sita and Lakshmana entered an uncharted forest.

ARANYAKANDAM

1

Dandakaranya

The forest situated between the rivers Narmada and Godavari in the Deccan was uninhabited by humans except for ashramas of various tapasvis and sannyasis. Living in lonely, dark jungles the saintly hermits exercised penance. While there were animals and birds who lived in harmony, these hermits were often attacked by rakshasas, evil-doers as opposed to devatas who were invariably described as good.

Daily Life in the Forest Ashramas

Travelling through Dandakaranya, Rama noticed many ashramas established by the tapasvis. A stunning aura created by a constant study of the scriptures and chanting by the tapasvis permeated these hermitages. Kusha and bark clothes were put to dry in every enclave. The floors were clean and one could see domesticated animals and birds in these ashramas in plenty.

The hermitages were dotted by large yagyashalas, and were stocked with pots and other containers to store the ahuti and ghee for sacrificial yagyas, deerskin, and samidha, pitchers full of clean, fresh water and fruits and flowers. Fruit-bearing trees had been planted in large numbers. Besides, there grew several old trees that provided shade to hermits and a home to birds.

Every morning and evening, the hermitages echoed with the sound of tapasvis chanting mantras from the Vedas. Pushkarni stream full of lotus flowers ran through this group of hermitages, making the place lovelier. Many hoary sages, dressed in black animalskin or bark, lived there. They subsisted on fruit and roots. By virtue of living a life of purity, restraint and piety, they emitted the glow of the sun and brilliance of the fire.

Prior to entering one of the cottages, Rama and Lakshmana untied the strings on their bow as a mark of peace and submission. The maharshi who lived in that cottage welcomed the trio warmly and blessed them. He was amazed to see the glow on the faces of the princes and the charming Sita. After offering them a comfortable place to sit, he addressed Rama and said,

'As a king you are superior to any one of us. You wield the power to administer justice and punish the guilty. You protect the weak, regardless whether you live in the city palace or in the forest hut. We, as hermits, have given up being harsh to anyone and punishing the guilty long ago. As of now, our only wealth is tapasya. It is your duty to protect us the way a mother protects her child.'

Sita and the princes set out again next morning. On their way, a rakshasa named Viradha, who tried to snatch Sita to make her his mistress, was killed by them. Soon they arrived at the ashrama of Rishi Sharabhanga who was busy in a conversation with Indra, who did not wait to meet Rama. He, instead, said that he did not want to interrupt Rama's mission of freeing the earth of the daityas, and sped to Swargaloka. Rishi Sharabhanga welcomed Sita and the princes, gave them directions to reach the ashrama of Rishi Suteekshna. Thereafter, he immolated his body to ascend to Swargaloka having served his purpose in this lifetime.

Suteekshna was meditating as the three reached his hermitage. Rama bowed to him and introduced himself, Sita and Lakshmana. The rishi welcomed them and invited them to stay in his ashrama as long as they desired. He called his ashrama a peaceful place, a favourite with rishis and munis who spent time there. Rama declined to stay there because he thought their presence would destroy the peace of the hermitage and be a hindrance to the penance of the hermits. They rested for the night in the Suteekshna Ashrama. The next morning, they bathed and ritually worshipped Agni and other gods. Thereafter, paying obeisance to the rising sun and taking leave from the rishi to depart on their journey, the three travellers said,

'We are keen to visit all the holy ashramas inhabited by mahatmas in Dandakaranya one by one. Give us permission to leave so that we can avoid the harsh sun of the day.'

Suteekshna blessed them and replied,

'I pray that there be no obstructions in your path and that your journey be peaceful. In this forest you will see several ponds full of clean water and lotus flowers, trees laden with fruit, blooming creepers, herds of gambolling deer, herons sitting on streams, eye-catching waterfalls, green glades and birds singing their songs. Travel wherever you will and come back to this ashrama when you will; you are always welcome.'

2

Sita's Advice to Rama and Lakshmana

The princes carried their bows and arrows and swords as a mark of their being Kshatriyas as well as for protection against wild animals, dacoits and the rakshasas who could attack anyone wandering in the dense forest. Sita, however, had a word of advice for Rama regarding his use of weapons. At an opportune moment, she said in a sweet voice,

'Arya, I am aware that you are a great man. Yet, in my humble opinion, you are moving towards adharma. As you are not prone to any passionate responses, you can easily avoid committing a sinful act.

'In this world, Kama leads to three flawed actions. Telling a lie is a major sin. However, worse than this are coveting another's wife and treating others cruelly without enmity or motive.

'You have always been devoted to me and I am sure you would never covet another's wife. You have been a model of truthfulness, dharma and filial devotion.

'You are one of those who have conquered their senses and emotions. Resultantly, you are always truthful. However, you have not been able to avoid committing the third sin, that of being violent and killing another being without reason.

'You have promised protection to the rishis residing in the Dandakaranya by killing the rakshasas. This worries me.

'I am your well-wisher. I do not approve of your wandering in the forest for this purpose. It is likely that you will use your arrows to kill the rakshasas who dwell in this forest. As fuel stokes a fire and makes it burn fiercer and brighter, weapons incite the killer in a Kshatriya.

'With faith in my love and regard for you, I ask you not to kill any rakshasa living in Dandakaranya if he is not inimical to you. Nobody approves of the killing of an innocent person.

'A restrained Kshatriya carries arms only for the protection of others. Arms and living in exile do not go together. This environment does not look upon the act of killing others kindly. You ought to respect the sanctity of the forest.

'Dharma leads to prosperity and ensures happiness; it is also a source of all that you desire. Dharma is the bedrock of this universe.

'A wise man follows the principles of renunciation as prescribed for the Vanaprastha Ashrama. He reduces his wants and enfeebles his body. Materialistic accumulation of goods, though desirable for a comfortable life, does not lead to spiritual elevation.

'I, therefore, ask you to lead a pious life according to the requirements of the tapovana.'

'O daughter of the King Janaka,' replied Rama after a thoughtful pause, 'you have uttered these words for my well-being because of your love for me. Your advice regarding the duty of a Kshatriya befits you and reflects your thinking.

'You have said that Kshatriyas carry a bow and arrow so that the weak can be protected. The munis living in Dandakaranya are a suffering lot. They have sought my protection against the unscrupulous daityas. The latter disrupt the yagya being performed by the ascetics and take away all the holy food collected for the occasion.

'Listening to their plaint, I have assured them of full protection. I cannot violate my promise in this lifetime.

'I do not have any dispute with your advice tendered to me out of love and affection. Your words reflect your upbringing and as my wife, you are dearer to me than my life. However, I cannot deviate from my truth: the promise that I gave to the hermits to protect them against all odds.'

3

Arrival at Agastya Ashrama

Ten Years of Wandering in the Dandakaranya

The journey through the forest dotted with streams, hills and waterfalls continued. Sita walked between the two brothers who carried their bows and arrows. On their way, they noticed chakvas, sarus, and swans either on the riverbanks or gliding over still waters. The area was dotted with lotus flowers of varied colours, blooming in abundance. They also spotted black bucks and deer with spotted skin moving in herds. The forest was teeming with all sorts of flora and fauna.

One evening Sita and the two brothers arrived at a huge lake wherein elephants were frolicking. The waters were full of fish and other aquatic creatures. Many graceful swans floated on its waters, as did flamingos with black and scarlet wings and pelicans with rose tinged white plumage.

To their utter surprise, all these natural wonders were accompanied by the sound of music floating over the waters of the lake. But they could not see any human beings in the area. Walking a bit further, they met Muni Dharmabhrita and enquired about the lake, and the source of the music they could hear. Respectfully he replied,

'This sarovar is renowned as Panchapsara. It is always full of water. Rishi Mandakarni created it through his powers as a tapasvi. Living in water, the rishi meditated for hundreds of years. He lived only on air during this duration. His penance upset Agni and other devatas lest he displace them in Swargaloka. They schemed to divert the muni from his path although he already had attained the knowledge of dharma in this and the other world. Five extraordinarily charming apsaras were sent to sing and dance in the muni's presence and to cater to all his needs. Mandakarni fell for the women and built an underground palace for them. He now lives inside the waters in the company of his five consorts. He has regained his youth. The apsaras sing and perform all other duties to keep him happy and there is music, dancing and dining in the underground palace all the time.'

Rama, Sita and Lakshmana moved from place to place in the large forestland, never staying at one place more than a few days at one time. In every hermitage, they were welcomed as honoured guests.

After the passage of ten years in this way, they returned to Suteekshna Rishi's ashram and asked for directions to the ashrama of Agastya Muni.

Suteekshna advised them to go southwest keeping to the side of the mountains. Walking along, they reached the ashrama of Agastya Muni's younger brother. They spent a night there and left to see Agastya Muni the next morning.

Arrival at Agastya Ashrama

They passed through thick foliage of neewar, kathala, saakhu, asoka, tinish, chirbilva, mahua, bel, tendu and other wild fruit-bearing trees. Flowering creepers embraced the tree trunks and monkeys jumped from tree to tree as chirping birds fluttered in multitudes.

Pointing to the trees on their path, Rama addressed Lakshmana thus:

'Look, how the leaves on these trees shine. The animals and birds are at peace with each other. This is a sign that we are close to Agastya Muni's ashrama.

'He is known as Agastya because he had stalled the mountains. Agastya made Dakshin safe from the attacks of the rakshasas. Since he moved here, the denizens of the night have quietened. They have become friendly and there is peace all over.

'Once upon a time the Vindhya Mountain advanced towards the sky to stop the sun in his movement. Mahamuni Agastya humbled him and since then the mountain has not grown higher and the sun rises each morning unobstructed. In the Agastya Ashrama, even the deer lives a disciplined life.

'I propose to spend the rest of the time of my exile in this ashrama. It is a place for the pure at heart, none tells a lie here, none cheats, there is no cruelty towards another, nor do devious and evil persons survive here. This is a befitting place for our stay.'

Agastya Gifts Divine Weapons to Rama

In the Agastya Ashrama, the maharshi warmly welcomed Rama, Sita and Lakshmana. Rama along with Vaidehi and Lakshmana bowed in the rishi's presence and touched his feet. With folded hands, they stood awaiting the muni to speak.

Agastya embraced Rama and offered him arghya with a few drops of water. He asked of their welfare and bade them to take a seat. He now offered ahuti to Agni, worshipped the guests as per rituals laid down for Vanaprastha and then served them a meal. Addressing Rama, Agastya said,

'You are the master of the universe. You are a warrior who follows dharma. I welcome you as a respected guest of this ashrama.'

Saying this, Agastya offered fruit, roots, flowers and other articles in welcome. He continued,

'O lion among men, I present you with a majestic bow designed by Vishwakarma. It has a gold plate studded with diamonds. Another weapon is a gift from Bhagwan Vishnu. Brahma gifted this superior, unfailing arrow shining like the sun to me. Further, I hand over to you two inexhaustible quivers full of sharp arrows burnished like fire, given to me by Indra. Here is a sword with a handle and scabbard both made of gold.

'Please accept these weapons in order to succeed in your fight against the rakshasas.'

Agastya requested Rama to spend the remaining years of his exile in his ashrama. However, Rama desired to live in a more solitary place. He wanted a place where they could live happily, which was soothing to the senses, and where samidha, kusha grass and water were available easily. He said,

'We would like to go and live in a place that is quiet, surrounded by dense trees, and has an ample water supply. We shall build a cottage at such a place and spend the remaining time of our exile in peace.'

After some thought, Agastya replied,

'Not far from here is situated Panchavati, home to large herds of deer. The area is rich in fruit and vegetables with sufficient water. You can go and build a cottage there with assistance from Lakshmana and fulfil the promise you had made to your father.

'I am aware why you do not want to stay here. You have determined to annihilate the rakshasas. It is not possible to do so here because they do not visit this ashrama.

'Panchavati is situated on the banks of Godavari with myriad flowers in bloom all year long. Mithilesh Kumari will certainly be happy to live there.

'Panchavati is situated north of the Mahua forest that you can see from here. At first, you will come to a large banyan tree standing tall just ahead of a high plateau. Beyond, there lies a hill and a short distance from there lies Panchavati.'

4

Panchavati

Rama's Friendship with Jatayu

On their way to Panchavati, they came across a vulture who was humungous in size. Taking him to be a rakshasa, Rama prepared to attack him and asked him who he was. Softly he replied,

'Son, consider me to be your father's friend. My name is Jatayu, son of Shyeni and a descendant of the Rishi Kashyapa and his wife Diti who had given birth to the daityas.

'I shall assist you in settling in this forest which is full of herds of deer and rakshasas. I shall guard Sita in your cottage when you and Lakshmana are absent.'

Rama bowed before Jatayu and greeted him respectfully. Assured of Sita's safety, they left her with Jatayu and moved on to the Panchavati grove to erect a cottage there.

Construction of a Cottage

The place was full of snakes, wild animals and deer with an abundance of wild flowers. Rama asked Lakshmana to select for their habitation a suitable site near a water body where Sita could feel comfortable.

After much consideration, they decided to build the hut on level land on the banks of river Godavari adorned by lotus flowers of many a hue. The flowers shone in their splendour like the very sun and emitted a captivating fragrance. The nearby hills echoed with sounds of various melodious birds.

Flowering creepers climbing around sal, tala, tamala, dates, kadamba, tinish, kathala, punnag, mango, asoka, tilaka, kewra, champa, sandal, shami, palash, and other trees made these hills look resplendent.

Lakshmana erected a vast thatched cottage using wood and grass.

At the outset, he constructed a wall with stones and mud supported by strong and shapely pillars. Large bamboos were placed diagonally on the pillars, branches of the shami tree spread on them and tied with sturdy ropes. He covered the roof with dry leaves and long grasses like sarkanda, kusha, and kans. He levelled the floors and coated them with wet mud.

Before entering the cottage, Sita and the two brothers worshipped the gods and offered them fruits and flowers. A delighted Rama looked at the cottage and warmly embraced Lakshmana. He said,

'My brave brother, I am mighty pleased with this effort of yours. Having no other reward to offer you, I hold you in a warm embrace.

'Lakshmana, you divine my thoughts correctly. You are knowledgeable in dharma. I believe that our father lives in a dharmatma son like you.'

The Arrival of Winter

The cycle of seasons gradually replaced the Sharad ritu with Hemant. The cold weather set in. One wintery morning, carrying pitchers on their arms Sita, Rama and Lakshmana were on their way to Godavari for a bath when Lakshmana said,

'Brother, your favourite season, the winter has arrived with its peculiar charm. While the cold air dries the skin, fresh corn sprouts and undulates in the fields. Water is so cold that one does not like to drink it. One likes to be near a fire.

'This is a season of contentment because grain and fruit are available to men in abundance. There is no shortage of milk. The sun has firmly moved into the south and the north looks lustreless like a woman whose forehead has been wiped of the vermilion tilaka.

'Undoubtedly, the Himalayas are the abode of snow but in winter the snow piles up as never before, and the Himalayas turn true to their name as the abode of snow.

'It is pleasant to move in the sunlight at noon. As opposed to the summers, shades do not charm anymore and sunlight seems pleasant.

'In this weather, the jungles look bare because the trees shed their leaves. The frost damages the lotus in the ponds.

'The nights grow longer and chilly. Nobody sleeps in the open. In the month of Pausha, the nights lose their lustre because of frost.

'Nobody desires to sit in the moonlight because the sun has taken away its comfort as well as charm. The sky looks dull because of the particles of frost suspended in the air. The moon looks like a mirror made dull by warm breath.

'The fields of barley and wheat are hidden by fog. Nevertheless, the forest looks bright at sunrise. The herons and saruses call aloud.

'The golden sheaves of rice, with pretty tufts shaped like the date palm flowers, are bent down with weight.

'In the distance the rising sun, hidden by fog, yet visible because of its rays, looks like the moon.

'Look, that wild elephant is thirsty. Yet it retracts its trunk the moment, in happy anticipation, it touches the freezing, unbearably cold water, to quench his thirst.

'The water birds sit near the bank. Yet, like cowards not entering the battlefield, they do not glide into water.

'A heavy fog hides the rivers. One can identify the sarus birds only by their trumpets for otherwise, they are invisible. Even the streams can be identified only by their sand banks moistened by dew.'

Having taken a bath in the company of Sita and Lakshmana, Rama looked glorious, as does Bhagwan Rudra after his bath in the Ganga, standing near Uma, Himalaya's daughter, and his mount Nandi.

5

Shoorpanakha Enters the Scene

Shoorpanakha's Flirtation

Rama settled to a peaceful life in the cottage at Panchavati.

One day when the two brothers were busy in conversation, Shoorpanakha, sister of the ten-headed Ravana, arrived on the scene. Looking at Rama she instantly fell in love with him. She found Rama of the complexion of a blue lotus, as captivating as Kamadeva, glorious like Indra, and imbued with a king's irresistible demeanour.

In appearance, she was a total contrast to Rama. She was of a scary appearance against Rama's charming face. Rama's waist was slim while she had an ungainly, large belly. Rama had large and lovely eyes, while hers were frightening. She had copper-coloured hair as against Rama's long shining black hair. Rama exuded kindness while Ravana's sister looked rough, disgusting and hideous. Rama's voice was soft while Shoorpanakha spoke in a thundering voice.

Rama was an epitome of everlasting youth while the rakshasi looked old and withered. A coquettish Shoorpanakha approached Rama and asked,

'O warrior, what brings you to this land of the rakshasas, dressed as a tapasvi and accompanied by a woman? You carry a bow and arrows yet sport matted hair on your head.'

Rama kept his cool and replied,

'There used to be a king, Dashratha by name, valorous as the devatas. I am his eldest son and my name is Rama.

'Here is my righteous brother, Lakshmana. This is my wife, Sita, daughter of the king of Mithila.

'In obedience to the command of my father and my mother Kaikeyee, and in order to act according to my dharma, I have come to spend a few years in this forest.

'I want to know about you. Who are you and what is your lineage? What is your name? Who is your husband? You appear to be a rakshasi who can change appearances at will.

'Why have you come to us?'

Burning with lust for the charming prince, Shoorpanakha replied,

'I am Shoorpanakha and, yes, I can change appearances at will. Frightening everyone, I wander alone in this forest. My brothers are mighty rakshasas, Ravana and Kumbhakarna, and Vibhishana who is a dharmatma and does not behave like a rakshasa. Two other brothers, Khara and Dooshana too are renowned for their valour.

'Rama, I am stronger and more valorous than my brothers. I have fallen in love with you and wish you to be my husband. What will you do with the ugly Sita who is unfit for you? I alone deserve you and, therefore, you should marry me. We shall spend a life making love, wandering on the hill tops and in Dandakaranya, enjoying the beauties of nature.'

Rama smiled and replied,

'Woman, I respect you. However, I am married. And knowing that for a woman like you, it might be difficult to live with a co-wife, I would not entertain your wish. Though, my younger brother is equally well-endowed. He is young, handsome and alone. In case he requires, he can take you as his wife.'

Impelled by lust, Shoorpanakha approached Lakshmana with a proposal for marriage. He tossed her back saying,

'O beautiful woman with large eyes, my elder brother alone is a befitting match for you, even if you have to be subservient to Sita to be his wife. I am a mere servant and you will have to be a dasi if you marry me.'

Continuing making fun of her, Lakshmana said,

'You have such a slender waist and attractive appearance. It would be foolish of a human to not take a beautiful woman such as you as his wife.'

Shoorpanakha approached Rama once again. She threatened him with eating Sita alive. Like a meteor striking Rohini as if to destroy the splendid star, she prepared to pounce upon Sita to tear her to pieces.

Rama shouted at the rakshasi advancing like the noose of Yamaraja to halt and directed Lakshmana to teach her a lesson.

In no time, Lakshmana severed Shoorpanakha's ears and sliced her nose.

Wailing and beating her breast, the rakshasi ran into the forest roaring like thunder. Reaching her brother Khara, she fell unconscious.

Looking at his sister's abject condition, Khara flew into a rage. He asked her,

'Who dared to disturb you in the forest we rule?

'Whoever has cut your limbs has put the noose of death around his neck. I shall kill him and throw his carcass to the dogs and vultures.'

Coming to her senses, Shoorpanakha replied,

'Brother, two young, handsome men have arrived in the forest. They appear to be strong and possess weapons. They are dressed in bark and deerskin. They live on fruit and roots and lead the lives of hermits. They describe themselves as the sons of King Dashratha and are named Rama and Lakshmana. A woman with a slim waist accompanies them. It is because of her that they have humiliated me as if I am an unprotected woman of ill repute.

'I want all the three of them to be killed so that I can drink their blood.'

An angry Khara sent fourteen of his bravest rakshasas to kill Rama, Lakshmana and Sita. Shoorpanakha's blood had coagulated on her nose and ears making her look more hideous. She led this party so that she could fulfil her desire of drinking their blood.

However, Khara's fourteen warriors were no match for the valiant Rama. He pierced their chests with fourteen arrows that came out on the other side like serpents crawling out of their hideouts. Drenched in blood, the rakshasas fell to the ground like tree trunks brought down by an axe.

Shoorpanakha fainted at this sight and after regaining consciousness, went back to her brother and lamented thus:

'My heart is filled with fear on seeing the warriors killed in an instant by the brave Rama. O king of the daityas, I am agitated, aggrieved, and fearful.

'Brother, if you have the strength, go and kill Rama yourself. If you are unable to kill those who harm rakshasas living in this forest, you are unfit to rule this forest.'

Khara Challenges Rama and Sends Dooshana to Fight

'I am moved by immeasurable anger,' roared Khara. 'Rama is no warrior in my presence. The life of that human being is ebbing and he shall soon be killed.'

Khara commanded his general, Dooshana:

'Gather a force of 14,000 soldiers ready to attack. They should be ready to die, rather than retreat.

'In order to kill the insolent Rama, I shall personally lead the Pulstya rakshasa warriors.'

Khara set out in a massive chariot glowing like the sun and pulled by speckled horses. It was as high as the Meru Mountain. Its wheels and body were gold plated with decorations of sun, moon, stars, trees, flowers, fish, mountains and birds. The horses had bells around their necks and tinkling anklets on their legs while the soldiers carried assorted weapons. Khara raised a tumultuous cry like thundering clouds and advanced to face Rama.

Clouds, the colour of grey donkeys scattered in the sky as the rakshasa forces marched to take on Rama. This was a bad omen for the rakshasa army. Khara's horses stumbled even on flat land carpeted with flowers while the earth was experiencing tremors. Although his left arm was shaking uncontrollably and he had a severe headache, he declared,

'I have the power to shoot down the stars in the firmament. If I am enraged, I can put even Death to the sleep of the dead. I have never lost a battle and today I will vanquish Rama to win another.'

Soon the rakshasa sena found itself facing Rama and Lakshmana. The latter too had noticed the advancing hordes. As a matter of precaution, Rama asked Lakshmana to move with Sita into a nearby cave. The chivalrous Rama burned with the fire of righteousness, like the doomsday fire. He appeared like Mahadeva carrying the Pinaka bow in order to disrupt the yagya of his father-in-law, Daksha Prajapati.

Surrounded by rakshasas, Khara looked like Saturn surrounded by a host of stars. His soldiers armed with spears, axes, maces and swords attacked Rama from all sides. The latter was wounded but not frightened. His archery was deadly and matchless. In no time, Rama cut down the enemy's swords, shields, and armour plates, horses pulling the chariots, drivers, mahouts, cavalry and foot soldiers.

Khara's brother and commander, Dooshana motivated his soldiers to advance, either to do or die, but the rakshasas kept falling. They threw trees and rocks in Rama's direction to disengage him from his fierce attack but to no avail.

Then Rama struck the enemy with the glorious Gandharva astra, which scattered thousands of arrows at one go in the direction of the asuras. Soon, the entire earth was carpeted with the dead bodies of the rakshasas.

Dooshana advanced with a furious force of 5,000 daityas. Rama bravely dealt with this onslaught. He cut Dooshana's charioteer into pieces and killed his horses. Dooshana advanced towards Rama on foot and tried to hit him with a mace bristling with long nails that looked like reptiles. Rama shot arrows with heads shaped like new moons and sliced both the arms of Dooshana. Like an elephant whose tusks have been pulled out, the daitya commander fell to the ground and bled to death.

Khara Dares Rama

It was now the turn of Khara to engage Rama in a fight, to either victory or death. However, before he could proceed, his commander Trishira volunteered to fight Rama and kill him. He declared that either he would be the cause of Rama's death or he would die fighting.

Rama fought Trishira like a lion taking on an elephant. He shot fourteen arrows, poisonous like snakes at Trishira's chest. In quick succession, the Raghava prince killed Trishira's horses and his charioteer. As the rakshasa commander tried to alight from the chariot, Rama split his chest with more arrows. Trishira's blood spurted from his body like lava from a volcano until he fell dead to the ground.

Khara was sad at his commander's death. However, he decided to take on Rama valiantly.

Although Khara walked like a lion and acted with the ferocity of the king of the forest, Rama faught him valiantly. Initially, Khara hit Rama near his heart and caused serious injury to the prince, cutting Rama's body armour to pieces.

Rama rallied his strength and using the Vaishnava bow given to him by Maharishi Agastya, one by one, he cut down Khara's flag and charioteer, his horses, and then hit him in his chest with six arrows in quick succession. One of the arrows hit Khara in his forehead, another two cut his arms and three half-moon shaped arrows burst into his chest.

Addressing Khara, who faced him standing on a ground full of the dead bodies of his soldiers, Rama said,

'O denizen of the night, the entire world condemns the cruel deeds performed by you, aided by your vast army consisting of elephants, horses, and chariots. An evil person like you, who harasses others, cannot long survive. He deserves to be killed like a poisonous serpent out in the open.

'The desire for something not gained is called 'kama'. A desire to attain more of what one already has, is called 'lobha'. Anyone who acts motivated by kama or lobha, without a sense of the evil nature of such activity, rather exulting in doing so, meets his end like a red-tailed ant destroying itself by biting a piece of hail.

'O rakshasa, you will reap the dire consequences of killing innocent hermits living and meditating in the Dandakaranya.

'The trees whose roots have become hollow do not survive for long. Likewise, the evil and cruel persons, denounced by everyone, cannot enjoy their dubiously acquired prosperity and power for long.

'Today, my arrows, like snakes coming out of their holes, will pierce you and drilling through the earth reach the nether world. You will follow the rishis whom you killed in this forest. However hard you try, today I shall break open your head like the tala fruit.

An angry Khara, his eyes blood-shot, laughing as if in delirium, retorted, 'O son of Dashratha, don't brag because you have been able to kill a few petty rakshasas. The chivalrous and the brave do not boast of their strength.

'Like brass revealing its impure character when tested in fire, you have uncovered your base reality and shallow character through false self-praise.

'Don't you see that facing you I stand with a mace in hand, steady like the immobile mountains that hide several metals in their core? I am powerful enough to dispatch the three of you with my mace like Yamaraja who carries a noose.

Denouncing Khara as evil incarnate, Rama challenged him to a fight.

Khara attacked Rama with the trunk of a huge sal tree plucked out of the earth. The latter cut this tree trunk into pieces with his arrows.

Rama was sweating and his eyes were red with anger. With a barrage of arrows, he grievously injured the daitya. Khara's wounds bled like a river but he still gathered his strength and rushed to hit Rama once again.

This time Rama shot at Khara with a glorious weapon, fierce and burning like Agni. As Shankara had burnt Andhakasura alive, Rama's astra set Khara on fire and the latter fell on the ground enveloped in flames. He died soon thereafter.

Agastya and other rishis surrounded Rama and thanked him for having killed the 14,000 rakshasas with their leaders. They said,

'We considered your arrival to be auspicious because we knew that you will kill the asuras. O son of Dashratha, you have made our life free of any impediments in the path of our meditation and yagya. Now the saintly rishis, living in different parts of Dandakaranya, will perform their religious rituals fearlessly.'

As she came out of the cave, Sita's joy knew no bounds. She embraced Rama in bliss to express her delight.

6

Maricha is Inveigled into a Conspiracy to Abduct Sita

Ravana Takes Offence at the Death of Khara

The territory, styled Janasthana, where Khara had ruled, was under the suzerainty of Ravana, the king of Lanka. As he received the news of Khara's death at Rama's hands, Ravana flared up. With anger seething in his eyes he told the messenger Anukampana,

'Who is it that courts death by devastating my territory and killing my general, Khara? Even Indra, Kubera, Yama and Vishnu cannot breathe in peace if they offend me. I am the death of Kala itself.'

Anukampana was speechless and feared lest he be killed for bringing such sad tidings. A little while later, assured of his life, he regained his confidence and narrated how Rama had single-handedly killed Khara, Dooshana and their forces.

'Rama came to the forest unaccompanied by any devata or muni. He is glorious of mien and is the bravest archer in the world. He is well versed in the knowledge of weapons used to wage a war. Upon Ravana's expressing a determination to take on Rama in battle and kill him, Anukampana dissuaded him saying,

'Rajan, please know of the prowess of Rama before you step further. Rama can reverse the flow of rivers; he can upset the arrangement of stars and planets in the heavens. Like a sinner's inability to enter Swargaloka, you along with all your forces or kin cannot defeat Rama in battle.

'However, I have a suggestion that, if implemented, can kill Rama easily. His wife Sita is the prettiest woman in the world. She is at the peak of her youth; with shapely limbs and sweet countenance, she is a rare gem among women. If you can devise a strategy to abduct Sita, Rama will not survive the separation.'

Maricha Dissuades Ravana

Ravana considered the idea and realized that this would be a befitting reply to the insult meted out to his sister and the rakshasas that had been killed. Riding his golden chariot driven by donkeys, he arrived at the Maricha Ashrama. He was welcome befittingly. On being asked the purpose of his sudden visit, the king of the rakshasas replied,

'Rama has killed my commanders Khara and Dooshana who guarded the frontiers of my kingdom. To avenge their deaths, I intend kidnapping his wife, Sita. I need your assistance.'

Maricha responded,

'O crown of the Rakshasas, which enemy of yours has advised you to do so? Does he want to pluck the crown of the daityas? Tendering you this vicious advice, he has indeed carved a path leading to the end of daityas.

'Rajan, Rama is like an elephant in musth whose smell frightens minor elephants. He is a lion in the body of a human being. He is an ocean of indeterminate depth.

'Lankeshwara, go back to Lanka and live happily. Do not engage Rama.'

Ravana contemplated on Maricha's words and thinking of Lanka, its people and his other commanders decided to heed this advice and returned to Lanka.

Ravana and His Splendour

However, Shoorpanakha had not yet had her vengeance. She arrived at her brother's court soon after. She saw Ravana sitting on his splendid golden throne on the seventh floor of his palace. He was invincible at the hands of devatas, gandharvas, ghosts and rishis. He had the frightening looks of Yamaraja. With ten heads and twenty arms, his canopy and the ornaments on his body made him look resplendent. He had sturdy arms, white teeth and the girth of a mountain.

Ravana had the strength to pluck out entire mountains. He was known to have destroyed several devatas under his elephant's feet. His deeds were against dharma and he was known as the ravisher of honour of women belonging to others. He had defeated Kubera on the Mount Kailas and taken control over the former's Pushpak Vimana that could fly in any direction at will. He had destroyed the divine

Chaitraratha forest of Kubera, Nandanavana of Indra and the Nalini stream full of blue lotus blooms. Ravana had desecrated hundreds of yagyas and killed many. A long time ago, Ravana had propitiated Brahma with meditation and offering his heads in sacrifice. Since Brahma refused to grant him immortality, he was granted a boon that he would be invincible to devatas, daityas, apsaras, animals and spirits. He did not include humans in the boon owing to his pride and arrogance.

Shoorpanakha Incites Ravana

Shoorpanakha, angry at her insult and grieved at the death of her brother, reprimanded Ravana and addressed him thus,

'Rajan, you have lost yourself in lusty pursuits and forgotten your duties as our protector and king. Beware of the danger facing you in the form of Rama. Your secret service, if any, has not informed you of the Panchavati battle where our dear and brave Khara and Dooshana were put to death by the merciless Rama. Do not act like an ignorant child but take measures to save your kingdom.

'If you do not awaken even now, you would soon be destroyed.'

His wailing sister's stern reprimand jolted the king. He said,

'O charming Shoorpanakha, who has disfigured you by cutting your nose and ears? Who is this man called Rama? How did he enter the dark and deep forest? What weapons has he used to kill my commanders?'

Shoorpanakha gave a vivid description of Rama and his companions, all the time expressing her anger in harsh words. She said,

'Rama is the eldest son of Dashratha, the late king of Ayodhya. He is handsome like Kamadeva, with large eyes and long arms. He lives dressed in bark and the skin of black deer. His arrows are released like poisonous reptiles from his bow that is ringed in gold and resembles a rainbow. He does so with the speed of lightning.

'He destroyed the rakshasas like a hailstorm annihilates the crops. He let me go only because he did not want to kill a woman. I was, however, humiliated by Rama and his magnificent brother, Lakshmana. Rama's wife, Sita accompanies him. He is deeply in love with her. She has large eyes and the face of a full moon. Her body glows like burnished gold. She has long, red nails. Her waist is thin and her limbs well formed. She is the daughter of Janaka, the king of Mithila.

'I have yet to see a woman more charming than Sita. She is prettier than the apsaras, Kinner and Gandharva women.

'That man is luckier than Indra who is loved by Sita, whom she embraces with joy and passion.

'This matchless beauty of adorable limbs is fit to be your consort, my brother. Her thighs are broad and her breasts are full. It was when I tried to persuade her to be your wife that Lakshmana disfigured me.

'I am sure that once you look at Sita, you cannot help being enamoured of her. If you approve of my proposal, put your right foot forward, kill Rama and make Sita your wife. Be confident of your strength because you are more powerful than Rama.'

Ravana Flies over the West Coast of India

Before making up his mind, Ravana carefully considered the consequences that might befall him after Sita's abduction. He decided to go ahead.

Moving in a splendid chariot drawn by luxuriously draped donkeys, Lankeshwara journeyed on the ocean shore. Ravana's chariot, Pushpak Vimana, could be steered at will in any direction. Flying over land the daitya king, of sapphire blue complexion, glistened like a cloud ringed by lightning and surrounded by flights of cranes.

The seashore had hundreds of trees rich in fruits and flowers. The valorous king looked at ponds full of cool waters and abounding in lotuses, and ashramas in which yagyashalas had been erected. Coconut and plantain trees stood tall and so did sal, tamala, and tala trees. Now and then, he noticed hundreds of celestial apsaras enjoying the breeze, as also devatas, rakshasas, and their consorts.

Advancing further, Ravana saw thousands of sandalwood trees oozing resin at their roots, intoxicating the air with rich fragrance. The nearby forests were rich in fragrant aloe and takkol fruit, flowering tamala trees, and bushes bearing round, red chillies. Heaps of pearls lay on the seashore and coral reefs under the water shone resplendently. The low hills parallel to the shore had peaks shining like gold and silver and were made lovelier by thundering cataracts of clear water. The king saw towns full of rich homes, lovely women, elephants, horses and chariots while flying in his chariot.

Crossing all these, Ravana arrived at Maricha Ashram once again. The latter enquired of him the reason for such an early return.

Ravana Requests Maricha to Assume the Form of a Golden Deer

'Dear brother, Maricha,' said Ravana,' I am an unhappy man at this time. In this situation, you are my greatest support. You are aware that in a habitation in the Dandakaranya, my brother Khara, sister Shoorpanakha, Dooshana and other rakshasas lived and prospered by harassing the rishis. Rama, although a human, has killed all of them and his brother Lakshmana has disfigured my sister, cutting her nose and ears. The princes have been sent into exile by their own father; I am sure there must be some reason behind it. He is a blot on the Kshatriya race.

'I do not care for any devata because warriors like you stand with me. There is none who equals you in chivalry, pride of a soldier, or dexterity in battle. You can create an illusion at will.

'If you transform yourself into a golden deer with silver spots, and amble in front of Sita in Rama's ashrama, she will send Rama and Lakshmana in hot pursuit to capture you. As soon as both her protectors are away, I shall abduct Sita. Lamenting for her, Rama will become weak and fall an easy prey to my assault.'

A stunned Maricha trembled with fear. His lips were dry and his face was drained of blood. Frightened to the core, he truthfully spoke words of persuasion:

'Maharaja, you are unaware of the reality of Rama who is brave beyond words, just like Indra and Varuna.

'We must not invite the wrath of Rama who has the capacity to wipe out our entire race. Sita was not born to be the cause of your death. Your life will be in danger if you abduct her.

'Because of a wilful and thoughtless king like you, Lankapuri and its rakshasas will be wiped out.

'Also, Ramachandra was not thrown out by his father. He has never crossed the bounds of dharma. Neither is he greedy, nor a blot on his race. He has never treated anyone cruelly and is living in exile to keep his father's word to his stepmother. Rama has conquered his desires and is a righteous being.

'Sita is protected by her virtue, her fidelity to her husband. As no one can disunite the sun from his resplendence, it is impossible to part Sita from Rama. How are you then going to abduct her forcibly?

'Rama is like Agni, a conflagration and his arrows the flames that swallow his enemies. Rama might turn out to be your Yamaraja.

'O king of the rakshasas, do not undertake this futile task. The day you face Rama on the battlefield, will be the end of you.

'I have faced Rama when he was just a child. As I considered myself a mighty rakshasa and Rama but a young child, I entered the Vishwamitra Ashrama to destroy the rishi's yagya vedi. Rama's arrow sent me hundreds of miles into the deep sea. I survived only because he had not willed to kill me.

'You are our king and if despite my advice against it, you wish to attack or offend Rama, you will witness the destruction of Lanka, your people, soldiers, kin and yourself.

'Rajan, there is no greater sin than cohabiting with someone else's wife. There are hundreds of young women in your harem. Shower your love upon them and protect your family and dynasty by leaving out thoughts of Sita.

'O my king, if you still wish to challenge Rama in the battlefield, I would request that you do not make me partake of this sinful deed. Shoorpanakha provoked Rama and suffered the consequences. That does not enable us to find a fault with Rama's conduct.

As a patient with a death wish ignores any medication, Ravana did not budge under Maricha's persuasion. Rather, he rebuked him sternly and said,

'Your words are futile like the seeds sowed in barren land. Nothing deters me from my resolve to abduct Sita and I propose to do so in your company.

'I am your king and you should speak to me respectfully, in sweet and pleasant tones. Additionally, I am your guest. It is not correct on your part to utter warnings in answer to my requests.

'Now, I wish that you carry out my command and have faith in what the king decides and asks you to do. Change into a golden deer with silver spots all over and wander as such in Sita's garden. She will crave for you and ask Rama to catch you to make you a pet. Let Rama chase you for a long distance and then mimicking his voice you should cry, 'Ha Sita! Ha Lakshmana!' Hearing this cry, Lakshmana urged by Sita will depart to assist Rama. In the absence of both the brothers, I shall easily abduct Sita. Half my kingdom will be your reward.

'I know you can help me in this and I am offering you a good bargain: half my kingdom for your valour. In this adventure, you might or might not be killed by Rama. But if you disobey and refuse to do as I say, I shall surely put you to death.'

Maricha attempted to dissuade Ravana but to no avail.

7

The Chase of the Golden Deer

Sita is Attracted by the Golden Deer

'I am ready, let us go. If I must die, let it be at Rama's hands.' Saying so, Maricha stood up to accompany Ravana.

The king was happy, embraced Maricha warmly, and made him sit in his splendid chariot. Said he,

'Create an insatiable desire in Sita's mind so that she compels Rama to chase you, in order to snare you or kill you for your skin.'

As Maricha reached near Panchavati, he changed himself into a deer as desired by Ravana and started ambling in front of Rama's cottage. The top of his horns shone and looked blue like sapphire. His face was freckled with white and black dots. It was lotus red and his ears were lotus blue. He had a long neck and a blue belly. His hind was creamy white and shaped like the mahua flowers. The golden tone of his skin was the colour of the saffron filament. His body was sleek and had an attractive glow. His hoofs reflected light like lapis lazuli; his legs were thin and his tail had the colour of rainbow.

The golden deer was grazing in front of Panchavati. He leapt to pluck fresh tree leaves. At times, he walked away and then returned to draw attention. He played, jumped and rolled in the ground. He joined the other herds but invariably came back keen to invite Sita's attention. He jumped like an acrobat whenever he neared Sita.

Videhanandini Sita, the one with intoxicating eyes, while plucking flowers and walking through the kanera bushes and asoka and mango trees, happened to look at the golden deer. She noticed that his entire coat was dotted with spots shaped like pearls and precious stones. He had lovely teeth and lips. The fur on his skin stood like thin threads of silver and copper.

Sita was astonished to see this unusually beautiful animal. With loving eyes, she looked at him without blinking.

Sita called Rama and Lakshmana to come and look at this exceedingly charming animal. Lakshmana cast a glance and declared that he suspected deceit and that this deer could be Maricha, the rakshasa who could change his form at will.

However, Sita's discretion had vanished with her fascination for the golden deer and by Maricha's deceitful illusion. She insisted that Rama must ensnare it and bring it to their cottage for their entertainment. She said,

'Rajan, although our ashrama is visited by several herds of sacred and pretty deer, some of a dotted coat, as well as by cows with black or white tails, by bears, and monkeys, I have so far never seen a deer like this one, so quiet, glorious and colourful.

'It is an animal of indescribable beauty. It bellows sweetly and its unusual limbs have won my heart. It stands fearless in front of me. It illuminates the forest like the moon.

'You ought to catch this deer alive. At the end of our exile, we shall take it along to Ayodhya where it will enhance the charm of our palace. Its divine looks will please Bharata and my mothers-in-law. In case you cannot catch it alive, I shall use his golden skin as a seat.

'I know I am being selfish. A pious woman must not goad her husband in her self-interest to do such a job. However, its astonishing body has excited my curiosity.'

Rama himself was amazed looking at the sapphire horns, the glow of the rising sun, spots like those of the star-spangled firmament, and the golden hue. Urged by Sita and getting curious on his own, he said to Lakshmana,

'See, how strong is her desire to catch this deer. It is in fact an extraordinarily charming animal. The fur on its spotted skin is fascinating, its tongue protrudes like a flame when it yawns, it shines like lightning and its belly is fair like seashells or pearls. Such an animal will not be found even in Indra's Nandanavana or in Kubera's Chaitratha forest.

'Lakshmana, kings go to hunt in forests. They shoot deer with their arrows. Hunting in forests is a source of wealth for a king because his exploration gives him information and access to hidden metals and minerals. A rich forest is a source of wealth for the state and it is important for the same reason.

'The skin of no other animal can be as attractive and pleasing to touch as the skin of this golden deer. Only two divine deer exist: one is the constellation, Orion, in the sky and the other is this spotted golden deer. Even if, as you say, it has been created by maya by some rakshasa, I ought to kill this animal in order to destroy the illusion of an evil daitya.

'Lakshmana, dressed in full armour, you will safeguard Sita while I go to catch this animal, dead or alive. Be very careful in my absence. I shall return soon with the trophy.'

Rama set out on the chase of the golden deer with a gold-handled sword, a magnificent bow bent at three places, and two quivers full of arrows.

The deer came into his sight, and then disappeared as if playing a game of hide and seek. As Rama ran in its direction, the animal ran on while all the time casting glances in his direction to make sure that it was being followed as desired. At times, it created a large distance between itself and the prince. At others, it came almost within reach. Soon it had drawn Rama far away from the ashrama.

The lengthening chase made Rama angry and tired him. He made up his mind to kill the beast rather than wait to trap him alive. Taking aim, Rama shot an arrow into its heart. The animal fell down with a loud roar. The rakshasa regained his form and remembering Ravana's command, shouted, 'Ha Sita! Ha Lakshmana!' His repeated calls frightened Rama, who thought of the consequences of Lakshmana coming to his rescue. While Maricha lay dying, Rama gathering fruit for their meals hurried towards his ashrama.

An Obstinate Sita Compels Lakshmana to Leave Her Undefended

Hearing Maricha's shouts, Sita was perturbed. She worried for Rama's life. She asked Lakshmana,

'This is your brother's cry for help. He seems trapped like a bull in the jaws of a lion.'

Lakshmana did not budge. He was well aware of Rama's prowess and sensed a trap. However, Sita would not be dissuaded. Distraught, she accused Lakshmana of betrayal. She said,

'Sumitrakumar, you are an enemy of your brother in the guise of a friend. You want Rama dead so that you can gain me. Do not forget that Rama is your master and that you are here to serve him. If his life is in danger, of what use will it be if you save my life?'

Lakshmana assured her saying,

'Videhanandini, there is none in the universe, whether a devata or a rakshasa, man or beast, gandharva or reptile, animal or bird, who can harm my brother who as a warrior equals Indra in the battlefield. In his absence, I cannot leave you alone. Do not grieve. All is well with Rama.

'What you heard was an illusion created by a rakshasa. At the moment my pledge is to protect you and I shall protect you under all circumstances. I cannot leave you alone.'

Sita flared at this disobedience. She shouted at Lakshmana,

'You are not an Arya. You are heartless, cruel and in disobeying me you are putting our family in peril. Your evil thinking is no surprise to me because that is how an enemy behaves. I can see that you accompanied Rama into exile so that you could put him out of your way and get me. Maybe, Bharata sent you to destroy Rama.

'However, remember that neither Bharata's nor your intentions will fructify. With a husband like Rama, charming as a blue lotus and with eyes like a lotus bud, I care nought for petty men like you. Without Rama, I shall not live for a moment on this earth. I shall drown in Godavari or hang myself with a rope from a tree. I shall jump to death from a mountain, or poison, or immolate myself.'

A lamenting and distraught Sita beat her belly in a fit of anger.

Lakshmana replied, his hands respectfully folded,

'Devi, I worship you and, therefore, I shall not respond to your accusations. It is usual for a woman to hurl such unfair accusations. Videhakumari Janaki, your words are like molten iron poured into my ears. I can sense that trusting an illusion more than me, you have lost your wisdom. This will take you closer to danger.

'I shall follow Shri Rama as you desire. However, I fear dire consequences of my absence.'

8

The Abduction of Sita

As Lakshmana left to look for Rama, Ravana's path was cleared to approach Sita. Everything was proceeding as per his devilish plan. The moment Lakshmana departed, the king of the rakshasas approached Videhakumari dressed as a hermit. He was dressed in a sheet of the colour of the light brown earth, carried an umbrella and had shoes on his feet. A tuft of hair stood on his head. He carried a kamandalu suspended on a stick resting on his left shoulder.

Thus dressed as a wandering mendicant, Ravana neared Sita, now alone in the absence of Rama and Lakshmana. He looked at the innocent woman like the frightful Saturn or Mars looking at Rohini when separated from the moon.

Frightened by the looks of the evil Ravana, the trees in the forest stood still, the breeze held its breath, and Godavari slowed down midstream.

Ravana Tries to Woo Sita

Hidden from her view, Ravana looked at the charming, weeping woman who had lovely teeth and lips. Ravana changed into silken yellow robes and struck by Kamadeva's arrows started reciting Veda mantras. Humbly addressing Sita who looked resplendent as Lakshmi away from her lotus seat, he said,

'You glow like burnished gold. Dressed in yellow silks, you look like a stream wearing garlands of lotus flowers.

'O woman with an auspicious face, are you Lakshmi? Are you Shree blessed with wealth, splendour, fortune, grace; Hree, modesty incarnate; Keerti; or an apsara? O woman with attractive hips, living by yourself, are you Rati, Kama's wife?

'Your eyes are large and flawless with red corners and black pupils. Your hips are broad and muscular. Your fleshy thighs look like an elephant's trunk.

'Your breasts are round, full, sensuously adorned by exquisite necklaces.

'O sensuous woman, with your fetching smile, flawless teeth, attractive eyes, you have conquered my affection just as a rivulet usurps its own embankment with its water. Your thin waist can fit into my fist. You have silky hair and sumptuous orbs touching each other. A woman like you is not to be found among the devatas, kinners or gandharvas. I have never seen anyone like you on this earth.

'I am deeply disturbed by your living in this forest abounding in animals of all sorts. It does not befit you to waste your youth in such harsh surroundings. This forest is meant for the living of the rakshasas who can change their form at will. Your place lies in a luxurious palace, in a prosperous and bustling city with fragrant gardens.

'Tell me all about yourself and also why and how do you happen to be here all by yourself?'

Maithili saw the mahatma and controlling her tears welcomed him. She organised various necessary things for the reception of an unexpected guest. She offered him a seat, arghya, water to wash his feet, and invited him to a meal. She said,

'Brahmin, please sit comfortably on this mat. Here is water to wash your tired feet. There is enough of fruit and roots grown in this forest. Have a meal of your choice in peace.'

Meanwhile, Sita looked around for Rama and Lakshmana but all that she could see was the large forest spreading till the end of her vision.

As Ravana had asked her, Sita introduced herself to him. She narrated the story of her birth in Mithila, her marriage with Rama after he had broken Shiva's bow into pieces, and Rama's exile through a manoeuvring by Kaikeyee. Continuing she said,

'O pious Brahmin, please rest a while. My husband will soon return with fresh fruit and vegetables. He will be happy to receive you with greater honours. In the meantime, may I know who you are? Tell me your name, gotra and family. What is it that makes you wander alone in this forest?'

In a loud and harsh voice, Ravana replied,

'Sita, I am Ravana, the king of the rakshasas. My name sends shivers into the mind of devatas, daityas and human beings, nay among all the three worlds. Looking at your golden hue and your body dressed in silk, my mind is centred on you to the exclusion of any other woman. I have abducted women from all over but I shall ask you to come and be my chief consort. Your well-being lies in that alone.

'My capital, Lanka is situated on the top of a hill surrounded by the sea. Living there you would enjoy wandering in my company in many a lovely forest. You will never desire to return to this forest. Thousands of maids will be at your service and you will not have a dearth of anything.'

Sita's Furious Response

The blameless Sita was offended at these words. Harshly responding to the rakshasa, she said,

'My husband, Rama is immovable as a mountain. He is valorous like Indra and deep like an ocean. Rama provides shelter to anyone who looks for it like a banyan tree. He is virtuous, truthful and fortunate. Devoted to him in mind and body, I am his loving wife.

'You evil denizen of the night, you are a jackal while I am a lioness. You cannot attain me. As no one can snatch the glory of the sun, you cannot even touch me. How dare you think of abducting Rama's wife? This will certainly be the death of you.

'Trying to abduct me is impossible like a dashing deer plucking the teeth of an angry and hungry lion chasing it. It is like raising the Mandarachala Mountain on a palm, or trying to survive after drinking a chalice of poison.'

Sita's body shook in anger as she further addressed Ravana,

'Do you hope to cross the oceans with a stone tied around your neck? Do you intend carrying the sun and the moon on your palms? What makes you think that you can dishonour valorous Rama's beloved wife? Compared to Rama, you are like a jackal against a lion, like a rivulet compared to an ocean and like a tasteless drink as against Amrita. You are as different from Rama as lead is from gold, mud compared to sandal paste and a cat in front of an elephant. You will not be able to live with my abduction when Rama challenges you in battle with his bow and arrows.'

Ravana Flaunts His Powers

After hearing Rama's praises from her in such a way, Ravana thought of impressing Sita with his words and valour. He said,

'I am Ravana who carries ten heads. I am the stepbrother of Kubera who I defeated in battle and took over his prosperous kingdom of Lanka as well his well-known Pushpak Vimana. When I am angry, Indra and the other devatas scurry in fear. The winds slow down when I stand. The sun loses his fierce lustre and becomes cold like the moon in my presence. Out of fear, the water in the streams stand still and the leaves on the trees are stunned.

'Beyond the ocean lies Lanka, as charming as Indra's Amravati. Fierce rakshasas inhabit it and white ramparts guard it. Its palace floors and walls of the passages are lined with gold, doors are set in lapis lazuli. The roads are full of horses, elephants, and chariots. In my city, the air echoes with the music of various instruments. The trees bear delicious fruit of several varieties.

'O woman with lovely eyes, come and live with me. You will soon forget Rama who, in any case, is not going to live long. Of what use is he to you after being banished by his own father? He may never be a king. He is bereft of wisdom to be leading a hermit's life. In battle, he will be weaker than even my little finger.

'If you spurn my advances, you will repent as Urvashi did when she disregarded Pururava. The king of rakshasas stands begging at your door. Kama's arrows have grievously injured him. Give him all your love and take care of him. If you accept his advances, you will rule Lanka and enjoy all comforts.'

Sita did not listen to Ravana's entreaties.

Seeing that his words had no effect on Sita, Ravana took a fierce form wherein he grew into a giant with ten heads. Once again, he addressed Sita. He said,

'You are out of your mind and have ignored my power and pelf in your ignorant love for Rama. Know that I can lift the earth in my arms, drink the oceans in a gulp and defy death. O woman, full of lust, proud of your looks, with my arrows I can bring down the sun and shatter the earth to pieces. I can change form at will. Look!'

In anger, Ravana's eyes turned red like flames. He changed his soft appearance into a fierce mien. He looked dark like a dense cloud, with heavy gold ornaments adorning him. Ten heads and twenty arms became prominently visible in this form. He further told Sita,

'O woman with lovely hips, come to me if you want to be the wife of a man reputed in all the three worlds. I am a suitable match for you. Live with me forever. Never shall I misbehave with you. I shall be a husband envied by others and one whose conduct is nothing but praiseworthy.

'Rama is at best a human being with a limited life span. He will never be a king and will die some day. O foolish woman, give him up and come with me. Rama is a fool to have given up a kingdom because a cunning woman asked him to do so and now lives in a forest teeming with wild animals.'

Sita's Cry in Wilderness

With these words and after Sita's persistent denial, Ravana advanced and caught hold of Sita's head by her hair and lifted her placing his right arm under her thighs. Soon his chariot appeared in view. Ravana placed her in his celestial chariot. She was least interested in the rakshasa king. Fearful and hurt, she repeatedly cried 'Rama'. In delirium born of fear, she called her husband, her brother-in-law, cried for help in wilderness and cursed the daitya king. She said,

'An evil person gets the return for his misdeeds in the long run. Kala has destroyed your faculty of thought and makes you commit such an evil deed. Rama will certainly put you to death. Today, Kaikeyee's ambition and that of her kith and kin, has been fulfilled. Even though I am the wife of the virtuous Rama, I am being abducted by a rakshasa.

'O kanera trees, tell Rama as soon as you can that Ravana has abducted Sita.

'Mother Godavari, I bow to you. Please tell Rama as early as possible that a rakshasa has abducted me.

'O birds, O trees, O devatas living on the trees, you be a witness to my abduction by Ravana. My husband is a brave man. He will certainly fight for me and get me back even if he has to fight Yamaraja.'

9

Jatayu Fails to Save Sita from Ravana's Clutches

Thus wailing and crying for Rama and Lakshmana, Sita noticed Jatayu, the king of birds, sitting on a treetop.

Drawing his attention to her predicament, she said,

'Arya Jatayu, this heartless daitya is cruelly abducting a helpless woman. You cannot stop him because he is strong, is fortified with arms and because his intentions are evil. Kindly inform my husband that Ravana has abducted his Sita.

Jatayu was asleep. Hearing Sita's wail, he woke up and saw Sita's plight. He stood up and raised his head high as a mountain peak and with his sharp beak addressed Ravana.

Jatayu Tries to Dissuade Ravana

'O ten-headed king, I am Jatayu, the king of vultures. I follow ancient religious practices and am always truthful. You must not commit this deplorable atrocity in my presence.

'A king who follows his dharma cannot touch another's wife. Rama has not wronged you and you have no reason to commit this despicable deed. His killing of Khara when the latter came to wage a battle was no crime.

'Please release Videhakumari immediately lest Rama destroy you with his fiery look just as Vritrasura was killed by Indra's thunderbolt.

'Who can justify a deed that is neither according to dharma nor adds to one's fame or glory? Why should anyone commit an act that would harm another?

'I am old and cannot fight you who carry many weapons. However, I shall not allow you to carry Sita away without resistance.'

With these words, Jatayu attacked Ravana's flying chariot and a bitter fight ensued. While the vulture king clawed at Ravana's body, the daitya king hit him with arrows and his sword. Jatayu was no match for Ravana who soon covered the former's body with a net of arrows. But Jatayu did succeed in killing the donkeys pulling Ravana's chariot as well as his charioteer. With his wings, he splintered the king's armour. However, Ravana did not let Sita go from his grip. Carrying her in his arm, he flew into the skies. Jatayu chased him and repeatedly clawed at the king, but to no avail. Ravana shifted Sita to his left arm and used his right arm to injure Jatayu. The latter cut the king's arms with his beak but Ravana grew new arms like serpents emerging out of their holes.

Ultimately, Ravana placed Sita on the ground and launched a full-scale attack on the bleeding Jatayu with fists and legs. He then sliced Jatayu's wings with his sword and felled him.

While Sita moaned Jatayu's injuries, Ravana lifted her and resumed his flight towards Lanka. Her yellow robes unfurled in the breeze and made her look like lightning flashes on a mountain. Her face set against Ravana's dark torso looked like the moon eclipsed by dark clouds. The flowers tied to her bun fell to the ground one by one. A gem-studded bangle came loose and fell to the ground. Her other ornaments too fell on the earth like meteors falling from the sky. A brilliant necklace skidding between her breasts looked like the Ganga descending from the heavens.

In a low voice, Videhanandini was crying, 'Ha Rama, Ha Lakshmana,' while glancing at the earth below. Her bun came loose and her hair flew in the wind. Her struggle with Ravana had smeared the tilaka on her forehead. Her face lost its glow.

While Ravana was carrying Sita, she noticed five mighty vanaras sitting on a hilltop. She tore a piece of her yellow garment, tied a few of her ornaments in it and threw them to the strangers in the hope that they might guide her husband when he came looking for her.

Ravana flew over Pampa sarovar in the direction of his capital, Lanka. He was full of joy and he did not realize that he had abducted one who would be the cause of his death. He shot like an arrow released by a mighty archer over forests, streams, mountains and ponds.

10

Sita Spurns Ravana's Advances; Ravana Offers Sita the Moon

Carrying his death incarnate in his lap, Ravana triumphantly entered his capital. The city had several broad avenues with thousands of rakshasas inhabiting it.

Ravana entered his inner chambers and deposited the wailing Sita on a luxurious bed. He summoned frightful pishachini maids and ordered them to guard her so that none could approach her without his permission. He said,

'I command you to provide her with whatever she asks for, pearls, clothing, gold, or gems. None of you dare misbehave with Videhakumari, knowingly or inadvertently.

'Like a pauper craving satisfaction in attaining wealth,' said he, 'I shall be satisfied only when I have killed Rama. I cannot sleep in peace until I have avenged the wrong done to me and my race.'

Ravana lived in a state of heightened lust, all the time thinking of making Sita his own. Soon, he approached her as she sat inside his well-appointed bedroom, surrounded by guards, shedding tears on her helplessness. Crushed by the weight of her sorrow, she looked like a sinking boat buffeted by strong winds in an ocean. She felt like a doe separated from her herd, surrounded by hungry wolves.

He compelled her to go around his palace in his company. His apartments were like a house of gods with high roofs. Quite a few buildings were seven storeys high. The rooms were full of women, and the gardens full of birds of several kinds. Eye-catching pillars of unique craftsmanship were covered with ivory, lapis lazuli, gold sheets, crystal, silver, and were studded with diamonds and sapphires. Celestial dundubhis played in the palaces. Even the stairs were paved with gold. Ravana forced Sita to climb them in order to look around.

The palace walls had window frames made of ivory and silver. Golden lattices framed several palace rooms in a row. The floors had been plastered with lime and brown earth and were decorated with tiles glistening like gems. Ravana pointed out each of the magnificent fittings and furnishings to Sita. She, of course, was overtaken by grief while looking at ponds and paths lined with flowers.

Trying to impress Sita, Ravana pointed at the large number of rakshasas at his command. He said,

'Vishala-lochane, my kingdom and life revolve around pleasing you now. I love you more than I love myself and am ready to offer all my riches to you. My palace is full of lovely women but my heart is enamoured with you. Dear, marry me and be my chief consort. If you do not agree to my wish, no advantage accrues to you. I pine for you. Be kind to me.

'Indra and other devatas cannot harm Lanka spread over hundreds of yojanas. What will you do with Rama who has no kingdom, walks on foot, lives like a hermit and is just a human being? He can never reach here. Give up thinking of him.

'As a husband, I am the most suitable for you. Accept me for your youth is not going to last forever. Live with me and enjoy yourself as long as it lasts.

'Do not wait for Rama to rescue you for ropes cannot tie storms nor can our hands stall rising flames. O beautiful one, there is none as brave in all the three worlds as can free you from my protective arms.

'Live here and rule over the vast kingdom of Lanka with me. Have a pleasant bath, anoint yourself with our holy waters, and start your life with me afresh. Whatever wrongs you might have committed in an earlier life, have been paid for by your life in exile. Reap the fruit of your remaining good deeds by living here. Fly as you will in the splendid Pushpak Vimana, which is delightful to travel in, and can be steered in any direction merely by willing to do so.

'Your beauty is eclipsed with sadness and it hurts me to see you thus.

'Sita, do not feel guilty because you might be violating your marriage vows in sleeping with a man other than your husband. I assure you that the shastras have sanctioned our love.

'I place my ten heads at your soft and glistening feet. Have pity on me and silence the storm of desire raging inside me. Ravana has never bowed in front of a woman; it is you alone to whom my request is addressed.'

In putting his words so persuasively, Ravana was of the opinion that Sita would comply.

Sita Spurns Ravana's Flattery

Although Sita was brooding over her misfortune, drowned in sorrow, spurning Ravana, Sita boldly replied:

'Rama is my husband as well as my god. Accompanied by Lakshmana he will soon come and destroy you. Had you tried to abduct me in his presence, you would have met the same fate as that of Khara and Dooshana

'A lowly man dare not step upon the altar at a yagyashala purified by the recitations of sacred mantras by the Brahmins. Likewise, you cannot touch me, the one who is the devoted wife of Rama. A sacred bond unites us.

'O Rakshasa, you can imprison me or cut me to pieces, but I shall never demean myself by submitting to your advances.'

Ravana Threatens Sita with Dire Consequences

Upon hearing such words, Ravana left his persuasive tone and tried to scare Sita into submission. He said,

'O lovely woman, your smile is irresistible and excites me beyond measure. Maithili, I will grant you a grace period of twelve months. If you do not accept my proposal, I shall order my chefs to mince your meat and serve it for my meal.'

Addressing his maids, Ravana commanded,

'Take her away, confine her to Asoka Vatika, guard her, and frighten her using all measures. Cajole her now and then so that she changes her mind.'

The rakshasis showed Sita the way to Asoka Vatika, a grove rich in trees that bore fruit of all kinds. It was fragrant with exotic flowers and resounded with bird song. Sita feared the rakshasis all around her and after Ravana's threat, felt like a doe surrounded by hungry beasts. The women surrounding her shouted and tried to scare her in various ways. Soon after, she fainted.

In the Brahmaloka, Brahma worried about Sita's condition. He sent for Indra and said, 'Sita is drowning in a pool of grief. She has discarded food and might not survive the separation from Rama. This must not be, for our plan to rid the earth of Ravana and his atrocities will never fructify in that case. There would be no cause for Rama to invade Lanka and kill Ravana.

'You should go and offer her food that will satisfy her hunger for as long as she lives.'

Accompanied by Nidra, Indra reached Lanka. Nidra put everyone to sleep. Indra identified himself and offered the divine havishya to Sita so that she would not require food or water offered by her guards.

11

Rama's Lament for the Missing Sita

Seeing Lakshmana coming for his rescue, Rama had divined how they had been tricked by the rakshasas into leaving Sita without a guard in the wilderness. He questioned his younger brother's wisdom in leaving Sita alone in spite of clear instruction not to. The latter explained in detail the circumstances and Sita's insistence that had forced him to leave her unattended.

On their way back to Panchavati after killing Maricha, Rama worried about Sita. The bad omens around him, the silent birds and sad trees instilled a fear of something bad having befallen his beloved Sita.

As feared, Panchavati was desolate and Sita was nowhere to be seen. Rama went all around their settlement searching for Sita. Like the lotus destroyed by frost in winter, each of the cottages was bereft of its glory. The rustling of the trees was like their moaning out of grief. The flowers had withered, deer and birds were silent, the gods of happiness seemed to have departed, and deer skins and kusha grass were scattered all around. It was a state of complete chaos.

Looking at the desolate cottage, Rama lamented,

'Where is Sita?
Has she been abducted or killed,
Or, has she just gone into the forest?
She may have gone to pluck flowers,
Or to fetch water from the stream.'

Rama's eyes turned red with tears of sorrow and his search in the forest did not lead him to Sita. He ran from tree to tree, looked into hills, and streams and ponds.

Submerged in grief, Rama asked the trees guarding Panchavati:

'Kadamba, my Sita was so fond of your flowers.
If you noticed her walking away,
Tell me of her whereabouts.
Her limbs are soft and silky like fresh leaves.
When last seen,
She was dressed in a yellow silken sheet.

'O Bilva, O Tala,
My darling's breasts are like your fruit,
Round and firm.
Did you notice her moving around?

'Arjuna!
My beloved had a special liking for your flowers.
She is of delicate limbs.
Is she alive or not?

'Kukubha, you ought to be aware of Sita's whereabouts
Because she is as magnificent as you are.
You are the king among the trees.
The bhramaras sing your paens as they hum.
You bear fruit, leaves and flowers.
So many creepers cling to you.
Tell me, where is my Sita?

'Asoka! While you are able to ward off grief,
I have lost myself to sorrow.
I too can call myself by your name,
If you help me find my beloved.

Jamun, if you had perchance noticed my beloved,
Resplendent like gold,
Tell me without fear where has she gone?

'O kanera! You bloom in rich colours.
Sita loved your flowers.
Did you see her coming your way?'

In his grief, the prince approached the trees such as mango, pomegranate, shala, bakul, punnag, sandalwood and kewra, one by one. Plaintively, he asked each of them where Sita could be.

Looking at a doe, Rama said,
'She had your eyes.
Has she joined your herd?'

Standing in front of an elephant, Rama asked,

'O superior being, her thighs are like your trunk.
Possibly, therefore, you might have noticed my Sita.
Won't you advise me about her whereabouts?'

In a state of delirium, Rama thought that he saw Sita running away.
Calling her to return, he said,

'O lotus-eyed, why run away from me?
I am sure that I have traced you.
Why not talk to me even when hiding behind a tree?
Don't you pity me?
You never made fun of me.
Why then do you ignore me now?

'The yellow silk you wear gives away your whereabouts.
I could see you though you ran.
Stop a while if you love me.

'However,
No longer am I sure of her identity.
The rakshasas have killed my Sita.
She had a charming smile.
My beloved Sita,
Of limbs as fair as the champaka flowers,
Of a long and glistening neck
That was meant to be dressed in necklaces,
The daityas have made a feast of her.

'Lakshmana, do you see her?
Where have you disappeared, my love?'

Lakshmana Consoles Rama

Rama bewailed the loss of his wife and did not know any peace of
mind. He was hallucinating and at times noticing a shadow, cried out

for Sita to return. Shaken to the core by grief, his emotions swirled like a whirlpool.

Lakshmana tried to assuage Rama's pain. Looking at his elder brother as if he was an elephant stuck in a quagmire, he said,

'Grieve not, my brother. We shall jointly make an effort to trace Janaki. She might have gone to enjoy the charms of the forest at the top of the hill. She could be relaxing on the banks of a lake full of lotus flowers, gliding swans and colourful fish. Please grieve no more. We shall find her.

'Arya, be patient. We have to look for Sita with vigour. An enthusiastic person is not afraid of even the most obdurate obstruction in his path.'

12

Rama and Lakshmana Set Out in Search of Sita

Rama and Lakshmana decided to look for Sita in the vast forest. They found no trace of her on the banks of the Godavari or in the orchards or gardens near Panchavati. They came across a herd of deer whom they questioned about Sita. The mute animals looked at the sky and started running due south. Lakshmana noticed this behaviour and persuaded Rama to continue their search in the southern direction.

Tell-tale Signs of Sita's Abduction

Soon they noticed some flowers scattered on the ground. Rama was sure that Sita had worn these flowers. Moving on, they noticed the footsteps of a daitya and the marks of Sita's feet on the ground. They saw her golden anklets lying broken here and there. These were soaked in blood. Nearby, lay broken golden armour, a shattered chariot, a dead charioteer, and the corpses of a few donkeys. As a sign of struggle, a broken bow was lying on the ground.

Pointing all these tell-tale signs to Lakshmana, Rama said that he would spare no one, neither a daitya nor a devata who might have committed the foul deed of abducting Sita. He declared war against the entire world.

Lakshmana's Words of Sanity and Determination

Lakshmana pacified his brother with a few words of advice:

'Arya, you have always been of a mild temperament, in control of your passions and a well-wisher of mankind. Do not let anger overwhelm you now. The moon is always lovely; the sun is ever glorious; the winds are always on the move and the earth is a model of patience. Likewise, you have always been honourable in conduct.

'For one person's sins you cannot punish the universe. Let me find out who was the master of this broken chariot. Who has separated its yoke, killed its donkeys and the charioteer, and smashed its wheels and spokes? All these indicate an intense fight to the finish.

'I notice the marks of one chariot, not of two. There are no marks of a horde of soldiers. Thus, the one who abducted Sita must have been alone, and was challenged. You cannot blame the entire population of this earth and heavens for this unholy deed.

'A king must award punishment commensurate with the crime and no more. A ruler must be kind and considerate and provide protection to everyone.

'Rajan, we have to find who has abducted Sita. We shall search the mountains, cross the rivers, look near the ocean, go through the caves and forests and sieve the ponds. We shall continue our effort till we find your wife.'

Rama wailed as if he had been rendered an orphan. His attachment to Sita had upset him beyond measure. Pleading for calm, Lakshmana kneaded his feet and said,

'Brother, if you do not patiently bear this misfortune as ordained by destiny, how would ordinary mortals do so with their limited strength?

'You are superior to other men in all respects. Have forbearance. In this world, which mortal is not subject to misfortune at some time or the other?

'Suffering and joy form a cycle in this universe; they come and go. Yayati, son of Nahusha, suffered even in Swargaloka as a result of his lust. Our family guru Vasishtha had a hundred sons who were massacred by Vishwamitra at one go. Even the mother earth, worshipped by all, is shaking all the time.

'The powerful sun and the lustrous moon on which the whole world depends, which are the originators as well as eyes of the universe, too, are eclipsed by Rahu. The greatest of gods are subject to the dictates of destiny. Where then do we, mere mortals, stand in comparison?

'Raghunandan, even if Sita, the Videha princess, dies, you ought not to grieve like a rustic. Knowledgeable persons like you do not lament even if faced with the gravest tragedy. They stay calm and do not give up rational thinking.

'Great man, use your intelligence to analyze the situation. Decide your course of action, what ought to be done and what avoided.

'You will gain nothing taking on the universe as your opponent. We have to find our evil enemy and uproot him from wherever he might be.'

Jatayu Unravels the Mystery of Sita's Abduction

Rama listened to his younger brother's words of wisdom carefully. Taking control over his grief, Rama, along with Lakshmana, started looking through the forest for Sita for any clue of her whereabouts. Soon they chanced upon an injured Jatayu, and saw his body splattered with blood.

Vomiting blood, Jatayu narrated the events leading to his battle with Ravana who was flying away with Sita. He said,

'May you both live long! Ravana has taken away my life as well as Sita whom you are looking for. I tried to help her and fought the daitya king. I smashed his chariot, broke his canopy, killed his charioteer and the donkeys, and inflicted severe wounds on him. However, he cut my wings and flew away with Janaki in his lap.'

Listening to Jatayu's words, Rama was deeply grieved and almost swooned. In a voice choked with agony, he said,

'Lakshmana, I lost my kingdom, was sent into exile and now my Sita has been abducted. Such is the extent of my misfortune that it could have set fire to fire. Today, if I jump into an ocean, the ferocious heat of my terrible destiny will evaporate its waters.'

Before Jatayu breathed his last, he informed Rama that Ravana had flown southwards with Sita in his lap. He asked them to continue their search and also that the omens were auspicious indicating their success.

The princes performed the last rites of Jatayu, and prayed for his soul at the banks of Godavari. Thereafter, walking like Vishnu and Indra, they set out to look for Sita.

13

Arrival at Pampa Sarovar

Rama and Lakshmana initially travelled south-west through paths that had not been treaded upon by men. The forest was dark, deep and frightening. Proceeding further, they entered a jungle known as Kroncharanya that looked dark as dense clouds. It abounded in various flowers and was inhabited by a large variety of birds and animals. From here, walking three kos east, they arrived at the ashrama of the Rishi Matanga.

Kabandha, the Monster

They continued their search for Sita and some time later, they came across a rakshasa by the name of Kabandha in another forest. He had a large body, and a broad chest but neither a neck nor head. His forehead and his mouth were on his stomach and his hair stood sharp and pointed. His forehead had a violently inflamed eye with a grey pupil and long lashes. He was repeatedly licking his mouth with his large tongue and survived on wild bears, tigers and birds.

Extending his arms, Kabandha took hold of Rama and Lakshmana in his grip. Addressing them, he said,

'I am famished and your arrival has only been to satisfy my hunger. I am not going to spare your lives.'

Although encircled in his arms, the brothers used their swords to slice the arms of the rakshasa before he could thwart their movement. The bleeding demon became pliant in a moment and asked them to identify themselves. In turn, he narrated the story of his downfall and requested them to cremate him, promising to tell them the whereabouts of a would-be friend who could help them in looking for Sita. He said,

'I am not endowed with divine knowledge. I do not know anything about Maithili. However, once my present body has been burnt, I shall regain my normal form and I shall be able to tell you of a person who knows about Sita and the mighty rakshasa who has abducted her.'

Kabandha, Released from Curse, Leads Rama to Sugreeva

Out of the burning logs on the pier emerged Kabandha, glorious and dressed in neat clothes, garlands and jewels. He climbed into a vimana yoked to swans. Lifting the vimana into the sky, he said,

'Know from me Raghava, how to reach Sita. A king can win over everything in this world by means of six devices, such as sandhi (reconciliation with the enemy), vigraha (invasion, war), yaana (attack), asana (opportunity), dwayidhibhava (duplicity) and samashraya (seeking protection of the more powerful friend or foe).

'A person in distress ought to look to another one similarly situated for help. Seek the friendship of a person who suffers like you. One such person is Sugreeva, a vanara, who has been ousted from his kingdom by his brother, Vali, Indra's son.

'At present, Sugreeva stays on the Rishyamooka Mountain with four other vanaras. This mountain extends to the lake Pampa. The valorous Sugreeva, the king of the vanaras, is glorious, dexterous, fearless, patient, wise, generous, truthful, and powerful. His brother, Vali, in order to usurp the kingdom, has thrown him out of their territory. Sugreeva is the one who will now assist you in looking for Sita.

'O brave Rama, destiny is irreversible and we suffer because fate willed it so. You must go as soon as possible to befriend Sugreeva. He too is looking for help in his misfortunes. Both of you can successfully help him. However, even if you cannot help him, Sugreeva will certainly assist you.

'He has deep knowledge about the rakshasa abodes and he will help you look in the mountains, caves, forests with the help of vanaras; he will certainly assist you in finding the whereabouts of your wife.

'Wherever your pious and devoted wife may be, on the Meru peak or in the Patala, Sugreeva, the crown of the vanaras, will ensure her return to you after killing all the rakshasas.

The Lake Pampa and the Rishyamooka Mountain

'If you go west from here on the path lined with flowering trees, you will be on your way to Pampa. You will notice the trees of jamun, priyala, kathala, banyan, pakad, tendu, pipal, kanera, mango, tilaka, naktamal, neel, asoka, kadamba, red sandalwood and mandar. Soon you will enter a forest as delightful as the Nandanavana. Like the Chaitraratha forest, this one sees a complete cycle of seasons.

'Traversing several hills and forests, you will reach the banks of Pampa that abounds in lotuses. Its banks are smooth, the sand is not slippery, the waters are free of weeds, and the land is plain on its banks.

'In Pampa, the sounds of various birds and animals are like music to the ear. Human beings do not disturb them and they have not experienced fear at the hands of hunters.

'On the banks of Pampa, you can enjoy the unlimited bounties of nature. The Pampa water is nourishing, cool, and a source of health and joy.

'Towards evening, you will notice large vanaras that live and sleep in the caves nearby. Yellow-skinned, they come roaring like bulls to drink water at the lake.

'A look at the flower-laden trees and at the waters of Pampa will lessen your sorrow. It is said that in old times, the pupils of the Rishi Matanga used to live on the shores of Pampa. Though they departed long ago, yet an ascetic named Shabari, who used to look after them, still resides there. She is aged and is always occupied in religious pursuits. She waits to see you before departing for Swargaloka.

'The forest there is known as the Matangavana. On the eastern bank of Pampa stands the Rishyamooka Mountain glistening with flowering trees. It is a dense forest difficult to access owing to reptiles and elephants inhabiting it.

'Raghunath, you will forget your sorrow when on the Rishyamooka Mountain you see bears, tigers, and men of a dusky hue like that of blue lotus and herds of deer racing each other and virtually invincible. A large cave shut by a door made of stone is situated on the mountaintop. At the eastern gate of this cave is a pond brimming with cool water and banked by fruit and flower-bearing trees. The pious Sugreeva resides in this cave. At times, he shifts to the mountaintop. You ought to befriend him.'

14

A Visit to Shabari's Ashrama

Soon after, Rama and Lakshmana arrived at Shabari's ashrama lying to the west of Pampa. Situated in pleasant surroundings, the ashrama was surrounded by innumerable trees. The ascetic stood with folded hands to receive them. The brothers in turn bowed and touched her feet.

Addressing Shabari, Rama said,

'Your tapasya has enriched you. However, have you conquered anger and pride? Are you able to stick to the path and the principles you have decided to follow? Are you happy in your mind and at peace with yourself? O sage of sweet words, has the service of your gurus been successful in all respects?'

Replied Shabari,

'Rama, you are the pride of mankind. The success of my tapasya lies in my being able to look at you today. Deveshwara, having welcomed you today, I shall certainly attain Swargaloka. Your kind glance has purified me.

'I had been told of your arrival here by my gurus when you were still at Chitrakoot. I have collected wild fruit and roots growing on the banks of Pampa for your meal.'

Shabari took Rama and Lakshmana around the ashrama and showed them the sites where her gurus had lived and worshipped. Thereafter, she asked for Rama's permission to immolate herself in order to join her gurus.

KISHKINDHAKANDAM

1

Rama Pines for Sita:
Vasanta Ritu at Lake Pampa

Rama and Lakshmana were still lingering on the shores of Pampa, planning to approach Sugreeva as advised by Kabandha, when the Vasanta ritu set in. In the flower-laden environment, Rama's grief for Sita's absence and for her unknown predicament made him restless. He wanted to reach out to her, look at her and love her. In poetic words he expressed his anguish to Lakshmana. He said,

'Sumitranandana,
How charming does Pampa look!
Its waters shine like gem-studded tiles, clean and bluish.
Lotuses of many a hue bloom on its surface while
The rich forest on its banks abounds in trees
Which grow tall and look splendid,
Like the peaks of the hills on its periphery.

'I suffer at the moment for Bharata's grief and
Because Sita has been abducted.
Yet, Pampa delights me with its flowers, its forest,
Its birds and fish,
The reptiles in its waters and on its banks, and the
Deer and other wild animals that roam nearby.

'The freshly sprouted grass,
Green, yellow and blue,
Delights the eye.
Thereupon, the trees have shed flowers,
Making it look like an expensive carpet.
While the creepers climb to wrap the trees all around,
The latter's boughs bend
With the weight of bouquets of flowers at their ends.

'Chaitra has arrived.
A mild comforting breeze blows.
It excites the mind like Kamadeva.
The flowers drop from the trees like rain from the clouds.
Swayed by the winds the trees dance and
Cover the lovely rocks below with blooms.
Look, the wind playfully flirts with
The flowers lying on the ground,
Or, still clinging to the boughs.

'As the wind blows shaking the flower-laden boughs,
The bhramaras swept off by the wind
From the branches of trees,
Give it a chase, droning paens about it.

'The wind emanating from the mountain caves
Sings in high octaves.
Intoxicated koels, cooing,
Provide a musical support.
Assisted by this orchestra, the wind imparts
Lessons in dancing to the swaying trees.

'The cool air running through the sandalwood trees
Comforts the body, assuages fatigue and
Scatters its fragrance all around.
In the forest
Full of honeybees and the fragrance of sandalwood,
Shaken by the breeze rich in the bhramaras' drone,
The trees, accompanied by music, appear to be dancing.

'Laden with massive trees,
Bearing flowers in limitless abandon,
The hilltops look splendid.

'The dancing and singing trees
Have dressed for the occasion:
Their arms are covered with bunches of flowers,
Their headdress is made of the bhramaras.
The flowering kanera looks glorious
In gold ornaments and yellow robes, like a human being.

'Sumitranandana!
Vasanta, echoing with hundreds of bird calls
Intensifies my agony caused by Sita's separation.
Kamadeva thus adds to the grief of a man
Already grievously injured by viraha.
The koel too, cooing joyously, appears to taunt me!
The waterfowl happily playing near the cataract
Adds to my desire for an early reunion with Sita.

'Look, even the female birds sitting snugly with their mates
Enjoy togetherness in their flock.
Listening to the bhramaras' drone,
Delighted,
They too sing pleasant songs.

'It looks as if the fires of Vasanta will reduce me to ashes.
The bunches of red flowers on the asoka tree are their embers.
Its fresh leaves are their flames, while
The drone of the black bees is the crackle of burning wood.

'Of what use is my life if I cannot be united with
The soft-spoken Sita who has fine eyelashes and lovely hair?
My beloved is so fond of Vasanta,
The season in which the splendour of the forest is enhanced and
The koel sings in melody everywhere.
Aided by the fuel provided by Vasanta
The fires of my grief, born of Kama,
Burn fiercer each passing moment.
They surely will consume me in no time.

'How glorious do the peacocks look
While dancing with their fans spread!
Their feathers, vibrating in the wind,
Are framed like lattices made of crystal and studded with gems.
Surrounded by their females, the lusty peacocks
Intensify the suffering of my separation even more.

'Lakshmana,
Do you notice the amorous movements of the peahen?
Spreading both his lovely wings wide,
The peacock chases his beloved and
Taunts me with his shrill cries.

'In the flowering month of Chaitra,
It is unbearable to stay here without my beloved.
You see, even the animals are so fond of each other.
Look at the lusty peahen presenting herself to her male!
Had Sita with large eyes not been abducted,
She too would have fondly approached me likewise.
In her absence, the heaps of flowers in the forest,
Enriched by Vasanta, hold no purpose for me.

'The flocks of birds, full of the joy of life,
Make love calls to their mates.
Singing melodiously and unrestrained,
They ignite my passion.
Imagine Sita's predicament if
Vasanta has arrived at the place in which
She has been confined.
Where Sita has been put in a solitary confine, for certain,
Vasanta cannot have access.
Despite this, how will my lotus-eyed Sita,
With black iris, survive in my absence?

'Even if Vasanta has arrived where she is,
Sita is helpless when her enemies rebuke or taunt her.
She is so young.
Her eyes are attractive like a lotus in bloom.
My soft-spoken beloved Janaki, will certainly
Kill herself in this Vasanta ritu.
Away from me, she cannot survive for long.
Of that, I am sure more and more, as I think.
Both of us are centred in each other
To the exclusion of anyone else, dear Lakshmana.

'The breeze that made me joyous when I was with Sita,
Enhances my grief when she is away.

'A black bee settles on the sprouts of a tilaka tree
That swings in the breeze.
It looks like the union of a lover with his impassioned beloved.
Look at the asoka that contrary to its name,
Multiplies the grief of those tormented by viraha.
It stands taunting me with its bouquets of flowers.
Lakshmana, the mango trees sprouting nascent blossoms,
Intoxicated by shringara and the ebullience of Vasanta,
Look like lovers who have anointed their bodies with sandal paste.

'The fragrant lotuses blooming on Pampa's surface
Glisten like the morning sun.
The bhramaras have sucked their honey [to their hearts' content.]
On Pampa's banks the cranes prosper,
The elephants visit to quench their thirst and the deer frolic.
The breeze generates waves on Pampa's surface.
The lotuses tossed back and forth, delight the eye.

'Sita's eyes are large like the lotus petals.
Fond she has always been of this flower.
Separated from her
I do not want to breathe a moment longer.
The cunning Kamadeva constantly reminds me
Of Sita who is inaccessible, being far away,
Of Sita who always spoke kind words to bless others,
Of Sita who always wished well to everyone.

'I can, maybe, restrain myself
But for the repeated onslaughts of Vasanta.
Whatever looked good when Sita was by my side,
No longer holds an attraction. It does not please me.
I like to look at the lotus flowers
Because their buds look like Sita's eyes.
The fragrant breeze,
Rich with pollen and blowing through the trees,
Flows like her breath.

'Sumitranandana, if you look southwards, you will notice
The resplendent, multicoloured kanera blooming on the hilltops.
Scraping the Rishyamooka hills, rich in minerals,
The winds blowing strong scatter their amazing dust.
The leafless palash trees, in full bloom everywhere,
Rise like flames in the distance.
The blooming malati, mallika, padma and karavira,
Nursed by the Pampa waters, are rich in fragrant, delicious sap.
The ketaki, sinduvar and vasanti creepers are loaded with flowers.
While the lovely creepers,
Like lusty women, chase the trees
Buffeted by strong winds and
Bending so low that they can be touched,
The wind blows from tree to tree, from one hilltop to another,
Enriched and intoxicated by scents and sap.

'Some of the trees are rich in bloom,
Loaded with flowers, scent and sap.
Some others bearing numerous buds look dark.

'A passionate bhramara flits from one flower to another,
Admiring beauty, tasting sweetness and
Looking at some others in full bloom.
Greedy for honey, it hides behind a flower,
Flies high and then flits elsewhere.

'Soft flowers shed by the trees
Carpet the earth.
The ground is comfortable
Like velvet mattresses meant for sleep.
Various flowers cover the rocks on the hilltops.
These look like beds of red and gold.

'Lakshmana, if we can find the pious Sita,
We shall stay here forever.
One need not go to Indraloka or return even to Ayodhya.
If I can live in joy with Sita
In this land, richly carpeted by green grass,
I need have no worries, nor a desire for other celestial pleasures.

'Blessed are they who can live with their sweethearts
On the banks of Pampa,
Breathing the breeze that blows rich in the aroma of fragrant lotus,
The breeze that blows cool, mild,
Salubrious and which washes away their grief.

'How shall I answer Janaka when he
Questions me about Sita's abduction?
Where is my Sita who followed me
Into a forest following her dharma
While I obeyed my father?
She is good to look at, lovely like a lotus leaf.
Her skin is unblemished and fragrant.
I miss looking at her each moment of my life.
I am losing consciousness, dear brother.
When shall I hear her laughter, her sweet words?
When shall I listen to her unparalleled words of wisdom?

'She was hardly sixteen when she followed me into exile
To suffer its immense hardship.
However, whenever she found me desiring her,
Or agonizing,
Forgetting her grief,
She talked to me in words full of joy and wisdom
In order to lessen my pain.

'In Ayodhya, what shall I tell mother Kaushalya
When she says, 'where is my daughter-in-law?'
Lakshmana, you please return to Bharata.
I cannot live without Sita.'

Lakshmana Advises Rama to Persevere and Have Patience

Lakshmana trying to assuage Rama's agony, in well-chosen and logical words addressed him thus:

'Do not grieve, my brother. Your emotions need to be controlled for us to search for Sita. Great spiritual souls like you are resolute, persevering and do not give up hope and effort. Each one of us has to suffer the grief of separation from one's near and dear ones.

'Ravana will not be spared for his evil deed even if he hides in the nether world, Patala. We will trace him, and get Sita back either honourably or by defeating him in battle.

'Dear brother, perseverance and determined effort are a source of strength in such circumstances and shall enable you to succeed.

'Give up your grief and stop acting like a lover separated fom the beloved. Nothing in the world is beyond the reach of a motivated person. We can free Janaki only with determined effort. You are a mahatma with a clear conscience. At present, you have forgotten your reality.'

Listening to Lakshmana's words, Rama overcame his delusion and attachment. He regained balance and collected his thoughts about Sita, Bharata and his kin. Leaving Pampa behind, the brothers moved forward in search of Sita.

Sugreeva, the king of vanaras noticed the arrival of the two princes from a distance. His first perception of them was that they were warriors sent by his brother and enemy Vali, to kill him. He and his warriors took shelter in the Matanga Ashrama to come up with a strategy to fight the enemy.

2

Hanuman, Sugreeva's Emissary, Approaches Rama

Sugreeva's Apprehension about Rama and Lakshmana

When he saw Rama and Lakshmana, fully armed, approaching his ashrama, Sugreeva was unsure of their intentions. Restlessly, he looked in all directions to see if there was an army accompanying them too. He was scared and sad. He consulted his ministers, expressed his fear and talked of his lack of strength to engage the outsiders in a fight. He said,

'The two warriors have certainly been sent by Vali. For disguise, they are dressed in bark as hermits. They have reached here walking through a forest difficult to access.'

Jumping over hilltops, crushing the trees on their path, Sugreeva's ministers soon gathered around him to offer protection. They stood with folded hands at the top of the Rishyamooka Mountain.

Addressing the frightened king, Hanuman, skilled in expression and conversation, said,

'Please give up Vali's fear while you are on this mountain. He cannot reach here. O Vanararaja, you are unable to think straight because you are disturbed and restless. Endowed with wisdom and logical reasoning, try to understand the motives of these visitors from their movements and act accordingly. A king who does not use the power of knowledge, intelligence and understanding, cannot rule over others.'

Sugreeva replied,

'Who would not be afraid of these men, armed with bows, arrows and swords? I suspect that they are Vali's friends. We cannot trust them without being sure, because Vali is clever in deceit.

'Hanuman, go and engage them in a dialogue. Try to discover their identity and motives from their conduct and ask them what brings them into this dense forest. Ascertain that there is no hidden motive in their visit.'

Hanuman's Diplomacy

Jumping over rocks, Hanuman arrived at the place where Rama and Lakshmana were resting. He assumed a hermit's form and clothing in order to establish credibility. Facing the two warriors, Hanuman humbly bowed in their presence and spoke sweet and polite words:

'O brave men, you appear to be truthful, powerful like the Rajarshis and the devatas, hermits and men of a firm resolution. Masters, what brings you to this forest? Your presence has added to the beauty of the fine trees growing on the Pampa banks. Your limbs glow like gold and you look like lions. You carry bows and arrows in this dense forest. What brings you to this inaccessible place?

'In you, the sun and the moon appear to have descended on earth. Have you come from Swargaloka? Your bows are gold-plated; the quivers, full of arrows deadly as snakes, look grand; and your swords are strong, broad and sharp with handles made of gold.

'I represent Sugreeva, a pious and brave vanara who has been thrown out of his home by his brother, Vali. Everyone knows me as Hanuman. I am the son of Pavana, the god of wind, although I am a vanara. I can change form at will and can go anywhere.

'Right now I am here in disguise for the benefit of Sugreeva. The pious Sugreeva wants to befriend you. I am his minister and representative.'

Addressing Lakshmana, Rama said,

'Sumitranandana, this wise man comes to us as a representative of Sugreeva for his master's benefit. He is perspicacious. Please respond politely and with warmth.

'None can talk so wisely unless he has studied the Vedas. He is a master of grammar because during this long conversation, he has not uttered a single misplaced word. In a remarkably brief introduction, he made his mission clear. He talked in pleasant words and was never at a loss for words. It shows his cultured upbringing.'

Following Rama's advice, Lakshmana spoke to Hanuman:

'O learned man, we are well aware of the qualities of the wise Sugreeva. We have arrived here looking for him. We accept his hand of friendship extended by you on his behalf.'

Next, Lakshmana narrated their tale of woe, of their exile and the abduction of Sita. He told Hanuman how Kabandha had asked them to approach Sugreeva for help in their mission. Further, he said,

'Rama, who could offer protection to the entire world, has today come to Sugreeva as his saviour. He needs Sugreeva's help in tracing Sita.'

Hanuman listened to Lakshmana and choosing his words wisely, said,

'Princes, Sugreeva, the king of vanaras, is in need of the friendship of wise men like you who have conquered anger, desire and lust. Fortunately, you have arrived on your own.

'He has been deprived of his kingdom and wife by Vali, his elder brother. He lives in fear away from his home from where he has been ousted.

'Sooryanandana Sugreeva will certainly help you to trace the whereabouts of Sita. Let us go to him.'

Saying this, Hanuman changed his form into that of a vanara and carried the two brothers on his shoulders to the top of the Rishyamooka Mountain.

Friendship Established with Sugreeva

Making them comfortable at the Rishyamooka Mountain, Hanuman summoned his king from the nearby Malaya peak after narrating to him the trials and tribulations Rama had suffered because of Sita's abduction. The vanara king warmly approached Rama and Lakshmana and extended his hand of friendship.

Striking two sticks of wood, Hanuman ignited a fire. With Agni as a witness, Rama and Sugreeva affirmed their friendship by a parikrama of the holy fire.

A delighted Sugreeva said, 'Now that we are friends, let us pledge to share our sorrows as well as joys.'

Sugreeva plucked a leafy, flowering branch of the shala tree and offered Rama a seat. Lakshmana was offered the flowering branch of a sandalwood tree to make himself comfortable, by Hanuman.

Sugreeva narrated the story of the loss of his kingdom and of his wife at the hands of his elder brother Vali. In turn, Rama assured him of his strength to kill Vali and retrieve his kingdom and wife. Pointing to his bow and arrows, Rama said,

'Glorious like the sun, the arrows in my quiver never miss their target. Their heads are pointed and sharp, and they fly like angry animals striking with the force of Indra's thunderbolt. Hit by them, Vali will crash to the ground like a shattered rock.'

In turn, assuring Rama of his help, Sugreeva said,

'A rakshasa has made you suffer the viraha of your wife. You will soon be free of this sorrow. I shall bring back your wife who is pure as the Vedas.

'A few days ago I noticed a rakshasa carrying a woman in his lap. She was crying, "ha Rama, ha Rama; ha Lakshmana". I guess, she must be Sita whom Ravana was carrying away against her will. In his lap, she looked restless. When she saw us on the mountain top, she took off some of her ornaments and threw them to the ground, tied in a piece of cloth. Here they are for you to identify.'

Looking at Sita's ornaments, Rama's eyes grew moist. With a ray of hope in his eyes he spoke to Lakshmana,

'Look at theses ornaments that Sita threw down. There is no damage to them. They must have fallen on a patch of grass.'

Lakshmana replied,

'Dear brother, I cannot identify these bracelets or the bangles; however, I recognize the anklets because I used to bow down at her feet daily. This is a good omen and assures me that our search for Sita will bear good results.'

3

The Killing of Vali

Sugreeva Lifts Rama's Morale

The friendship between Rama and Sugreeva, though accomplished in the presence of Agni, required affirmation in ways more than one.

Sugreeva tried to calm Rama who was shattered by the separation from Sita. He said,

'I am totally unaware of the place in which the rakshasa, evil incarnate, resides and where he has hidden your wife. I have no idea of his strength or to which family he belongs. Yet, I shall do my best to find her and restore her to you. It is, however, necessary for the accomplishment of our mission that you let go of your sadness and take up the responsibility of a warrior.

'My wife too, has been snatched from me. However, I have given up grieving and am looking for ways to be united with her. It does not befit you to be immersed in grief forever. Patience is a virtue that you have to embrace till you find Sita.

'He does not suffer, who, when faced with the loss of a dear one, or with a financial crisis, or with a life-threatening situation, uses his intellect to find a way out. A fool, who is always upset and who does not know his mind's prowess, helplessly drowns in his sorrow like a leaking boat full of water.

'Lovingly, with folded hands, I pray that you be happy and determined and not allow the clouds of sorrow to cast their shadow upon you.

'I offer this advice as a friend and not as a guide. In the name of our friendship, shed your grief forever.'

Rama wiped his tears and said,

'Sugreeva, you have done whatever you had to do as a well-wisher. Your assurance has assuaged my nerves.'

Sugreeva's Tale of Woe

Sitting on the leafy branches of a sala tree, Sugreeva narrated the catastrophe that forced him to take shelter in the forest. He said,

'O self-enlightened Rama, a friend helps another whether he is poor, rich, happy or unhappy, innocent or guilty. Noble souls sacrifice their wealth, happiness and even their country for their friends.'

Rama nodded in agreement.

Sugreeva continued,

'Vali is my elder brother and is a well-known warrior. Upon our father's death, the trusted ministers of the kingdom crowned him king of Kishkindha.

'Some time later, a fierce demon Mayavi, who could change his form at will and coveted Vali's wife, attacked Kishkindha at night. Vali chased him over a long distance. Mayavi sought shelter in a large cave hidden by grass and splinters of wood. Vali, asking me to guard the opening, went after the demon.

'I waited at the opening of the cave for one full year. I feared that Vali had been injured or killed by Mayavi. One day a stream of foaming blood spurted out of the cave. I heard the roar of many danavas as well. Following this, I was certain that they had killed my elder brother. I placed a stone slab at the mouth of the cave to avoid the demons coming back and returned to Kishkindha. After mourning for the appropriate time, I was anointed the king so the kingdom could run effectively.

'Soon after, Vali returned. He had killed the danavas and their chief in a fierce battle. He was enraged at finding me sitting on his throne. Unfortunately, seeing his anger towards me, the ministers had arrested him. I tried to pacify him but to no avail. I told him that I accepted his superiority and his kingship and also explained how I had waited at the cave opening for him for one year.

'However, Vali rebuked me sternly. He called me cruel, heartless and selfish. He alleged that although he had entrusted me with his safety, I had shut the mouth of the cave with a stone slab deliberately so that he perishes inside.

'Vali threw me out of the kingdom and took my wife. Now I wander from place to place out of fear from which, Rama, you alone can salvage me.'

Tale of Vali's Bravery

Sugreeva continued narrating to Rama episodes highlighting Vali's valour. He said,

'Vali is a patient and mighty warrior. Before sunrise, he traverses the distance between the east and the west coast every day. Likewise, he goes from the south to the north without a trace of fatigue. He lifts huge rocks from the hilltops, throws them up like a ball and then catches them in his palm. He defeated a danava, Dundubhi who had the strength of a thousand elephants and was as high as the Kailas Mountain.

'Dundubhi arrived at the gates of Kishkindha and challenged Vali with a roar like that of a buffalo. He had sharp horns that made him look fearsome. He uprooted the trees all around, dug the earth with his hooves and scratched the massive doors of Vali's palace with his horns.

'Vali, who had been spending time with his women, heard the danava's roar. Surrounded by his wives, like the moon in the midst of stars, he emerged angrily and faced Dundubhi with equally blood-shot eyes. The latter offered Vali the privilege of completing the revelries of that night.

'Vali was not the one to wait till the next day. He caught hold of Dundubhi's horns, lifted him into the sky, spun him around a few times and threw him away. Then he crushed him to death.

'When Dundubhi was being spun aloft in circles, a few drops of his blood were scattered by the wind in the ashrama of Muni Matanga. The angry rishi cursed Vali and asked him never to enter the ashrama. Otherwise, he would meet with death.

'Rama, I live here in this ashrama because Vali cannot enter for fear of death.'

Sugreeva Puts Rama's Valour to Test

'However, how can I be sure that you will vanquish Vali, O Rama?' said a worried Sugreeva.

'How do you want to be assured that Rama will be able to kill Vali?' asked Lakshmana with a laugh.

Pointing to a row of seven sala trees standing tall in front of them, Sugreeva said,

'Once upon a time Vali had pierced through each one of these trees one by one with his arrows. If Rama is able to pierce even one tree at one go, I shall be convinced of his capability.

'Even if he can, with one kick, remove the skeletal remains of Dundubhi to a distance of 200 dhanusha, I shall be convinced that Rama can kill Vali.

'You see, Vali has never been defeated in a battle. He does not like being challenged.

'My friend, you are like the Himalayas to me. I have sought your protection as a friend. I am not trying to frighten or insult you.'

Rama smiled playfully and put one toe through Dundubhi's skeleton. Lifting his foot, he threw away the mass of bone at a distance of ten yojanas.

He then shot an arrow that piercing all seven sala trees, cutting through the seven layers of the earth, went straight into Patala. It then rebounded and returned to Rama's quiver.

Sugreeva lay prostrate before Rama, touching his feet and offering obeisance. Rising, he said,

'Who can face you on the battlefield, O Rama? With one shot, you have pierced seven mighty sala trees, the mountains and the earth. My sorrow has vanished in acquiring a dear friend like you who is valorous like Mahendra and Varuna. I am assured that I shall be freed from Vali's wrath.'

Vali Is Challenged

At Rama's instance, Sugreeva stood outside the doors of Kishkindha and challenged Vali. An angry Vali, like the setting sun, came out speedily and started hitting Sugreeva with fists and maces. Rama who stood hiding behind a tree could not shoot at Vali because the two brothers looked alike.

Sugreeva, feeling let down, ran back into the Matanga Ashrama. Vali chased him and entered the ashrama in a rage.

Accusing Rama of betrayal, Sugreeva said,

'Raghunandan, what sort of valour did you exhibit in not attacking Vali while you could? You went into hiding while I bore the brunt of my brother's anger.'

Hearing Sugreeva's pathetic complaint, Rama said,

'In dress, height and behaviour both of you are alike. I could not distinguish between you and Vali. Being in doubt, I did not shoot my arrow. Put on this flowering creeper as a garland and fight Vali. We shall not fail this time.'

Wrapping the flowering creeper around his neck, Sugreeva advanced like an evening cloud adorned by a flight of birds. Raghunath, Lakshmana and Hanuman accompanied him.

Reaching Kishkindha, Rama and Lakshmana stayed behind a thick grove of trees while Sugreeva challenged Vali to come out and fight. He thundered like a thick cloud blown by strong winds.

Tara Tries to Dissuade Vali

Vali heard Sugreeva's roar in his inner chambers. His yellow body burned with anger and his eyes glowed red like charcoals on fire. Tara, his wife, was frightened. To her the omens were not favourable. Taking him in her arms, she said,

'Give up the anger that has overtaken you like a river in spate. Give it up as a man discards a garland used in the bed at night. Fight your brother in the morning. Despite your being the mightiest of warriors, I do not advise your rushing into battle at this hour.

'I have another reason to advise you to show restraint. Sugreeva had taken shelter in the Matanga forest when you defeated him yesterday. His coming again to challenge you is a matter of concern and suspicion. He must have come back with strong supporters. That is why he roars like a lion.

'Prince Angada visited the forest a few days ago. From his informants, he learnt that two valiant sons of the king of Ayodhya have arrived and that it is impossible to defeat them in battle. They have promised help to Sugreeva. One of them, Rama, is known for vanquishing the armies of his opponents. He is reputed to be radiant like the pralaya fires. For the virtuous, Rama is like Kalpavriksha.

'I pray that you anoint Sugreeva as the Yuvaraja. After all, he is your younger brother. Make Rama your friend and regain the affection of your brother. Sugreeva deserves your love and affection; he is a wise man. Win over his confidence by giving him wealth, position and respect.

'I lovingly request you to listen to my advice.'

Vali did not pay heed to his wife's wise advice and acted in defiance of good councel as if his time to perish had come. He thundered in reply,

'Lovely woman, I cannot tolerate the roaring of my brother; he is my enemy and is challenging me to a fight. If Rama is truthful and a protector of dharma as per your description, how can he side with Sugreeva? He knows the distinction between right and wrong. How can he commit a sin?

'I shall shatter Sugreeva's pride. However, I shall not kill him. I shall beat him with fists and trees till he runs away.'

A sobbing Tara embraced her husband and chanted mantras wishing him victory.

Vali came out to fight his brother Sugreeva and hit him with his fist. Sugreeva's mouth started bleeding. He in turn plucked a sala tree and hit Vali hard causing grievous injury.

The brothers fought savagely, showing no mercy and hitting each other as hard as they could. However, Sugreeva seemed to be losing the battle and reminded Rama of his promise.

Rama was ready with his bow and arrow. He balanced the fierce arrow on his bow and pulled at the string as if Yamaraja had readied the Kalachakra. Rama let the arrow go roaring like a thunderbolt. Sparks of lightning flew from the arrow as it hit Vali on his chest. Seriously injured, the glorious Vali fell to the ground. His blood oozed until he lay submerged in it. Indra's son, Vali, lay flat like a flowering asoka tree felled to the ground.

Rama's arrow had opened the pathway to Swarga to Vali. He was soon going to attain the highest status in the heavens. Acknowledging his valour, Rama and Lakshmana approached the fallen warrior who even though lying lifeless, looked invincible like Mahendra. He resembled the sun shattered by Kala at the time of Pralaya.

Vali's Rebuke to Rama

Although he was gradually losing consciousness, Vali addressed Rama who was filled with pride at having brought him down in battle. He said,

'Raghunandan, you are the son of Dashratha and your darshana is sought by everyone. What honour have you earned for your family by shooting at me who was not at war with you?

'Rajan, every living being on this earth is full of praise for you. They say that you are truthful, well-behaved, glorious, an embodiment of satva, a man of good conduct, one who feels for others, kind-hearted, a well-wisher of his people, always enthusiastic, and aware of propriety under all circumstances.

'Rajan, a king is supposed to have his desires under control and an unwavering mind. He is expected to be kind, patient, truthful, chivalrous and just in meting punishment to the criminals. I put faith in your qualities and in spite of being forewarned by Tara, came to fight Sugreeva.

'Owing to your being righteous, I believed that you would not target me without a warning. However, now I realize that you have no conscience, that you are evil incarnate though apparently you profess to follow the dictates of dharma.

'Though dressed as a saint, you are a sinner. You are like embers covered under ashes.

'I had neither insulted you nor did I create turbulence in your city or kingdom. Why did you kill me who was innocent?

'Kings fight over land, silver and gold. These three are the root cause of strife. Here, no such wealth is available to attract a fight.

'Polity, submission, diplomacy, punishment and persuasion are attributes of the raja-dharma. In acting the way you have, you have proved yourself to be a slave to your passions, easily moved by anger and used to acting without restraint. You are temperamental and have punished me without a cause, losing a sense of propriety, without humility and without a trace of kindness

'You have committed a sin in killing me in battle stealthily.

'I could have traced Maithili and restored her to you in a day. If that is the only reason why you helped Sugreeva, then you have made a mistake. I would have thrown Ravana, with a noose around his neck, at your feet.

'Sugreeva's ascension to the throne at my death is unobjectionable. However, your killing me with deceit is highly flawed and unjustified.

'If you can justify your action, please say so after careful consideration.'

Vali fell silent. He was in great pain and lay like the lustreless sun, a cloud bereft of water or an extinguished fire.

Rama Justifies His Action

Rama had been listening to Vali's rebuke patiently. In well-chosen words, he addressed Vali on the real significance of dharma, artha and other superior virtues in human conduct.

'Vali, you are unaware of the meaning of dharma, artha or kama. You have denounced me like an ignorant child.

'The entire country with her mountains, forests and rivers belongs to the Ikshavaku rulers. They are, therefore, empowered to punish the humans, the birds as well as the animals. Bharata rules truthfully and is well aware of his duties. He has authorized us to spread the rule of dharma. We punish anyone who has deviated from the path of righteousness.

'You preferred kama over all other principles in your life. You never followed the righteous path of a king. You obstructed dharma and those who are truthful have always condemned your conduct.

'The elder brother, the father and the guru who imparts knowledge, all the three ought to be respected like a father by a man of righteous conduct.

'Dharma requires that a younger brother, a son or an intelligent pupil, ought to be treated like a son.

'O Vanara, the attributes of dharma are subtle and difficult to understand.

'If you ask me the reason why I shot the arrow at you, then listen. You are cohabiting with the wife of your younger brother in violation of all the rules of Sanatana Dharma. Sugreeva is still alive, but driven by lust, you have captured his wife Ruma who is like a daughter-in-law to you. You have sinned, O Vali. According to established practice, the punishment for this crime is death.

'I have made friends with Sugreeva. I treat him like my younger brother, Lakshmana. To regain his kingdom and his wife he is ready to help me to reach my abducted wife. I have given him my word and I shall keep it.

Vali shed tears of remorse at these words of Rama. Like an elephant rendered immobile in a quagmire, he said in a quivering voice,

'I accept my sin, O Raghava. I have violated my dharma.

'I have received punishment for my sin. Now I am not worried for myself, or for Tara or for my relatives. I worry for my beloved son, the virtuous Angada who wears a golden armlet. I have brought him up with love and care. He will be extremely unhappy in my absence and will wither like a flower on a fallen tree.

'He is just a child, Shri Rama. He is my only son born of Tara. Look after my warrior son.

'Be kind to Sugreeva as well as Angada. You are their protector as well as mentor from now, and I am sure you will lead them on the right path, away from evil.

'I wished to die at your hands and that is why I ignored Tara's advice and came to wrestle with Sugreeva.'

Rama spoke words of wisdom. He said,

'Vali, you cannot override the dictates of Kala. This punishment has wiped out your sins. Give up your sorrow, attachment and fear. Be assured that your son Angada will be as safe with Sugreeva and me as he has been with you.'

4

Tara's Grief

Learning of the devastating result of her husband's fatal fight, Tara rushed to the site with her son Angada. On her way, she noticed her husband's guards running in fright like the deer who have lost the leader of their pack. Stopping them in their tracks, she said,

'You used to be the advance guard of Vali who was like a lion. Sugreeva, greedy to be the king, asked Rama to murder his elder brother. Why do you run like deserters?'

The vanara chiefs replied,

'Devi, you should protect your son who is alive. Rama is like Yamaraja who struck down the huge trees, rocks and thunderbolt-like arrows thrown by Vali. You please return and anoint Angada as the king of Kishkindha. We shall be at his service.'

Tara responded,

'What relevance does life, a kingdom, or even my son have for me, whose husband, Vali, the lion of the vanaras is no more?'

Moving ahead, Tara saw Vali lying on the ground smeared in blood and mud. Rama and Lakshmana accompanied by Sugreeva, stood nearby.

Talking to her husband who was breathing his last, Tara said,

'Wake up O king; you deserve to lie on a bed of luxury and not on this uneven ground. Discarding my body, why do you cling to the earth?

'You disregarded my advice and have been punished for usurping Sugreeva's wife. You will continue to frolic with the apsaras in Swargaloka who, looking at your handsome face, will be enamoured of you.'

Facing Rama, Tara rebuked him saying,

'Rama, you have committed sacrilege by killing Vali who was fighting his brother. Your act is condemnable. I can see that you have no remorse at having committed this crime as a consequence of which I shall have to spend my remaining years as a widow.

'Angada, have a last look at your brave father. You will not see him again on this earth.

'Brother Sugreeva, your brother, whom you considered your enemy, is no more. Enjoy your kingdom and Ruma, uninterrupted.'

Hanuman tried to pacify the wailing Tara who looked like a fallen star. He said,

'Devi, we reap the fruit of our actions, wise or unwise. Your situation is lamentable. Why lament for the one who has gone? This body is transitory like a bubble of water.

'Your son, Angada is alive and looking after him is your responsibility.

'You are the mistress of this kingdom. Angada and Sugreeva, both of them are in mourning. Kindly motivate them to move ahead. Let us perform the last rites of the late king. Then we shall anoint Angada as the king. That will give you peace of mind.

However, Tara was adamant. She said,

'Between having a hundred sons like Angada and burning myself holding my brave husband in my arms on his funeral pier, I shall any day choose the latter. As far as Angada is concerned, his welfare lies in Sugreeva's pleasure. His uncle matters more to him than his mother.'

Vali Enjoins upon Sugreeva to Look after Angada

While Vali was about to breathe his last, he opened his eyes and with difficulty looked around. First, he talked to Sugreeva. Affectionately and in clear words, he said,

'I considered you to be my enemy under the delusion of some evil deeds done in an earlier life. We were destined not to live happily as loving brothers. Now, you be the king of the vanaras. I give up my life, my kingdom, my considerable wealth and my glory. Please do as I say.

'Treat Angada as your son. He is brave and glorious like you and will always stand by you. He may be young but he is not a fool. Tara is subtle in her thinking. She is extremely wise. She can sense danger in advance. You can follow her advice without hesitation.

'Carry out the job entrusted to you by Shri Rama.

'Here is my celestial gold necklace wherein Lakshmi resides. Its powers will disappear if I die. However, if you put it on while I am alive, Lakshmi will look after you.'

While Sugreeva put on the celestial necklace, Vali looked at Angada and said affectionately, with tears in his eyes,

'Son, always try to judge correctly the time and place for any activity. Firstly, determine how much respect a person warrants. Behave accordingly. Learn to bear joy, happiness and sorrow as they come. Learn to suffer patiently. Be kind, generous and forgiving.

'You shall always obey Sugreeva and his enemies should be your enemies too. Serve Sugreeva whole-heartedly and he will, in turn, give you all you desire.

'Never be too friendly with anyone nor be totally indifferent. Both these approaches are undesirable.'

Saying so, Vali breathed his last.

Although Sugreeva had asked Rama to kill his elder brother, looking at Vali's dead body, he shed copious tears. He said,

'Raghunath, Vali had spurned me and maltreated me. I was so angered that I urged you to kill him. However, now that the deed is done, I am overcome with remorse that might last a lifetime.

'Raghunandan, however selfish a man might be, he will not prefer his brother's death over the power and pelf of a kingdom. I never wanted Vali's death. However, good sense deserted me. While he played the elder brother even while beating me with the trunk of a tree, I behaved like a vanara impelled by kama, krodha and a fickle temperament.'

In the meantime, Tara approached Rama and asked him to kill her as well. She said,

'Raghunandan, if you kill me, I can join my husband because he cannot live even for a moment apart from me. In Swargaloka, he will pine for me. Even the prettiest of apsaras cannot entice him.'

Rama consoled Tara saying,

'Do not consider death as an option, O wife of a warrior. The Creator created this universe with joy and sorrow co-joined. We are subservient to His will and, therefore, we cannot overrule His dictates.

'Your son will be the Yuvaraja and you will be happy as before. That is your destiny. The wives of brave men do not wail helplessly like this.'

To the assembled vanaras, Rama said,

'We have had enough of mourning and weeping. It is time to perform the king's last rites. Vali has attained moksha having been killed by me.'

A celestial palanquin was readied to carry Vali's body for cremation. It was made like a chariot with a grand throne for the king. With its frame made of red sandalwood and lotus flowers with shining petals, orange like the rising sun, used in abundance, Vali's body seemed like that of an incomparable king. Vanaras scattered gems over the palanquin as the procession moved forward. The surrounding mountains wept with the mourners. On the banks of the river Tungabhadra that ran meandering through the Kishkindha mountains, the mortal remains of Vali were cremated with appropriate rites.

5

Varsha Ritu

The last of religious rites for Vali being over, the vanara warriors, accompanied by a sorrowing Sugreeva, approached Rama to invite him to Kishkindha and crown the new king. Rama declined as his father's command prohibited him from entering a village or town for fourteen years. He advised Sugreeva to anoint Angada as the Yuvaraja because the latter was a wise man and a warrior. Rama said,

'The chaumasa, the four months of the rainy season, has set in. We are in the first month, Shrawan when the rainwater enriches the streams. It is not time for any military adventure. Go to your kingdom while I stay here with Lakshmana. This large cave is pleasant and airy with abundant source of water. As the month of Kartik approaches, you shall initiate efforts to trace and kill Ravana.'

Sugreeva's Coronation

Sugreeva was crowned king ceremoniously. His courtiers brought offerings of a white umbrella studded in gold, two flywhisks that had handles made of gold, gems, seeds and medicinal herbs, and flowers, clothes, unguents, flowers grown in ponds and in earthen beds, intoxicating sandal paste, several scents, fragrant condiments, rice, honey, ghee, curds, powder, tiger skins, gold and precious stones.

On a raised platform was placed a throne of gold on which the Brahmins seated Sugreeva facing east, as they chanted holy mantras for his consecration.

Enjoying his newfound kingdom and the company of his wife, Ruma, Sugreeva soon forgot his promise to his benefactor Rama.

The Prashravanagiri Cave

Rama and Lakshmana moved to a nearby hill called Prashravanagiri. The place resounded with the calls of cheetahs, the deer and the roar of lions. Besides, one came across bears, monkeys and langurs. The woods were thick with trees and abounded in creepers and wild bush. The hilltop looked like a pyramid of clouds.

They settled in a deep cave at the top that provided full protection from the rain. Standing on a ledge, Rama pointed out to Lakshmana:

'The mountain with rocks looks lovely. We stand atop several seams of minerals. The thickets of trees and the widespread creepers make the hilltop look velvety. The birds sing and the splendid peacocks call all the time.

'Its loveliness is enhanced by the bushes of malati, kunda, sindhuvar, and the flowering arjuna, kadamba, shirish and sarja trees. In the river, the lotus shines as pieces set in a tapestry. Our cave will protect us from the south-west showers. We can use a large flat, coal-black slate that lies just outside the cave as a comfortable seat.

'The northern ridge looks black like a mound of coal or dark clouds piled on each other while the southern ridge is fair like the peaks of Kailas. Look, on the other side of the cave, near the Trikuta hill, the river Tungabhadra flows leisurely like Mandakini.

'Tungabhadra, with her clear-cut shores, as the playing field of the royal swans and the sarus birds and as a repository of many a precious gem, appears to scatter her laughter all around. Red lotuses bloom here and blue ones there, interspersed with the white ones. Hordes of munis use her water.

'Lakshmana, if we stay here we shall be pleasantly occupied. I can also hear the sound of celebrations in Kishkindha, of the songs sung by the vanaras and the sonorous music of various instruments.'

In spite of the few comforts that were available while living on the Prashravanagiri, viraha rocked Rama in Sita's absence. He was unhappy, sleep eluded him particularly when he saw the moon rising in the east at night. Often, he fainted while shedding tears of sorrow.

Frequently, Lakshmana asked Rama to give up sorrowing all the time, to patiently and bravely await the arrival of autumn when the search for Sita could begin. 'Control your sorrow,' said he. 'Bear with your suffering for the four months of the rainy season.'

Varsha Ritu

'The sky is hidden by the clouds that look like mountains.
The time has come when the rains bring water to the earth.

'The sky, as a young bride,
Nourished by the waters of the oceans for nine months,
Helped by the rays of the sun,
Gives birth, from her womb, to water, the elixir of life.

'It looks easy to ascend the spiralling clouds into the sky and
Garland the Sun god with strings of jasmine and arjuna flowers.

'The evening sky is dyed orange.
The clouds are red at the core,
Their edges white and warm.
A wounded sky
Looks dressed in a blood soaked white bandage.

'The sky, like an amorous lover,
Is short of breath because the breeze blows mild.
The evening colours his limbs and the forehead red
As if with red sandalpaste.
However,
His cheeks look pale like the clouds.

'Earlier, scorched by the summer heat,
The earth, now soaking the fresh showers,
Gives out vapour
Like the suffering Sita when she sighs.

'The winds, saturated with rain,
Blowing out of the clouds' belly,
Cool like camphor,
Fragrant with the scent of kewra,
Can be sipped in cups made of our palms.

'The mountain where the arjuna blooms,
Where kewra scatters its scent,
Is being anointed by streams of water flowing downwards,
Like Sugreeva whose enemies have been silenced.

'Like the Brahmacharis [learning their lessons],
The mountains, wrapping the dark clouds as deerskin, and
Putting on the streams of rain as Yagyopavit,
With tunnels through which blows the wind,
Are busy in chanting the Veda mantras.

'The lightning strikes the sky like a golden whip.
The firmament,
Grievously injured, roars in pain through the clouds.

'Crisscrossing the dark clouds, the lightning
Appears to me like the tapasvini Sita
Writhing in the lap of Ravana.

'Of course, the amorous couples
Prefer the environment when
The stars, the planets and the moon are hidden behind the clouds,
and
When the sense of direction has been lost.

Sumitranandana, look at the kutaja blooms
Resplendent on the hilltops.
At places, they have wilted, impacted by the hot vapour
Emitted by the earth soaked in the first showers.
At others, they rejoice in the arrival of the rains.
While I suffer from Sita's separation,
The kutaja flowers inflame my passion.

'On the ground,
The dust has settled.
A cool wind blows.
The summer heat harasses no longer nor spreads disease.
While the kings do not mount an offensive,
The travellers, away from home, return.

'Wildly flow
The mountain streams, full of fresh water.
Mixed with the brown of the rocks and minerals,
Their waters are red.
On their surface, float the kadamba and sarja flowers.
The peacocks' calls mingle with the sound of gurgling waters.

'The rains add to the magnificence of the forests.
Nursed by them the grass grows tall and green.
The peacocks rejoice, dancing as if in a festival, while
The clouds pour incessantly.

'Surrounded by flocks of cranes,
The clouds, carrying their weight of water,
Roar and move forward.
Now and then, they halt and rest
Upon the mountain peaks; then, they set out again.

'Covered by nascent grass,
Crisscrossed by tiny, maroon indragopikas,
The earth glistens like a woman
Who has wrapped herself in a parrot-green covering
With stripes of purple-red.

'As the chaumasa begins,
Nidra nears Keshava at a leisurely pace.
The rivers rush to meet the ocean.
The joyous cranes fly to touch the clouds.
The beloved impelled by kama presents herself to her lover.

'Hurt by showers, the bhramaras,
Sticking to the kadamba branches,
Slowly exude the thick honey extracted by them
From the juice of the flowers.

'Looking at the branches of the jamun trees,
Loaded with large, juicy fruit,
Dark like mounds of powder coal,
It appears as if swarms of black bees
Have closely settled on them to sip their sap.

'The forest glade, rich in
The kadamba, sarja, plantain and arjuna trees,
Soaking the sweet rain water,
Resounding with the calls of
Intoxicated peacocks dancing in abandon,
Appears more like a madhushala [tavern].

The thirsty papihas delightfully sip
The raindrops falling from the sky
Like pure white pearls into cones made by the tree leaves,
A gift from the Lord Indra.
Drenched in the rain,
Their feathers reflect glorious colours.

'The forest resounds with a festival of music.
The drone of the bhramaras sounds as sweet as veena.
The croaking frogs sound as if notes are sung.
The clouds thunder like a mridanga player.

'The surging streams [like lusty young women],
Carry the geese [like breasts] floating on their waters.
Demolishing their restraining banks which are weak and worn out,
Cutting into their embankments,
Carrying fresh flowers as gifts,
They rush to meet their master,
The ocean, for consummation.

'The dark blue clouds, full of fresh water,
Floating close to each other as if merged together,
Look like mountains fused into each other
After volcanic fires have melted their rocks.

'The elephants [gajendra] run amok.
The bulls [gavendra] are busy in the pursuit of pleasure.
The lions [mrigendra] flaunt their valour.
The high mountains [nagendra] look inviting.
The kings [narendra] are quiet [for this is not the time to wage a
war.]
Indra [surendra] is busy playing with the clouds.

'The clouds wandering in the sky
Put to shame the roar of the ocean waves with their thunder.
With a massive discharge of water,
They flood the rivers, ponds and reservoirs and
Submerge the entire earth.

'As the subjects consecrate their king
With the holy waters brought in pitchers,
The mountains are anointed with water
Bestowed by Indra and
Brought in the pitcher-like clouds,
Carried by the winds.
Thus, awash, they present
A fresh face and their splendid wealth.

'Thick clouds hide the sky.
During the day the sun, and at night the stars are invisible.
The earth has quenched her thirst with fresh water.
All around there is darkness.
For lack of illumination,
Difficult it is to move in any direction.

'Eye-catching rivulets of water run in every direction.
They look like the pearl necklaces worn by devanganas
Come unstuck during passionate lovemaking.

'The birds retire to their nests.
The lotus has folded.
Malati buds are opening.
It looks like sunset.

'The rains have brought enmity,
As well as the roads, to a standstill.
The kings' adventures to wage a war are on hold.
The armies in the field rest wherever they are.
The rains have cooled the fires of enmity between the warlords.

'The month of Bhadrapada has arrived.
It is time for the Brahmins to study the Vedas and
For the learned to recite the Samaveda.

'Bharata, the king of Kausala must have
Made provision for all his requirements during these months.
The Saryu ought to be in flood this season.

'After the defeat of his enemy,
Sugreeva having ascended the throne of his vast kingdom
Enjoys with his woman.
However, Lakshmana,
I have lost my kingdom as well as my wife.
I suffer like the embankment swept by the flood.
My grief intensifies.
How do I while away the four months of rain?
Ravana, my enemy appears to be invincible.

'It is not an opportune time for undertaking a journey,
Nor are the roads easy to navigate.
I, therefore, did not make a demand on Sugreeva
Even as he bowed at my feet.

'He had suffered a long time.
His wife has joined him after ages.
Moreover, my assignment is not simple.
Therefore, at the moment,
I do not want to disturb him.
Surely at the right time
He will fulfill his obligation to me.'

Rama continued, 'Desirous of Sugreeva's happiness and the purity of water in the rivers, I silently wait for autumn. A warrior, once he has taken an obligation, will certainly return it. However, if someone forgets a good deed done to him or deliberately turns his face away from a benefactor, he hurts the sensibilities of a good person.'

Lakshmana agreed with Rama's point of view and hoped that Sugreeva would keep his word.

6

Sharad Ritu:
Lakshmana Grows Impatient

Hanuman Reminds Sugreeva of His Commitment

Among Sugreeva's ministers, Hanuman was the wisest. Son of Pavana, the wind god, he understood the rules of governance and diplomacy as per the scriptures. He appreciated devotion to one's duty and was one of the few who remembered Sugreeva's obligation to Rama.

The rains were over. Clouds or flashes of lightning disappeared from the sky. The sarus cranes flew and sang their swooning duets. The moonlight painted the sky with a sandal white paste.

Hanuman was aware that Sugreeva, his objective achieved, was indifferent to the exercise of dharma and artha. While Ruma was restored, he had also made the same mistake as his brother Vali by marrying his wife Tara. He ignored good counsel by his ministries and became engrossed in revelries.

Soon, Hanuman approached Sugreeva and in pleasant and wise words, logically argued his case. He said,

'Rajan, while you have acquired a kingdom and fame, you have still to settle a friend's debt. Please attend to it and strengthen your friendship.

'It is time to start looking for Sita. Rama is our benefactor and a man of unique virtues. He is at present dependant on you but hesitates to remind you that time is running out for him. We ought to set things in motion before Rama brings up the subject.

'Kapishwara, once you order, nothing can stop your forces whether on land, over water, in the sky or in the Patalaloka. Your vanaras cannot be defeated.'

The wise Sugreeva ordered Neel, one of his generals, to summon all his forces, even those guarding the borders of his empire. He also desired Hanuman to apprise the senior vanara chiefs of the decision.

Virahi Rama and the Advent of Sharad Ritu

As the season changed and the sky emerged from the clouds, Rama suffered more and more because of his longing for Sita. He looked at the clear skies and the soothing moonlight. His pain of being away from his beloved was heightened by his thoughts of Sugreeva's indifference because of his preoccupation with his harem. The effort to trace the whereabouts of Sita had not even started. It was a matter for concern.

Rama longed for Sita. He thought:

'Her words were sonorous like the call of the sarus cranes.
At the ashrama,
Listening to their love calls, she spent her time.
How does my innocent Sita entertain herself now?

'Looking at the asan trees, pure like gold and in bloom,
Finding me missing from her side,
How can she ever be happy?

'Her limbs are lovely.
Habitually, she speaks in sweet tones.
Exhilarating, musical sounds of the rajahansa
Used to awaken her in the morning.
Who looks after her now?

'Without Sita who has the eyes of a fawn,
There is no joy for me, although
I freely wander near streams, sarovars, orchards and forests.

'When the Sharad ritu is in full swing,
Kama excites lust even more.
I hope that desire does not torment the passionate,
Charming Sita.
Firstly, she suffers from her separation from me.
Secondly, being young,
She might find the pain of viraha intolerable.'

Lakshmana Asks Rama to Meditate

Like the papiha thirsting for raindrops and praying to Indra for the onset of rains, Rama continued to lament his loss. Returning from the

forest after gathering fruit, Lakshmana found his brother in a sad
state of mind. Sympathizing with his grief, Lakshmana said,

'Arya, there is nothing to be gained by surrendering to kama,
forgetting your valour, and ignoring your strength. Submerged in
shameful grief, you have lost your focus. Concentrate your mind in
samadhi. Why not take recourse to yogic meditation and ward off
your worries?

'Brother, give your whole-hearted attention to the essential tasks.
Be happy. Never lose your focus. Do not pity yourself. Rather, gather
help and add to your resources.

'Sita is yours and yours alone. She will not yield to another man.
She is like a flame which none can touch without being burnt.'

Rama replied,

'What you suggest is useful in the present and beneficial in the
future. Your approach is diplomatic and is in line with the concept of
sama, dama and dharma. However, it is not advisable to expect
results without having made efforts.'

Thinking constantly of Sita whose eyes resembled a lotus in bloom,
his mouth parched, Rama talked of the advent of the Sharad Ritu,

'Now that he has saturated the earth with water and
Matured the grain,
The hundred-eyed Indra feels blessed.
The clouds that thundered sonorous and deep,
That floated over the hills, the trees and the towns,
Having exhausted their water, are now at peace.

'[During the rains]
The clouds, blue like bouquets of blue lotus,
Had coloured the sky blue all over.
Like elephants no longer in musth,
Those clouds have lost their prowess.

'Saumya, the rain clouds were heavy with water and
Fragrant with the arjuna and kutaja scents.
Those ferocious clouds that floated all over,
Churning the sky with the force of gales,
Are now at peace.

'O sinless Lakshmana,
The thunder of the clouds,
The trumpet of the elephants,
The peacocks' calls and the roar of the cataracts
Have suddenly been silenced.

'The fascinating mountain tops,
Slashed by the water pouring out of the mighty clouds,
Look smooth and clean.
Wrapped in moonbeams,
They appear to have been plastered in white.

'The Sharad ritu has scattered her bounty
In the branches of the saptaparni trees,
In the glory of the sun, the moon and the stars, and
In the antics of the massive elephants.

'The autumn bestows Lakshmi with its own splendour.
The latter looks resplendent, uniquely glorious,
In several manifestations.
However, most of all,
She displays her magnificence,
When the lotus blooms
With the first rays of the rising sun.

'Imbibing the fragrance of the saptaparni blooms,
The winds blow to announce the arrival of the Sharad ritu.
Droning bhramaras sing its praises.
The wet earth runs dry.
The elephants ooze more of musth,
Thanks to this season.

'Fond of flirtation,
The hansa frolic with the chakravaka.
Flying together from the Manasarovar,
They have descended,
On the riverbanks.
Covered with the lotus pollen,
Their large feathers look stunning.

'Looking at the skies bereft of the clouds,
The peacocks in the forest,
Shedding their colourful fantails,
As if discarding their jewels,
Stay away from the peahens.
Losing their glory,
Joyless they sit, lost in thought.
[For a lover,
This is a scene of desolation and deprivation.]

'In the forest,
Several asan trees stand tall,
Their boughs bent with
Bouquets of fragrant flowers at their tips.
Looking like gold, they please the eye and
Make the forest glow.

'The elephants are indolent,
Although they wander with their mates.
They ooze musth in excess, are full of lust and easily excited.
They love the lotus flowers and forests.
The fragrance of the saptaparni blooms enhances their libido.

'The sky sparkles like the edge of a sword recently honed.
The rivers flow at leisure.
Rich in the aroma of the white lotus,
The breeze blows mild and cool.
The horizon is dark no longer.
Rather, the sky is all aglow.

'The heat has dried the mud.
After a long interval,
One can see the dust rising.
The kings are ready to wage battles against their enemies.

'Standing among their herd of cows,
Joyously, the bulls bellow with full force.
The autumn makes them look glamorous.
Dust has covered their limbs.
Their libido aroused, they itch for a fight.

'Walking at leisure, the she-elephants,
Of good breed, waiting to be mated,
Surround their male oozing musth and are ready to copulate.
Equally excited, passionate,
They follow him into the forest.

'Their foreheads oozing musth,
Frightening the ruddy geese and ducks with their trumpets,
The elephants
Frolic and playfully slurp water from the ponds
Brimming with full-blown lotus flowers.

'The flamingos and the geese happily alight into
The streams where the mud on the shores has dried,
Where herds of cows flock to sip water,
Where the sarus cranes flirt and sing in melody,
Where the water is clear and the sands sparkle.

'The deadly poisonous, variegated snakes that had
Hid in holes, frightened by the onset of rains, and
Lay listless, starving,
Crawl out of their holes with the change of season.

'What a surprise!
The passionate Sandhya, [like an amorous Nayika],
Disrobes herself of the firmament.
She is delighted at the caresses of the moonbeams.
[Like the whites of her eyes,
Anticipating pleasure,]
The tiny stars twinkle.
The Sharad night, dressed in the moonlight,
Enchants like an alluring damsel wrapped in white.
The rising moon is her pleasant face and
The stars her wide-open, attractive eyes.

'Making a meal of ripe sheaves of rice,
With boundless joy,
The flocks of cranes speedily flying in lovely formations,
Look like well-knit garlands of flowers,
Tossed by the winds,
Floating in the sky.

'The lake is full of lotus flowers.
A solitary flamingo floats in sleep.
The waters reflect the vast, cloudless sky,
Illuminated by a full moon and
Enriched by glimmering stars all over.

'The beautiful ponds look like
Shapely women dressed in finery and elegant robes.
Flocks of flamingos form their waistbands.
Blooming lotuses make their necklaces.

'The tall, new sedge growing on riverbanks,
Adds to their fascination.
The grasses sway in a gentle breeze.
Smiling through their tiny buds,
They glisten like spotless, freshly washed silks.

'The amorous bhramaras, and the bees,
Joyously follow the fragrant breeze into the forest.
Dexterous in sucking the honey from the flowers,
Persistent, they wander in order to gather
The pollen, from the lotus and the asan trees,
That powders them fair.

'In Sharad ritu,
The water is clear,
The rice crop has ripened,
The breeze blows mild and
The moon is spotlessly clean.
The rains are over.
The herons [kroncha] call and
The season smiles through its flowers in bloom.

'Tying the fish like a waistband,
The streams flow languid like the delicate brides,
Walking in the early morning,
In a daze, having enjoyed the night with their lovers.

'Like a bride's face, the rivers shine at their mouth on which,
Resting there in a row,
The chakravaka [the ruddy geese] have painted a yellow tilaka.

The lotus flowers are tattoos to beautify the comely face
Hidden by the apron of the white sedges.

'Tall grasses and asan trees have enriched the forest that
Resound with the drone of the joyous bhramaras.
Kamadeva, the mighty archer,
Traverses the forest with his bowstring stretched,
Ready to shoot and angrily punish the lovelorn lovers.

'Satisfying the human beings with heavy rains,
Enriching the rivers and ponds with water, and
The earth with a rich harvest of rice,
The clouds have disappeared from the skies.

'Like a coy woman during her first union,
Compelled to open her thighs by and by,
The rivers, where waters have receded,
Show their naked banks to the onlookers.

'Saumya, the water in the ponds is clean and settled.
The ospreys quack.
Gaggles of geese gather all over.
The birds make the ponds look lovelier.

'O prince!
The time is ripe for enemies of long standing and
For kings desirous of conquering another,
To wage a war.'

Coming to the point, Rama said,

'Here is an opportunity to set out on the road to victory. However,
I do not see any sign of Sugreeva, nor efforts made by him for this
purpose.

'I am dejected because Sita is not here. I have waited through the
four months of rainy season with great difficulty.

'Like a chakvi following her male, the blessed Sita accompanied me
to the Dandakaranya, inhospitable and frightening, as if she was
visiting a garden. Lakshmana, I have been separated from my beloved.
My kingdom has been snatched and I have been exiled. Even in this
desperate situation Sugreeva is not lifting a finger to help me.

'He has gone back on his word.'

An Ultimatum to Sugreeva

'Lakshmana, call on Sugreeva and tell him that he is going back on his words in forgetting the obligation, a promise given to me, after I restored his kingdom.

'It is surprising that Sugreeva has forgotten the fate of Vali. He has forgotten that he had promised us to trace Sita's whereabouts. Living lecherously, he has not noticed that the rains are over. Tell him about my anger and that the road on which Vali has been transported is still open. Ask him to fulfil his promise or face the consequences of my enmity and anger.'

7

Lakshmana Visits Kishkindha

While the kind-hearted and generous Rama was grieving and pining for his wife, in order to assuage his anger, Lakshmana said,

'Arya, Sugreeva cannot tread the righteous path traversed by decent persons. He does not appear to believe in the friendship cemented between the two of you with Agni as a witness, because of which he was restored to his kingdom.

'Sugreeva has lost his wisdom. His women engage all his attention. He does not intend honouring his commitment. He must be dispatched to keep company with Vali and Angada made a king and asked to help trace Sita.'

As Lakshmana, with his bow and arrow held high, prepared to move speedily towards Kishkindha in great anger, Rama spoke to pacify him. He said,

'Sumitranandana, it does not become a righteous man like you to kill a friend. Amongst men, the best ones overcome their anger with subtle wisdom. We must stick to our commitment to be Sugreeva's friends and try to remind him of his obligation.'

A pacified Lakshmana, though inwardly angry and upset, walked towards Kishkindha looking glorious like a rainbow. Wise as Brihaspati, Lakshmana thought over how to address the problem with Sugreeva. Kishkindha, situated in a valley, was inaccessible to outsiders. The vanara guards confronted Lakshmana. This upset him once gain. Sugreeva, who was enjoying Tara's company in his bed, did not come out to receive the prince.

However, as soon as Angada learnt of the arrival of Lakshmana, he came out and greeted him with folded hands. The Raghava prince asked him to inform his uncle of his arrival and to remind him of the promise he had made to Rama while cementing their friendship.

An intoxicated Sugreeva lay with Tara, his eyes red and unfocused.

He wore a garland of golden flowers. When Angada and his ministers explained the situation to him, his comprehension cleared and he asked Tara to receive the angry Lakshmana, pacify him using her wise words and womanly guile and escort him into the palace. He said,

'I have not uttered a word against Rama or Lakshmana. Why are they angry with me? A friend's unjustified anger bothers me. It is easy to make friends but difficult to sustain the relationship.'

Hanuman, the wisest among Sugreeva's counsellors, tried to sort out the situation. He said,

'Maharaja, Rama cannot be inimical to you whom he helped without caring for public condemnation when he killed Vali. The fact that he has sent Lakshmana as his emissary shows that he cares for you.

'You forgot your duty to help them trace Sita. You were too occupied with pleasures of the flesh. The skies are clear now and the rainy season has passed. It is time for the kings to set out on their expeditions. Lakshmana has come because you ignored all this.

'Mahatma Rama is unhappy because his wife has been kidnapped. Bear with it even if Lakshmana is harsh with you. You are in the wrong. Hence, you have no way out except to make peace with Shri Rama and Lakshmana.'

Kishkindha was lavishly built. The avenues were broad and the gardens full of flowering plants. Several buildings were as high as the Meru Mountain or Vindhyachala. The air was redolent with the fragrance of sandalwood and of intoxicating liquors. Massive doors made of solid gold guarded the inner palace. Expensive tapestries covered the luxurious beds, made of silver or of gold. Entering the gates, Lakshmana heard the melodious voice of the singers to the accompaniment of veena.

A Beauteous Tara Pacifies an Angry Lakshmana

Sugreeva was afraid of facing an angry Lakshmana. At his instance, the beauteous Tara walked over to the prince. She was slim, coy and by nature, humble. Her eyes were red and intoxicated. Her gait was unsteady. Golden threads dangled from her waistband. Having imbibed liquor, Tara was not restrained like a woman. She sensed that Lakshmana was delighted to look at her. Fearlessly, she spoke her words of wisdom:

'Why are you so angry, O prince? Who dare disobey you? Which idiot enters a conflagration raging in a dry forest?'

Tara's assuring words set Lakshmana's doubts at rest. He could see that she was sincere. Responding, he said,

'Tara, I admire you for thinking well of your husband. However, he is squandering his wealth of dharma and artha by ceaselessly indulging in kama. Why do you not show him the path of righteousness?

'Rama and I are overtaken by grief because Sugreeva forgets his promise to us. We had decided to wait for the rains to pass; it is time for Sugreeva to leave his irresponsible ways of conduct and fulfil his vow to us.

'If an obligation is not repaid in time, dharma is destroyed. A broken friendship with sincere friends, leads to loss of artha.

'What is your advice, Tara, in this matter? How do we achieve our goal?'

Tara asked Lakshmana to forgive Sugreeva because he was a sincere friend, and a well-wisher. She said,

'How can a person of a noble character be angry with another less qualified? O prince, how can anyone who is a repository of the sattva guna, such as you are, defy the rules of proper conduct and be so angry? I am aware of Sugreeva's fault. While you kept your word, he has overlooked his commitment.

'Please forgive Sugreeva and treat him as your younger brother. Even maharshis can go astray when overpowered by kama.

'By the way,' said Tara, rolling her intoxicating eyes, 'Sugreeva has already commanded all his vanara forces to assemble here, to be assigned their duties in Sita's pursuit.'

Tara led Lakshmana to Sugreeva's chambers where he was sitting with Ruma in a close embrace. Young women decked in finery surrounded him. Looking at him thus, Lakshmana once again flew into a terrible rage.

Sugreeva, trembling out of fear came down from his throne and apologized to Lakshmana for his forgetfulness. However, Lakshmana rebuked him soundly, and said,

'You have belied your promise to Shri Rama. If you fail to grasp what he has done for you, you will end up meeting the same fate as your brother.'

Tara, lovely as the moon, interrupted at this point. She said,

'Kumara Lakshmana, Sugreeva is after all the vanara king. You ought not to address him in such harsh terms. He does not deserve such bitter rebuke from a friend like you. He is not a cheat, nor is he cruel, ungrateful, devious or untruthful. Undoubtedly, what Shri Rama has done for him, is unprecedented and very difficult. With his blessings, Sugreeva has regained his kingdom, his wife Ruma and me. As Vishwamitra was lost in his infatuation for Menaka, my husband too forgot his duty towards Rama while with us.

'Kumara, the body needs food, sleep and sex. Sugreeva had been deprived of these comforts for very long and thus, once he got them, he lost his sense of time.

'On his behalf, I apologize to you. My son Angada will fulfil all his obligations. Believe me, Sugreeva can give up his kingdom, his treasury, Angada, Ruma and even me for your sake.

'Ravana cannot be defeated without the help of vanaras who obey the orders of Sugreeva. They have been summoned to assemble here for further orders.'

Listening to Tara humbly making her point according to the rules of propriety, Lakshmana was pacified. Trying to please the fiercely powerful Lakshmana, Sugreeva said,

'I regained my glory, my kingdom due to the kind efforts of Shri Rama. Who can repay even a fraction of such an obligation? Dharmatma Rama will destroy Ravana without any assistance.

'Lakshmana, when your brother pulls at his bow, its echo makes the earth and her mountains quiver. I shall follow Shri Rama when he advances at the head of the armies to kill Ravana.

'Kindly forgive me if I have committed a crime out of love, affection or trust.'

Listening to such words, and knowing that measures had already been initiated to gather the vanara army, Lakshmana was pacified. Speaking warmly, he said,

'Vanararaja, my brother has gained strength by associating with a humble person like you.

'Please come with me. Your friend is grieving because his wife has been abducted. Come and assuage his sorrow.'

Before his departure to meet Rama, Sugreeva directed Hanuman to summon millions of vanaras owing allegiance to him from every nook and corner of the country. He said,

'I command that all the fierce vanara warriors who can change their form at will and who, with their giant torsos, can hide the sky like the clouds or the mountains, assemble here without loss of time.'

Sugreeva travelled to meet Shri Rama in a royal palanquin made of gold and carried by several vanaras. Alighting, he stood before Shri Rama with folded hands. Looking at the vanara army, standing in massive strength, Rama was delighted. Lifting Sugreeva's head up from his feet in both hands, Rama lovingly and respectfully enclosed him in his arms and addressed him thus:

'O brave one, O king of the vanaras, that king alone is superior among others who wisely uses his time for dharma, artha and kama.

'It is time that we made an effort to trace Sita. Please consult your ministers and generals.'

Sugreeva replied,

'Great warrior, I had lost my glory, wealth and my kingdom and owe it to your kindness that I have regained them. If I do not repay your debt, it will be a blot on my dharma. I have assembled the vanara chiefs from all over the earth. They can change their form at will, are chivalrous like Indra. Some of them reside on the Meru and the Vindhyachala mountains. All of them are on their way and will arrive soon.

'I shall certainly provide you with hordes of the mighty vanaras who can kill Ravana in a fight and restore the Mithilesh Kumari Sita to you.'

Once again, Rama embraced Sugreeva. He observed,

'Friend, it does not surprise me when Indra rains; the sun, glorious with his millions of rays, overtakes the dark night; or when the peaceful moon illuminates the night with his effulgence. It is in their nature to do so. Likewise, Sugreeva, the terror of enemies, it is not unusual for a man like you to make your friends happy by obliging them. I know that you are truthful. It is in your nature to serve your friends.

'Empowered by you, I shall vanquish all my enemies in battle. You are my well-wisher and you can help me. It shall be soon that I kill Ravana with my piercing arrows.'

The Arrival of Vanara Forces

While Rama and Sugreeva were busy conversing, a storm blew and covered the sky with dust, hiding in its wake even the fierce sun. Numerous vanara warriors with bodies large as the Himalayas, and fierce jaws covered the land. They roared like thundering clouds. Tara's valiant father, handsome like a golden peak, and the glorious father of Ruma led their forces. The wise Kesari, Hanuman's father, shone like the morning sun. Thousands of soldiers accompanied him.

The brave Gavaksha who looked frightening, led the langurs. Neel was large in body and blue of complexion and was surrounded by ten crore monkeys. Jambavan led the bears. Among the other generals one noticed Panasa, Dhoomra, Gavaya, Darimukh, Maind and Dwivid, Gaja, and Gandhamadana. The Yuvaraja Angada came accompanied by millions of soldiers.

Sugreeva introduced his generals to Shri Ramachandra. He said that all of them had proved their mettle in wars and were known for their chivalry and patience. They could fight on the land and on the sea. He asked Shri Ramachandra to take command and direct his forces as he liked.

Rama responded by saying that their first priority was to find where Sita was being held captive and if she was alive or dead. They had to find the whereabouts of the kingdom of Ravana. He said,

'Once we get news of Sita and the place where Ravana rules, I shall issue appropriate orders in consultation with you. Next to Lakshmana, you are my dearest. You are brave and wise. You are aware of your duty and are our well-wisher. I trust you as you understand our objective and provide assistance for the same.'

The Search Parties Leave for Different Territories

Sugreeva ordered four teams to go searching in four directions. He gave them detailed instructions about the geography and topography of the places they were to travel to in search of Sita. He asked them all to return within thirty days.

Sugreeva asked one of the commanders, Vinata to lead his group towards east. He said,

'Look for Sita in the mountains, inaccessible forests and the banks of streams. Look for her on the Bhagirathi Ganga, the delightful Saryu, Kaushiki, Kalinda-nandini Yamuna, Saraswati, Sindhu and Shonabhadra with clear waters. Look for her in the provinces of Brahma-mala, Videha, Malwa, Kashi, Kaushala, Pundra desha and

Anga. Go to the sites where the silk worms are reared, search in the silver mines, climb the mountains to reach for the islands beyond. Do not ignore looking for Sita in the dense forests.

'Look for Sita in the caves of Udayachal mountain and in the forest nearby. The horizon turns orange when the sun rises. Brahma created this place in the beginning and it is the gateway to the earth and to Brahmaloka. That is why we know it as Poorva Disha.'

Having dispatched a search party to the east, Sugreeva with his knowledge of the specifics, ordered a contingent of valorous and skilful warriors to look for Sita in the south. This team comprised among others, Hanuman, Neel, son of Agni, Brahma's chivalrous son Jambavan, Gandhamadana, Angada and their soldiers. He warned them of several inaccessible places situated on their path. He said,

'You will thoroughly search the Vindhya mountain that is rich in diverse trees and creepers. It has thousands of peaks. You will cross Narmada replete with reptiles, Godavari, that delights the senses, Mahanadi, Krishnaveni and Varda rivers. Look for Sita in the cities of Utkal, Mekhala, Dasharna, and Avantipuri.

'Visit Vidarbha, Rishika, Mahashika, Kalinga and Kaushik regions in search of Sita. Look carefully in hills, around rivers, in the caves and in the forests. Visit Godavari several times. Do not neglect Andhra, Pundra, Chola, Pandya and the territory of Kerala.

'Climb the Malaya Mountain where the peaks glow with minerals. The hills are rich in flowering gardens and the tops of each slope are adorned with sandalwood trees. Look carefully for Sita's whereabouts. The apsaras frolic on the banks of the celestial Kaveri wherein the waters run clean and pure.

'The supreme Muni Agastya, effulgent like the sun, sits at the top of the Malaya Mountain. With his permission, you can cross the Mahanadi river that abounds in crocodiles.

'Advancing further, you will reach the divine, gem-studded, massive golden gates of the Pandya capital. Reaching the shore, you should decide, after careful thought, your next move. Maharshi Agastya has planted a lovely golden mountain in mid-ocean and named it Mahendragiri.

'Beyond the ocean, there is an island, a hundred yojana wide. Human beings have no access to this island. Go round this island vigilantly looking for Sita.

'That country belongs to the evil Ravana, king of the rakshasas who is glorious like Indra. He is the one we have to kill. Look for Sita in all places. In case you are sure that she is not there, go beyond Lanka to look for her.'

Sugreeva assured ample reward to anyone who returned within a month with information about Sita: 'All of you are incredibly brave and strong. Make an effort that results in finding the whereabouts of princess Sita.'

Sugreeva now summoned Sushena, Tara's father and bowed to him in respect. Sushena was dark like a cloud and a great warrior. Also present was Archishman, a renowned vanara chief who looked splendid like Indra and was surrounded by a horde of vanara soldiers.

This group was directed to go to the west, to Saurashtra, Bahleeka and Chandrachitra regions. Sugreeva asked them to look for Sita in the lands full of punnag, bakul and udyalaka trees and in kewra groves. He asked them to walk along the rivers full of cool water and flowing westwards. He said,

'Most of this land is desert. The rocks are high and cold. The places surrounded by hillocks are inaccessible. Looking for Sita, travel up to the western ocean. The waters abound in large fish and crocodiles, so be on your guard. Conduct a thorough search in kewra orchards, tamala forests and coconut groves. Find out if Ravana maintains a palace there. Scour the Maurvi region, the Angalepapuri town and the Alakshit forest. At the mouth of Sindhu lies Somgiri mountain with one hundred peaks, with dense forests. The vanaras should change their form and look for Sita on mountaintops and in the caves.

'After some distance, you will arrive at the Meru, the king of mountains that had been blessed by Surya in ancient times.

'Vishwakarma built a grand palace atop Meru's peak which provides all sorts of luxuries. Look for Sita there as well. Beyond this, vanaras cannot proceed. I am unaware of what lies yonder in the darkness of the night. You should come back within a month and report.'

Sugreeva now summoned a vanara chief, Hitaishi Shatabali. Addressing him, he said,

'Proceed with a hundred thousand vanaras descended from Yamaraja, and your ministers, towards the north that is adorned by the Himalayas as an ornament. Look for Sita, the wife of the illustrious Shri Rama everywhere.

'Visit Malechha, Shoorasena, Bharata, Kamboja, Kuru, Yavana and Shaka territories. In the Himalayas look in the lodhra and padmak bushes, in the deodar forests for Vaidehi.

'Travelling through the Sudarshana Mountain, carefully searching through forests, near waterfalls and in the recesses of deep caves, you will arrive at the Mount Kailas, gloriously white. Vishwakarma had built a palace for Kubera that looks like a white cloud. It is plated with Jambunad gold. In a sarovar nearby, lotuses bloom in abundance. While the apsaras frolic in its waters, several varieties of water birds, such as flamingos, float on its surface.

'You must look for Sita and Ravana on the Kailas peaks that shines like the moon. Search in the caves thoroughly.

'Soon thereafter you will reach the Kroncha Mountain where there are valleys carved by the Lord Skanda. Several divine rishis, worshipped even by gods, reside there.

'Travelling beyond the Kroncha Mountain, crossing several streams, mountains and valleys, looking for Sita everywhere, you will notice the Somgiri mountain, the abode of Vishnu, Shankara and Brahma. You cannot go beyond this. Even devatas cannot do that. There is neither sunlight thereafter nor the boundaries of any country. I have no knowledge of what exists beyond.

'Come back within a month with some good news so that we can repay Shri Ramachandra. I shall reward you handsomely.'

8

Shri Rama Gives Hanuman a Ring for Identification

From the team going to the south, Sugreeva specially sent for Hanuman because he firmly believed that being the best among the vanaras, he could accomplish this task. Addressing him the king said,

'Kapishrestha, I have never known your movement to be obstructed on the earth, in the skies, on the horizon, in the devaloka or over the oceans. You are familiar with the territories inhabited by humans, devatas, asuras, gandharvas, reptiles, mountains and seas. You have inherited the qualities of unobstructed movement and speed from your warrior father, Pavana. There is none as glorious as you on the face of this earth. Hence, you must devise a plan to trace the whereabouts of Sita.

'Hanuman, you are a master of the art of diplomacy. In you alone, I see valour, wisdom, chivalry, timely conduct and an understanding of the right choice of time and place. '

Listening to Sugreeva addressing Hanuman, Rama learnt how much the success of their mission depended upon the latter. He could see that Hanuman too thought that he could certainly deliver success. Delighted at the thought, Rama placed in Hanuman's hand a ring engraved with his name that would help him in identifying himself in Sita's presence. He said,

'Kapishrestha, this token of identification would convince Sita that you have met me. She can then fearlessly talk to you. '

Hanuman received it, bowed at Rama's feet and left with his group. Among his hordes, Hanuman looked resplendent as the moon surrounded by the constellations in a clear sky. Bidding him farewell, Rama said,

'O brave Kapishrestha, I depend on your valour. Try your best to retrieve Sita with all your might.'

No Trace of Sita

Counting thirty days from the date of departure, three groups of vanaras returned from the east, the north and the west without success.

The southern team led by Angada and Hanuman arrived at Vindhyachala mountain and looked into caves, valleys, forests, around rivers, ponds, bushes, and around hilltops, but without finding a trace of Sita. Disappointed, disheartened, the group sat near a tree where the wise Angada addressed them to lift their morale. He said,

'We have thoroughly searched in forests, near streams, in inaccessible places, on the mountains and in the caves. However, we have been unsuccessful in finding a trace of either Janaki or of the devilish rakshasa who abducted her. We have used up most of the allotted thirty days. The king, Sugreeva is strict in compliance of his orders.

'Bypassing sloth, sleep and regrets, we shall continue our effort. The one who makes an effort reaps the fruit of success. Therefore, we must not give up making an effort because we are dejected.'

Swayamprabha, the Aged Hermit Leads the Vanaras to the Ocean

Tar, Angada and Hanuman leading, the vanaras continued with their search in the caves and dense forests of the Vindhyachala mountain. As they arrived at the Nairityakon peak, the time limit of thirty days prescribed by Sugreeva was exhausted.

They noticed a cave where the door was open. It was known as Rikshabil and was guarded by a rakshasa. The vanaras were thirsty. Noticing several kroncha, hansa, sarus and wet chakravaka birds coming out, they concluded that water was available in the cave. Hanuman pointed to the birds and the green trees near the cave entrance. 'There ought to be a well or some other source of water nearby,' he said.

Almost losing consciousness because of thirst, holding each other's hands, the vanaras entered the cave and were stunned to find a forest without darkness with golden trees emitting the glow of fire. Sal, tamala, tala, nagakeshara, asoka, champa and kanera trees were blooming. Unusual golden bunches of flowers and red, fresh, and tender foliage crowned the trees. Pavilions of lapis lazuli had been erected under them.

It was an unusual sight. Birds were perched on lotus leaves and glistened like gems. The vanaras saw several ponds where massive golden fish floated. The architects had extensively used gold and silver in several mansions. The windows had curtains of pearl strings. The lattices were made of gold. A number of houses, however, had been constructed with earthly construction materials. Large beds and seats studded with gems and gold were lying around. Gold, silver and bronze utensils were stacked all over and so were incense and sandalwood sticks. The vanaras noticed an abundant supply of fruit and victuals besides expensive clothes, snug blankets, deerskins and costly carpets.

Looking around the cave, Hanuman saw a woman dressed in bark and black buckskin. She was meditating and seemed healthy. Giant like a mountain, Hanuman bowed to the aged tapasvini and asked her, 'Devi, who are you? Who owns this cave, these jewels and these mansions?

'Devi, we have been suffering from hunger and thirst for long. Suddenly we entered this dark cave to see such marvels. We fear this place belongs to the asuras who can create illusions. We are unable to fathom who the glorious person is to have assembled such divine goods, golden chariots, places made of silver, windows made of gold, and fragrant trees loaded with fruit and flowers inside a cave.

'How do gold lotuses sprout in these clear waters? Why do even the fish and tortoises appear to be golden? Is it due to your tapasya or someone else's? We are ignorant in such matters; kindly enlighten us.'

The devout tapasvini replied,

'O mighty vanara, you might have heard of the illustrious Maya, an expert in creating illusion. He created this golden forest with his powers and expertise. He was the architect of the asuras. He prayed to Brahma for a thousand years, performed austere tapasya, and was rewarded with Shukracharya's knowledge and skill in architecture. He later fell in love with Hema, an apsara. Enraged at this, Indra hit Maya with a thunderbolt, and made him flee. Brahma gifted this forest with its wealth for eternal enjoyment to Hema.

'My name is Swayamprabha and I am Merusavarni's daughter. I am the caretaker of Hema's palaces. She, now a close friend of mine, is proficient in dance and music.

'Why are you here? What brings you to this inaccessible place? How did you find it?

'In any case, have your fill of pure food, of fruit and vegetables. Thereafter, narrate me your tale.'

Hanuman briefly narrated how Rama, the son of Dashratha, had arrived in Dandakaranya and how Ravana had forcibly abducted his wife Sita. He told Swayamprabha of Rama's friendship with Sugreeva and how Angada and other warriors had been sent to find the whereabouts of Sita in the south, a direction overseen by Agastya Muni and protected by Yamaraja. He said,

'We have scoured all the forests. We intend now proceeding to look for her in the oceans. We were tired and hungry when, resting near a tree we noticed this massive, dark cave covered by creepers and large trees. We walked in to look for some food and water. Now we are under your protection. Following the atithi dharma, you have offered us food and fruit, which we have enjoyed to our satisfaction. Kindly tell us how do we repay your obligation?'

'I am happy with you, O vanaras who can outdo others in speed,' said the omniscient Swayamprabha. 'Busy in the practice of religious austerities, I expect nothing from anyone.'

Looking at the gentle, harmless and pious tapasvini, Hanuman said,

'We seek your protection because you follow dharma. Kindly show us the path ahead.'

Swayamprabha guided them out of the cave in no time. Assuring them, she said,

'Here is the imposing Vindhyagiri. Just across you can see the Prashravanagiri in front of which rolls the ocean. It is for you to go ahead and for me to return to my home.'

The vanaras looked at the mighty, limitless ocean where Varuna resides. Its frightening waves roared continuously. However, they had a cause for worry because the allotted thirty days were over. Vasanta was approaching and the branches of the mango and other trees were bent with sprouts and flowers.

Addressing his followers, the wise Angada whose shoulders were muscular and whose arms were long and thick, respectfully submitted, in sweet tones, to the vanara leaders and their followers:

'Our allotted thirty days were over while we were wandering in the cave. We have to consider our next step. We are occupied in pursuits beneficial to our king, but till now have failed to meet our objective. Hence, we shall surely lose our lives if we go back after the stipulated time being over and without success. To me, the best course appears to be to fast unto death.

'By temperament, Sugreeva is harsh and also the ruler. He will never grant us pardon. I am sure this shall be the end of me. As it is, he never crowned me as the Yuvaraja. Rama did it.'

Tar, another vanara chief suggested that they enter Swayamprabha's cave again and spend the rest of their life in comfort.

Hanuman's Efforts to Bring around a Reluctant and Disheartened Angada

Hanuman found the fear of others rooted in imaginary thoughts rather than facts. He thought that a rebelling Angada would oust Sugreeva and become the king. He was aware that Angada, Vali's son, was a storehouse of the eight types of wisdom, of the four virtues of sama, dama, danda and bheda and the fourteen qualities of a superior leader. Angada had always been chivalrous, powerful and brilliant.

Keeping in mind the interest of his master Sugreeva, Hanuman decided to drive a wedge between Angada and the other vanaras. Using sama, dama and bheda, he successfully isolated Angada from the other vanaras. Hanuman decided to use the fear of danda to bring Angada round. Addressing him, Hanuman said,

'Taranandana, undoubtedly you are as powerful as Vali, your father. You have the capacity to take care of the kingdom as firmly as he could. However, these vanaras are fickle. Away from their wives and children, they might not carry out your wishes. You can never win us over with danda.

'A powerful person can afford to keep quiet while opposing a weak enemy. However, the latter can never live happily while nursing an enmity with the former. Those who contend that this cave will hide and protect them like a mother, are living under delusion. Lakshmana's arrows will easily tear it apart like a bowl made of leaves.

'O brave Angada, the vanaras will desert you the moment you start residing in this cave. I am aware of their decision. They will never forget their children. Living hungry, sleeping in discomfort, and facing inconvenience, they will regret their decision to side with you and hence, would soon desert you. Deprived of the support of your well-wishers, you will be as powerless as a straw.

'However, when you humbly accompany us after our success, Sugreeva will certainly name you to succeed him as a king when the time comes. Your uncle is a follower of dharma. He cares for your happiness and has no son except you. Therefore, we ought to go back to him.'

However, Angada disagreed with Hanuman. Responding to the latter's humble, dutiful and loyalist arguments, he said,

'Your argument that Sugreeva is stable, pure at heart and in mind, is not cruel, is simple, brave and patient, does not appear correct to me. How can it be said about a man who has with evil intentions married his elder brother's queen, who was like a mother to him, in his brother's lifetime? The man who forgot his promise to Shri Rama even after Raghava's fulfilling his side of the bargain, cannot be seen as responsible.

'I was born to be his enemy. How will Sugreeva let me live? He would want to make his son, whether worthy or not, the successor.

'It is better that I fast unto death rather than spend time in bondage. O vanaras, permit me to stay here while all of you go home. Please convey my regards to the king Sugreeva, to the powerful Raghava brothers and give solace to my mother Tara.'

Saying thus, Angada spread a kusha asana and weeping copiously, sat down in a fast unto death. Other vanaras also wept in sympathy and decided to sit with him on a fast.

Arrival of Sampati, Jatayu's Brother

Suddenly they heard a frightening sound from the skies. The innards of the caves echoed like thundering dark clouds.

Soon after, Jatayu's brother Sampati, known for his chivalry and enterprise, appeared on a cliff in front of the fasting vanaras. Coming out of a Vindhya cavern, delighted to look at the vanara warriors, he said,

'Just like the fruit of good deeds done in an earlier life, I have been presented with a feast without much effort. I have been hungry for a long time and shall make a meal of whosoever dies fasting.'

The vanaras were taken aback by this sudden misfortune. Angada lamented how the circumstances had conspired against them. Narrating the course of events since Rama's exile, he tried to persuade Hanuman as well to give up his life, fasting.

As Angada described how Ravana had abducted Sita and how Jatayu had given his life trying to save her, Sampati perked up hearing his brother's name being mentioned respectfully. The king of vultures, with a sharp beak, loudly asked,

'Who is talking of the death of my brother Jatayu, who was to me dearer than my life? What sort of battle did he wage against the rakshasa in the Janasthana? He was younger to me. He earned praise for his virtues and chivalry. O warriors, take me down from the inaccessible cliff. I desire to climb down but I cannot; the sunrays have burnt my wings. I am eager to learn how my chivalrous brother met with his end. How did he befriend the king Dashratha, Shri Rama's father, while Jatayu was at Janasthana and the latter at Ayodhya?

9

Sampati Provides a Lead to Sita's Whereabouts

The vanaras led by Angada were suspicious of Sampati's motives. However, preferring to meet their end at his hands rather than submitting before Sugreeva for a sure death, they brought him down from the cliff. Angada narrated to him the entire history of the Raghuvansha, of Rama's exile, of Sita's abduction and of the fight between Jatayu and Ravana. He informed Sampati of their decision to fast unto death rather than face Sugreeva's wrath.

Hearing their pathetic tale, Sampati shed tears of sympathy. He said,

'I am old and my wings are burnt. I do not have the strength to avenge my brother's death. Once, while returning from Swargaloka after scoring a victory over Indra, I tried to save Jatayu from the harsh rays of the sun. In doing so, the fierce heat of the sun destroyed my wings. I fell down on this mountain and have been here ever since. That is why I never learnt of my brother's death.'

Angada said,

'If you are Jatayu's brother and if you know where the rakshasa resides, please let us know.'

Sampati replied,

'Although I cannot help Shri Rama in person, I shall certainly help him with my information. I know the Varuna loka, about the places where Vishnu planted his three steps as Vamana and have also been a witness to Amrita manthan and the Deva-Asura sangram.

One day, I saw evil Ravana flying with an abducted, charming woman adorned in heavy ornaments. The respected woman was crying, 'Ha Rama, Ha Lakshmana,' and was throwing her ornaments to the ground. I believe that she was Sita because she repeatedly called Rama's name.

'Ravana, the rakshasa is the son of the Rishi Vishrava and a brother to Kubera. He resides in Lanka, a fascinating city created by Vishwakarma, in an island in the ocean 400 kos away from here. The palaces in Lanka and their picturesque gates are made of gold. In that city, Vaidehi, dressed in yellow silks, spends her time in grief. She is under arrest in Ravana's inner apartments. Several rakshasis stand guard over her. In case you reach there, you can see her.

'By helping you I shall avenge my brother's killing by Ravana. Presently, your task is to work out how you can cross the sea. I would like to go to the seashore with your help so that I can offer holy water to my late brother, Jatayu.

The vanaras acted accordingly.

Sampati narrated his life's events in full to the assembled vanaras. While concluding his story, he found that his two wings were restored. The new wings were of red colour and their reappearance made Sampati happy beyond measure. He said,

'With the blessings of Rajarshi Nishakar, I have again grown my wings once burnt by the fierce heat of the sun. Regaining my wings bodes well for your success in finding Sita.'

Assuring the vanaras in these words, Sampati, in order to test his prowess in flying, flew away from the hilltop.

It uplifted the morale of the vanaras. Keen to find Sita, they, brave as the god Pavana, moved south following the Abhijit nakshatra.

10

Hanuman Agrees to Fly to Lanka

Now that they had a lead on Sita's whereabouts, the vanaras were somewhat joyous. They walked to the shore full of hope and expectation. The vast ocean lay in front; the vanaras camped on the northern shore of the southern ocean.

At places, the ocean looked asleep because of the absence of tides and its roar. At other places, it appeared to be frolicking with mild waves rolling on its surface. However, there were places where the mighty tides arose as high as the mountains. The vanara warriors were in a fix looking at the exciting and mighty ocean. 'What ought to be our line of action?' they thought over.

It was Angada's turn to assure his forces. Addressing the frightened vanaras, he said,

'Warriors, do not surrender to dejection or doubt. Despondency is a flawed condition. He who doubts himself when an opportunity arrives to show his valour, loses his glory and fervour. Success evades such people.

'Which great warrior among you can jump the length of this ocean and help Sugreeva to fulfil his promise, and whose efforts will make us successful in our mission and allow us to return happily to our women and children?

'If anyone among you considers himself capable of performing this task, he may please volunteer and gift us the freedom from fear.'

Hearing Angada, the entire horde of the vanaras stood lifeless like wood. There was none who came forward.

Angada Restrained from Going to Lanka

Breaking this wall of silence, Angada said in all humility, 'I can jump the one hundred yojana span of this ocean. However, I am not certain that I can return.'

Responding, Jambavan, ever skilful in his use of words, said,

'O mighty Yuvaraja, we are well acquainted with your ability to traverse long distances with speed. You might cover in one go a hundred thousand yojanas. You have the capability to return as well. Yet, you being our master, we cannot permit you to go. My son, the master who commands others, cannot be ordered about. You can send anyone amongst those who are at your service.

'You are the root and core of our mission; and the wise opine that such a root must be protected. We can succeed in our mission if you support us.'

Angada replied, 'If I do not go and none else is ready to try, then we have no option but to fast unto death.'

Hearing this comment, the jewel in the crown of the vanaras, Jambavan wisely remarked,

'O warrior, we shall not allow any diminishing of your mission. I propose to inspire a valiant person who would satisfactorily accomplish the task.'

Hanuman's Birth and Prowess Described

Hanuman was sitting by himself in a corner when, keeping in mind the despondency of their forces, Jambavan addressed him. He said,

'Hanuman, learned in shastras and one of the bravest among us, why do you sit alone and silent? You are as brave as our king is, and in strength, you compare with Rama and Lakshmana. You are renowned in power and speed like Garuda. Your strength, glory, and forbearance are superior to any living being. Why then, do you not offer yourself to cross the ocean?'

Hanuman did not answer, at which Jambavan continued thus:

'Let me tell you about your glorious birth and unusual virtues. Punjikasthala was an apsara who was foremost among her tribe. Under a curse, she was born to Kunjara as a vanara. She could change her form at will and her charm was incomparable on this earth. She was named Anjana. Growing up, she married vanara raja, Kesari.

'Once upon a time, Anjana, in human form, glowing with charm and youth, was wandering upon a mountain peak that was dark like a rain cloud. Pavana, the god of winds, blew her sari away. He looked at her plump thighs, at her raised breasts set close to each other and her lovely face.

'Pavana, who had forcibly disrobed her, fell in love with her as he looked at her charms. He was excited in mind and body and wanted to make love to her. He enclosed her passionately in his arms.'

'However, Anjana was a devout woman, loyal to her husband. Agitated, she said,

'Who are you? How do you dare to violate my chastity?'

Pavana replied, 'O beauty with broad hips, I do not intend violating your vow to be married to one man alone. Please shed your fears, if any. However, O praiseworthy woman, I have, embracing you in my thoughts, made love to you. Consequently, a wise child, unusually brave will be born to you. That great, effulgent child will have the powers of leaping, crossing and flying like me.'

'O great vanara, hearing this, your mother was delighted. Later she gave birth to you in a cave. Once, as a child, seeing the rising sun and taking it to be some fruit, you jumped into the sky to eat it. You did not experience fear or anxiety even after flying 300 yojanas, although the sun's heat blasted you.

'As you neared the sun, an angry Indra hit you with a luminous thunderbolt breaking a piece of your chin. Since then you have been known as Hanuman.

'Looking at you being hit, Pavana who carries the scents of the world around, angrily gave up flowing in the three worlds. All beings were devoid of air and felt suffocated. Upon propitiation by various gods, Pavana mellowed.

'Brahma, pleased that order was restored in the world, blessed you with a boon that no weapon can kill you on the battlefield. Even Indra, finding you unaffected by his strike, blessed you saying that you would exercise control over your death and that you would die only when you wished and not otherwise.

'Thus, Hanuman, you are Kesari's legitimate son. Your valour makes your enemies shudder. You are also the auras son of Pavana and, therefore, you are effulgent like him. Being his son, you can jump over any distance like Maruta.

'We are weak. You alone are superior to us in wisdom and physical prowess. I had such powers in youth, but no longer can I exercise them under the effect of age.

'The entire vanara army desires to see your valour. Stand up and cross this ocean at one go. Step forward like Vishnu measuring the universe.'

Listening to Jambavan, and inspired by his words, Hanuman realized his prowess. To the delight of the assembled vanaras, he showed them his virata form.

Hailing victory for Hanuman, the vanaras roared and were filled with hope. Listening to their encomiums, Hanuman started expanding his body. Simultaneously, he thought of his strength while joyously moving his tail in a circle. His brilliant face glowed like a fire in a jungle. Bowing to the elders he said,

'The god of winds, traversing the skies is all powerful. He wields limitless power. He is a friend of Agni and he can shatter mountains with his blasts. I am the son of that mahatma and like him, I am capable of jumping over large distances at one go. With the force of my arms, I can part the waters of the ocean.'

'I can make a trip round the earth and return without setting a foot on her. I can fly in the skies beyond the stars and the planets. Certainly, I shall with great speed cross the ocean in one leap and land at the other end.

'I am quite certain that I shall succeed in tracing Vaidehi. I believe that I can pull out the entire Lanka landmass from the sea and carry it on my palm.'

When Hanuman of the inexhaustible glory, was roaring of his prowess, all the other vanaras looked at him in amazement. His words had the power to extinguish the grief of his companions. Hearing him, Jambavan, the commander-in-chief of the vanaras, remarked,

'O brave son of Kesari, O son of Pavana with an immeasurable speed, you have vanquished the sorrow of your companions. We wish you well and we shall now pray for your success.'

Addressing the vanaras, Hanuman said,

'When I jump from here, none in the world can withstand my force and speed. I shall plant my foot firmly on Mahendra Mountain that alone can provide me support.'

Taking measure of his steps, Hanuman strolled on the Mahendra mountain peaks. Such was his weight that the mountain cried like an elephant in the grip of a lion. Its rocks scattered and new waterfalls started flowing.

Concentrating on his mission, Hanuman thought of Lanka as he planned his long leap across the ocean.

SUNDARAKANDAM

1

Hanuman Crosses the Ocean and Arrives at the Island of Lanka

Hanuman had made up his mind to reach Lanka where the abducted Sita might be living. His task was difficult and no outside help was available. Standing tall, his neck and head held high, looking like a well-fed bull, the valorous and patient Hanuman, joyously strolled on the sea-green grass glistening like sapphire. He looked magnificent like a fearsome and powerful lion which had crushed herds of deer under his feet.

The flat land on the hilltop looked colourful because of blue, red, lotus-white and grey mineral rocks. Hanuman bowed with folded hands to the sun, Indra, Pavana Brahma and other devatas, and sought their blessings to cross the ocean. Facing east, he bowed to his father Pavana, in particular, and then expanded his body to go south. The vanara elders and army looked at him in adoration.

Hanuman Prepares to Leap

As Hanuman pressed on the mountain with his powerful feet and expanded arms, the latter shivered as if in tremor. Cataracts burst from the hilltop like musth oozing from the forehead of an elephant in heat. Mahendragiri erupted with fire and smoke under Hanuman's pressure and spat rocks of pumice.

Looking brilliant like Agni, Hanuman moved his body, shook his limbs and the hair on his body and roared like a massive cloud. He got ready to leap upwards. Like Garuda throwing a serpent skywards, he threw his twisted and hairy tail into the sky. He supported his large arms on the mountain, pulled his limbs into his belly and brought his feet together. He tensed his arms and neck, looked upwards at the sky, breathed deep and held his breath.

Addressing the vanaras, Hanuman said,

'I shall fly to Ravana's Lanka with the speed of Rama's arrow. If I do not find Sita even there, I shall bring Ravana as a prisoner. However, I am sure of returning blessed with Sita or after destroying the city of Lanka.'

Hanuman Jumps Skywards

Ignoring any possible impediments, Hanuman, the ace among the vanaras, jumped upwards with great speed. The draught plucked several trees in its wake. Sucked upwards by the forceful movements of his thighs, the trees followed him some distance, as if to bid farewell.

Hanuman, fresh shoots and flowers sticking to his body, looked resplendent like a mountain illuminated by fire-flies. The surface of the sea, carpeted by colourful flowers, resembled the firmament full of stars. Hanuman appeared to be gulping the vast ocean and his massive tides. It looked as if he might swallow the sky itself.

Hanuman looked resplendent like the sun traversing the ocean in this manner. With his tail, Hanuman looked like a meteor traversing the sky.

While he flew over the water, Hanuman cast a shadow partially submerged in the ocean. Impelled by his movement, the ocean waves rose high. The powerful winds generated by Hanuman's movement, along with the clouds in the sky, created turbulence in the roaring waters. Vanarakesari Hanuman's shadow was ten yojana broad and thirty yojana long and for this reason, looked all the more fascinating. Massive white, orange, blue and red clouds following in his wake looked splendid. Disappearing into and appearing out of the clouds, he played hide and seek with them like the moon.

The Ocean Orders Mainaka Mountain to Rise

The sun did not harass Hanuman because he was going to accomplish a job for Shri Rama. Pavana helped him all along. Even the ocean, remembering his obligation to the king Sagara of the Ikshavaku dynasty, made sure that Hanuman was not inconvenienced. He requested the submerged golden Mainaka Mountain to rise and provide a place for Hanuman to take rest. The golden mountain had been stationed there by Indra to block the exit of the asuras from the Patalaloka.

The golden Mainaka, with his wealth of trees and creepers, came out of the saline waters like the sun rising from behind a curtain of clouds. In a short time, he displayed to Hanuman his peaks. Illuminated by a glorious, rising sun, his high, golden peaks appeared to draw a straight line in the sky. His golden peaks turned even the steel-grey sky into gold. To begin with, Hanuman thought it to be an obstruction that had suddenly surfaced out of the salty ocean. Hitting the highest peak with his chest, he pushed the mountain downwards. Mainaka was delighted at this physical contact with the great warrior and roared with joy. Assuming a human form, standing on his own peak, he said,

'You are occupied with a most arduous mission. Kindly take rest for a while on my peaks. The ancestors of Shri Raghunath had, in ancient times, augmented the waters of the ocean. Now you are acting for his benefit. Hence, the ocean desires to help you going by the tenet of Sanatana Dharma, that a good turn deserves another. The ocean desired me to welcome you and offer you a place to rest for some time.

'Kapishrestha, I offer you delicious fruit and roots for a meal. Enjoy my hospitality, relax a bit and then go ahead with your mission. O son of Pavana, I consider you the best of vanaras who can jump a long distance.

'For a wise man rooted in dharma, even an ordinary guest is an object of worship. How can I welcome a guest of unusual valour like you? You are the son of mahatma Pavana, the crown of the devatas. In energy, power and speed you are like him. If I worship you, I shall be offering worship to Maruta himself.

'However, there is another reason.

'Brother, in the Satyayuga the mountains had wings and they could speedily fly like Garuda in any direction. Their unrestrained flights frightened the devatas, the rishis and the human beings, lest they fall to the ground and cause havoc. An angry Indra sliced the wings of lakhs of mountains with his thunderbolt. As the angry Devaraja advanced at me, your father Pavana, pushed me into the saline ocean and thus saved me.

'O son of Vayu, O Kapishrestha, therefore, I have immense regard for you. I shall always hold you in high esteem. Our relationship is founded on virtues. It is after ages that I have an opportunity to return your father's favour. Therefore, oblige me as well as the ocean by accepting our hospitality. Assuage your fatigue and let me worship you and treat you affectionately.'

Hanuman Responds to Mainaka's Offer of Hospitality

Hanuman replied, 'I too am delighted to meet you, Mainaka. In listening to your pleasant words, I have enjoyed your hospitality. Do not for a moment imagine that I have not accepted your courtesy. Do not worry or grieve on this account.

'My mission compels me to hurry. I have promised the vanaras that I shall not break my journey anywhere.'

A Panoramic View of the Southern Coast

As an assurance, Hanuman touched Mainaka with his hand and continued with his flight. With his virtues of patience, resourcefulness, wisdom and capability, he wanted to make sure he succeeded.

Flying over a hundred yojanas, almost at the end of the water line, Hanuman noticed a green forest with trees lined in a row. He saw the Lanka Island surrounded by a variety of lovely trees. Looking behind, he also noticed the Malaya Mountains and their orchards on the southern edge of the sea, just like those on the northern coast.

Realizing that he had assumed a huge form to fly to Lanka, he returned to his normal form. Hanuman landed at the tree and mineral-rich crown of the Trikuta Mountain that had several tiny peaks. On its slopes, kewra, coconut and mint plants grew in abundance. Descending to the seashore, he looked at Lanka situated on a hilltop. The city glowed like the prosperous and pretty Amaravati.

2

The City of Lanka

Once again, climbing the peak of the Trikuta Mountain, Hanuman calmly observed the magnificent Lanka. He felt no fatigue. All around him were fragrant, flowering trees, well-planted orchards and regular pathways. He strolled through pine trees and observed kanera, lemon, date palm, ketaki, kadamba, asoka, asan, kovidar, kutaja, and priyangu plants in bloom. Ponds of various sizes were full of swans, flamingos and other aquatic birds. Lotus plants floated on water. All around these water-bodies, seasonal flowers were in bloom.

The City of Gold

The city of Lanka was protected by several moats adorned with a variety of lotus. Ravana had made special arrangements for protecting the city since he had abducted Sita. Fierce rakshasas, carrying bows and arrows, kept a watch all over.

The protective walls around the city were made of gold. Several buildings were high as the hills and white as the autumn clouds. Roads were painted white, were raised above the ground level and meandered through the city. The main doors in the city walls were also made of gold, with paintings of plants and creepers all over them. Vishwakarma had designed Lanka as if he was creating a beautiful woman: the sturdy protection walls as her thighs, the forests and the limitless ocean were her clothes, weapons like shataghni and lances were her tresses. The high-rise buildings across the city seemed like ornaments.

The northern gate of the city was high like the gate of Alkapuri situated on the Kailas Mountain. The tall buildings appeared to support the sky as a roof. Looking at the fierce asuras moving around carrying lances and other weapons, Hanuman thought:

'It would be futile even if the vanaras reach here. Even the devatas cannot conquer Lanka in a battle. The place is dangerous. What will Raghunath achieve by coming to this inaccessible place that is protected by Ravana? There is no scope for trying for a conciliation '

'Moreover, none other than the four high-flying, mighty vanaras, Angada, Neel, the wise Sugreeva and I can reach here.

'Of course, at first, I ought to find out whether Sita is alive or not. I shall think of all the other issues after meeting her.

'I cannot enter Lanka in my present form because the city is guarded by powerful and heartless asuras. If I want to look for Sita successfully, I ought to enter the city at night and that too unseen by anyone.'

Having thus made up his mind, eager to have a darshana of Vaidehi, Hanuman waited for the sun to set. At the opportune time he reduced himself to the size of a cat and jumped into the city. With amazement he looked at the broad avenues, at the numerous mansions, golden pillars and windows, houses that were eight storeys high, and at the floors of those mansions which were studded with sapphire crystal and covered by gold plates. Lattices with curtains of pearl strings made the rakshasa residences look splendid.

Simultaneously, Chandradeva, with thousands of beams, surrounded by sparkling stars, appeared on the horizon. In order to assist Hanuman, he spread a canopy of moonlight all over Lanka. Hanuman looked at the rising moon that had the luminosity of a conch, the whiteness of milk, and the colour of a lotus root.

3

Lanka at Night

Hanuman entered Lanka, a city beautified by lovely orchards and ponds, and situated on the Trikuta Mountain, that loomed like a massive cloud under the garb of night. Mansions painted white like the autumn clouds, enhanced its charm. The city was protected by mighty warriors. Elephants in musth stood by its magnificent gates. Massive golden fortifications protected the city of Lanka. Hanuman, full of joy and enthusiasm, climbed onto one of the fortifications and cast a wondrous glance all over. The golden gates added to the city's grandeur. The doors had cornices made of sapphire and were studded with crystal, pearls and diamonds. While the indoors resounded with music of different instruments and ornaments, the outdoors echoed with the melodious calls of the herons, peacocks and swans.

Casting a glance in every direction, Hanuman found Lanka attractive like a stunning woman attired in pretty clothes and attractive jewellery. She wore her fortifications as her robes and palaces as her ornaments. The domes hiding the missiles on the fortifications looked like her breasts. Brilliant lights and the mighty planets had vanquished the darkness of the city.

4

Hanuman Looks for Sita

Hanuman, bypassing the massive gates of Lanka, jumped inside over the rampart, and landed in a square. It was as if he had placed his left foot on the enemy's head.

He walked on a road littered with flowers. As the sky looks lovely when covered by white clouds, the fascinating city looked enchanting with its mansions painted in white. Inside their homes, people laughed and played on musical instruments or listened to music.

Homes of the Asura Aristocrats

Some of the asura homes had been designed in the form of lotus, some in the form of a swastika. On certain others, the swastika had been painted on the walls. Certain homes opened in every direction except the south, making it auspicious for gaining wealth. All the buildings had been decorated on all sides with flowers in different motifs.

Hanuman listened to enchanting lyrics being sung in manda, madhyama and uchcha melodies. He heard the tinkling of bracelets and anklets of dancers who were as charming as apsaras and who expressed the suffering of love while dancing. While he heard many a woman's ornaments tinkling as they went up or down the stairs, he could also hear men clapping to a beat or just shouting.

To his surprise, he found many asuras reciting holy mantras and others busy in studies. He found many rakshasas loudly reciting eulogies of Ravana.

Ravana's Informers and Soldiers

In the heart of the city, Hanuman noticed several informers of the king. Some of them were dressed like beggars, yogis, naked sadhus, religious men with matted hair, and still others who had put on deerskin. Quite a few rakshasas carried swords, maces, shataghni, bows and arrows. They had put on armour as if ready for a battle.

The asuras walked with garlands around their necks. They applied sandal paste on their bodies and foreheads and put on a variety of dresses and expensive jewels. A few wandered aimlessly.

A hundred thousand soldiers protected the centre of the town while some stood alert in front of Ravana's palaces.

Ravana's Palace

Ravana's palace stood on one of the peaks of the Trikuta Mountain. It was surrounded by moats abounding in white lotus. This glorious palace was as pretty as Swargaloka and was guarded by hordes of guards. It resounded with the sound of music. Near the palace gates one could see chariots, vimanas, decorated horses, palanquins, and four-tusked elephants in musth, dressed from head to toe in tapestries. Hanuman gained an entry into Ravana's palace and looked around. The moonlight shone splendidly to give him a clear view of the palace.

Lanka in Moonlight

As the moon rises,
His cool beams alleviate
The heat as well as the evil in the world.
The ocean tides rise high, and on the earth
The living beings bathe and glow in a new light.

Under the moonlight,
Lakshmi looks brilliant as she does
On the Mandarachala on the earth,
On the great oceans at twilight, and
On the lotus floating on sheets of water.

Chandradeva looks glorious in the sky,
Like a swan in a silver cage,
A lion in a Mandarachala cave, and like
A warrior riding an elephant in musth.

The moon, his face marked with a deer horn,
Looks splendid like
A bull standing triumphant with his sharp horns,
Like the mighty and white Himalayas rising high, or
Like an elephant with tusks capped with gold.

Purified, by waters cool and masses of snow,
Of all his faults,
Chandradeva appears in the sky,
Unblemished.
Helped by the rays of the sun,
His darkness has vanished.
Even his shadows look bright because
Lakshmi, illumination incarnate,
Resides with him.

Like a majestic lion resting on a rock outside a cave,
Like an elephant looking splendid in a vast forest,
Like a king looking resplendent on attaining a kingdom,
Bestowed with pure light,
The moon looks bright.

As the night descended,
The darkness enveloped the earth, and
The asuras indulged in killing animals and having meat.
The women looked forward to wanton indulgence.
With the rise of the brilliant moon,
Her darkness vanquished,
Even the night is blessed like Swargaloka
That is revered by all.

In the moonlit night,
The melodious sound of veena delighted the senses.
The women of noble character slept beside their husbands.
In the moonlit night,
The rakshasas of a gentle disposition,
Though looking amazingly fierce,
Indulged in their pastimes at midnight.

Men and Women of Lanka

During his wanderings, the wise Hanuman looked into several homes. Rakshasas, intoxicated with their prosperity inhabited some, while drunkards lived in some others. Outside some homes, he saw horses and chariots, and inside, royal furniture. Majestic warriors were to be seen in plenty.

There was no dearth of quarrelsome asuras. Under the influence of liquor, they used unpleasant words. In fits of anger they slapped their chests or their women. Hanuman saw some asuras fondling their women, others busy in painting lovely images and still others pulling the strong bow strings to their ears.

Hanuman observed charming women applying sandal paste on their bodies. He saw some others sighing deep in anger after quarrelling with their lovers or husbands.

Hanuman noticed many wise, world-renowned rakshasas with elegant speech, balanced mind, and meaningful names. They were men of varied mien and complexion. A number of them were handsome, men of noble qualities, and of a dignified conduct.

Hanuman looked at several daintily dressed women, impressive in looks, pious in conduct, who had put on tasteful jewels and ornaments. Their attention was either focussed on their lovers or they were busy imbibing liquor. They glowed like stars and were sweet of temperament. He saw some extremely charming, yet shy women who, lost in bliss, were lying intertwined, like two birds, with their men at midnight.

Many women sat on the rooftops of their mansions, busy looking after their husbands. They were devoted, loyal to their men, religious as well as amorous. Happily they sat in the laps of their lovers. The brave Hanuman, the pride of the vanaras, saw some stunningly good-looking women who were overjoyed in the company of their lovers. Garlands of flowers enhanced their charm. He saw women who cast oblique glances. He saw rows and rows of jewels arranged like flashes of lightning.

However, nowhere did he find the delicate Sita. He searched long for Sita who had walked steadfast on the path of Sanatana Dharma, who had eyes and ears only for Shri Rama, who loved him and him alone, and who was loved with equal intensity and commitment by her husband.

Hanuman was looking for Sita, the foremost among women, who, suffering from the viraha agni, shed tears and deeply sighed in grief all the time. He searched for Sita, who used to wear a priceless pendant around her neck, who had lovely eye lashes, whose voice was melodious, who looked attractive like a peahen dancing in the forest, who looked like the new moon covered by a cloud, or like a streak of gold, covered with dust.

5

Hanuman Looks for Sita in Ravana's Palace and in Other Places

Inside Ravana's Palace

Moving along, vanarashrestha Hanuman, who could assume any form, took stock of the buildings of Lanka. He entered Ravana's palace that was protected by walls shining like the golden sun. He saw pictures in silver frames hanging on the walls, doors embedded with gold, and amazing staircases.

Ravana's palace was full of hordes of precious artefacts, jewels, and the best of furniture. Stunning beauties, always full of joy, casually strolled in the palace. When they walked, Ravana's palace echoed with the music of their ornaments.

In the palace one could hear the sound of bheri and mridanga and the echo of conches all the time. Prayers were recited daily and havana was performed on festive days. Hanuman moved fearlessly in the attached gardens, and in the mansions occupied by senior courtiers such as Prahasta, Mahaparshva, Mahodara and others. He visited the residences of Indrajit, the warrior son of Ravana; Kumbhakarna, who was dark and large as a cloud, and Vibhishana, both brothers of the king.

Ravana was protected by rakshasis with ferocious eyes. Some of them carried maces, lances and other weapons. In Ravana's palace, Hanuman saw arbours surrounded by creepers, plants of several varieties, art studios, wooden slopes for sports, and rooms furnished for entertainment and merry-making. The palace was as high as the Mandarachala Mountain, a place fit for the seekers of pleasure, a treasure house of gems and jewels, with vaults for safeguarding valuables. It had hundreds of high terraces and domes. Its floors were wet with wine and honey. Its air resounded with the sound of dancing anklets, the clinking of bangles, the playing of mridanga and other sonorous instruments, and clapping.

The Pushpak Vimana

After having seen grand mansions and immaculately constructed buildings all around him, Hanuman noticed the unique Pushpak Vimana, high as the clouds, glowing like gold and pleasing to the senses. The vimana could travel at a great speed, anywhere, in any direction over large distances and could be steered by the will of the owner.

Pushpak Vimana was built like a palace with sapphire clad golden windows. It had rooms that stored conches, weapons, arrows and swords. The rooms were painted white with scenes of ponds full of blue lotuses and attics full of flowers. It was superior to any other vimana in the possession of the devatas. Long ago, Vishwakarma had constructed it in Swargaloka for Brahma. The latter had gifted it to Kubera, Ravana's elder brother, from whom the rakshasa king took it away by force.

The walls of the Pushpak Vimana had been painted imaginatively to evoke nature in its splendour. There were images of the vimana being carried on the wings of flamingos, or flying on the clouds, flashing lightning.

A vast variety of colourful birds made of silver, sapphire and coral were affixed to the walls. These birds in their loveliness appeared to instill amour, as if assisting Kamadeva. They had eyes made of coral and wings that had flowers of a golden hue.

Hanuman was amazed to arrive at the Pushpak Vimana which loomed large like a picturesque mountain with caves, fragrant trees and bouquets of flowers. However, he was worried at not having found, after so much effort, the unhappy Sita lost in Rama's thoughts. The pious Hanuman was sad at this turn of events.

6

Hanuman Enters Ravana's Harem

Ravana's Private Apartments

In the centre of the palace, Hanuman noticed a large and sophisticated lodge, one yojana in length and half this size in width. It rested on silver and gold pillars, with figures of wolves at their base. Looking for the large-eyed Sita, he went around this building. Soon he arrived at the king's private apartments. The place was full of Ravana's rakshasa wives and conquered princesses. Ravana looked to be more prosperous than Kubera, Yama and Varuna.

In some rooms the roofs were high, and brightly lit. The steps, windows and ventilators were made of gold and marble, and the pavilions were of sapphire and emeralds. The floors were studded with unusual coral, priceless gems and rare pearls.

Besides the bejewelled steps, this place was decorated with ivory figures. It appeared to fly on the wings of high pillars. Its floor was covered by an expensive carpet with motifs of mountains and forests. The palace looked as large as the earth itself. It echoed with melodious bird song and was divinely fragrant. Hanuman could smell the inviting fragrance of several varieties of drinks, condiments and cereals.

The palace was furnished with all possible supplies as if it was the Kamadhenu of Vasishtha Muni. None could be unhappy in Ravana's inner chambers. Like a mother, the palace satisfied all the five senses of Hanuman. He thought that he had arrived in devaloka, or in Indra's capital, or had ascended to Brahmaloka, the ultimate goal for any being.

Hanuman looked at a row of golden lamps burning simultaneously, as if lost in contemplation. The entire palace appeared to be on fire with the light of these lamps, with Ravana's glory, and with the brilliance of the jewels worn by the women.

Ravana's Harem

Hundreds of charming women lay on expensive carpets, dressed in colourful clothes, each one uniquely dressed. They had garlands around their necks. It was post midnight. They were fast asleep after revelry, liquor and sex.

Hanuman smelled the fragrance of lotus from the mouths of these sleeping beauties. Deep in sleep, their faces reflected the joy of the lotus that blooms when the night ends. Yet, they charmed as does the lotus that has just folded its petals as the night approaches. Looking at them, Hanuman thought of the amorous beings who prayed and hungrily pined for a touch of such faces, like intoxicated bees reaching for the lotus in full bloom.

The Kapishrestha looked at the sleeping women lying like stars fallen from the sky and assembled at one place. They had imbibed liquor, danced, played on music and sung songs. As a result of all this activity, their hair was dishevelled, their garlands crushed and scattered, and their pretty ornaments loosened and displaced. The sindoor in the parting of some of these women's hair had been smudged, the anklets of some had been thrown away, while some others were covered by pearls from broken strings. Necklaces shining as the sun and the moon lay high on their breasts and looked like hansas sleeping on the mounds in a pond. Sapphire pendants raised on their breasts looked like kadamba ducks. Their necklaces of gold were like the chakravaka. The women lying asleep thus resembled rivers in which a variety of ducks floated. Their thighs resembled the embankments.

The grooves made by the pressure of necklaces and pendants on their delicate limbs and nipples were so precise that the impressions looked like real ornaments.

The colourful cloths covering the faces of Ravana's wives, all charming in different ways, looked like glorious buntings. Even their ear rings shook in rhythm with their breath. Always excited by the natural fragrance of his mistresses' breathing, Ravana was all the more pleased by their breath laced with the aroma of liquor made from molasses.

Some of the intoxicated women slept with their bracelet covered arms as pillows. A few others had made a roll of their fragrant clothes for supporting their neck and head. One of them lay on the breasts of another while another one supported herself on someone else's arm.

In this manner, under the influence of their passion for Ravana and liquor, these women lay in deep sleep with their hips, thighs, waists and backs intertwined and supporting each other. They had slender waists and lay in each other's arms experiencing the delights of a lover's embrace.

Like the spring breeze sending a shiver through arbours of flowering creepers, the women appeared to vibrate when their clothes undulated with their breath. With their bodies intermingled, these beauties looked like flowers in a garland stuck together, or like flowering creepers inextricably intertwined.

The king's wives included daughters of Rajarshis, Brahmarshis, asuras, devatas and the gandharvas. A few had been conquered in battle. Some others, moved by lust, had offered themselves to Ravana to be at his service. None of them had stayed against her wishes. Ravana had not abducted anyone by force. They loved his unique, divine and unearthly qualities.

Sita alone was one who had been abducted against her wishes. While other women were totally dedicated to Ravana and loved none but him, Sita's absence in the harem was yet another proof of her unending love and dedication for Rama.

The wise Hanuman brooded over the situation. Hanuman considered Sita to be superior to all those present in Ravana's harem. He condemned the mighty Ravana's act of deceitfully abducting her by approaching her in disguise. He thought that it would be better for all concerned if Sita too could spend her time happily with Rama, her husband.

7

Hanuman Mistakes Mandodari for Sita

Looking around, Hanuman noticed a raised platform made of marble and studded with gemstones. Several large beds made of sapphire with ivory legs, had been placed thereon. In a corner of one of the beds, Hanuman noticed a canopy, white like the moon and festooned by exquisite garlands of asoka flowers. Several women stood around waving fly-whisks.

Ravana's Glory

It was then that Hanuman first saw Ravana, who was fast asleep. He was a handsome man, dressed in fabulous jewels and splendid clothes. He was beloved of the virgins and a source of joy to the rakshasas. Red sandal paste on his limbs made him look like the sun at dusk. Wearing glowing earrings, with large, red eyes, long arms, golden robes, and resting after a night of debauchery and liquor, Ravana looked splendid.

Hanuman was frightened at the sight of the king. He moved slightly away and climbed another step to reach another terrace from where he could, unnoticed, observe Ravana, the ferocious lion. The sleeping king's bed looked magnificent like the Prashravana Mountain where sleeps a fragrant elephant. His large arms bore the marks of Airavata's attack with the sharp ends of his tusks, in a battle. His shoulder was muscular and thick and carried the marks of vajra wounds.

Ravana's arms were powerful and well-built, and Hanuman realized from marks on it, that they had been injured by Vishnu's chakra as well. His fingernails and thumbs bore auspicious marks. Spread-eagled over the spotless bed, his palms looked like two cobras with five hoods each. Hanuman imagined how in the battlefield, these arms would have reduced the yakshas, nagas, gandharvas, devatas and asuras to tears.

Ravana's lotus face, glistening in the light of his gold earrings, glowed all the more in the unusual reflection of light from his golden crown, studded with pearls that lay beside his head. Below the waist, his body was covered by a loose, white silk sheet. His torso, however, was wrapped in expensive yellow silks. Lying on his luminous white bed, Ravana looked like a mighty elephant resting in the limitless waters of the Ganga.

At the four corners of the king's bed, four golden lamps had been lit. Their light highlighted every limb of Ravana like lightning illuminating a cloud and making it visible.

Ravana and His Harem

Hanuman noticed some of the mighty king's favourite wives sleeping at the foot of his bed. Ravana's mistresses, beautiful women with narrow waists, intoxicated with liquor and exhausted with making love, lay asleep in a dishevelled state wherever they could. The finest of danseuses, the one who had been specially crafted by the Creator, the one who could move her limbs with delicacy and dance with exquisite grace, although fast asleep, looked as if she was still expressing shringara-bhava.

Another lay clasping her veena to her chest. She looked like a water lily stuck to a boat in the river Mahanadi. Still another, with kohl in her eyes, was fast asleep with a small musical instrument by her side. A delicate accompanist with attractive breasts lay asleep on her tabor like a woman pressing her long lost lover to her body. A lotus-eyed young woman clung to her veena like a woman lying asleep in a passionate embrace with her lover.

However, apart from these women in plenty, Hanuman saw a stunningly charming woman lying on a separate bed. She had put on pearls and jewels. She enhanced the loveliness of the palace. She was fair of complexion and had a golden glow. She was Ravana's beloved, mistress of the harem, named Mandodari. Taking her to be Sita, Hanuman was overjoyed. He whipped his tail and jumped like a vanara. Playfully, he climbed a pillar and then jumped to the floor.

8

The Search Continues

However, Hanuman soon regained his composure and concluded that the magnificent woman lying next to Ravana could not be Sita. He was worried. He thought that separated from Shri Rama, Sita could neither sleep nor eat, neither put on makeup, nor dress in silks or put on ornaments. She would never take liquor, he thought. He was sure that Sita would never surrender to another man, even if he was the lord of the devatas because no devata could equal Shri Rama.

Hanuman, therefore, concluded that the woman lying next to Ravana must be someone other than Sita. Settling this doubt, Hanuman resumed his wanderings of the Madhushala in search of Sita.

Leaving aside Ravana who slept like a bull surrounded by cows in a cow-shed, Kapishrestha Hanuman walked into the kitchens and the dining halls of the palace. He saw all varieties of provisions spread over the place. A variety of pickles were kept alongside the meats. Savouries were stored side by side with liquor made by fermenting grape and pomegranate juices with sugar and honey.

Indulgent Lifestyle

The pleasure hall had been lavishly decorated with flowers. Sturdy sofas and golden beds were placed fastidiously. Empty drinking vessels were scattered all over, along with bracelets, anklets, fruit and crushed flowers. Hanuman saw tables loaded with tastefully arranged dishes prepared by master chefs. Natural extracts of trees vied with wines and liquors made from molasses, honey, mahua and other flower saps or from resins.

Here too, Hanuman found women sleeping intertwined. Intoxicated, some of them had undressed the others before clasping them in a close embrace. Hanuman savoured the fragrance of cool sandalwood, liquors, wines, honey, sundry flowers, toilettries, and incense wafting on a mild breeze.

Hanuman felt guilty about peering at the women lying asleep. He thought that this was the end of his dharma and virtue. He had not only looked at women belonging to others, but also he had seen Ravana, the evil incarnate, the one who had abducted another's woman, from close quarters.

However, applying logic, Hanuman argued thus:

'No doubt Ravana's women were sleeping innocently, completely unaware of their surroundings and I have seen them in this condition. Yet, my mind never went astray with lust. It is the mind that steers our senses towards good or evil, the desirable or the undesirable. Fortunately, my mind did not deviate from the path of propriety.

'I could hardly look for Vaidehi in other places. A woman's place is among women. One cannot search for an abducted woman among female deer.'

Hanuman Arrives at Asoka Vatika

In trying to find Sita's whereabouts, Hanuman successively visited arbours, studios and rest houses. However, he could not find any trace of her anywhere. The thought of Ravana having killed Sita for not giving in to his will haunted Hanuman.

Hanuman thought over his predicament. Not having traced Sita so far, there was no reward for his valiant effort in crossing the ocean in a jump. Worried about the reaction of Angada and Jambavan, and the pain that it would cause Shri Rama, Hanuman at first decided to fast unto death. However, soon he pulled himself up. He thought that a passionate desire to achieve one's objective alone was the secret of success. Hanuman, therefore, decided to look for Sita in places, howsoever well guarded, that he had not visited so far. He went to basements, pavilions built in the city squares, and houses of pleasure. He opened doors, knocked at gates, entered and exited galleries. Not finding Sita anywhere, he felt sad.

Hanuman was sure that Sita would never have surrendered to Ravana. Therefore, she could have been kept captive in some secret chamber. Hanuman also thought over the desirability or otherwise of informing Shri Rama about the possibility of Sita's demise. He was sure that Shri Rama would not be able to survive such devastating news. Hanuman finally decided against informing Shri Rama about Sita's possible death. He knew that his presence in Lanka would keep everyone's hope alive. He argued with himself:

'Taking one's life is harmful in many ways. A living being tastes success sooner or later. Hence I too will live and attain my objective as well as happiness.'

The persevering Kapishrestha thus made up his mind to kill Ravana, whether Sita was alive or not. It would be a sweet revenge for his heinous deed!

'I shall carry his dead body over the ocean and hand it over to Shri Rama.

'I shall continue my search for Sita, wife of the glorious Shri Rama until I can take her along to him.'

Asoka Vatika

Hanuman reached the Asoka Vatika surrounded by large trees and realizing that this place was still unexplored, entered in search of Sita. Before setting foot in the Asoka Vatika, he bowed to Shri Rama, Lakshmana, Sita, Rudra, Indra, Yama and Vayu and prayed for success in his mission.

He was aware that the place was heavily guarded by Ravana's guards. Even Bhagwan Vayu, the life breath of the universe, moved there like a breeze. Hanuman changed into a diminutive form. Once again he prayed to Brahma, the self-created, all the maharshis and to various gods for their blessings to accomplish his mission.

As he approached the Asoka Vatika, Hanuman was immersed in the thoughts of Sita.

'When shall I be lucky to look at her face?' he thought. 'She who is endowed with the delicate beauty of a spotless moon, and is Shri Rama's beloved. How shall the helpless woman shackled under Ravana's control, ever cross my path?'

THE PRINCES LEARN VARIOUS SKILLS

[The Mewar Ramayana Manuscripts. 1649-1653. Courtesy: The British Library, London]

THE BRIDES ARE WELCOMED

[The Mewar Ramayana Manuscripts. 1649-1653. Courtesy: The British Library, London]

DASHRATHA ANNOUNCES HIS DECISION TO ANOINT RAMA

[The Mewar Ramayana Manuscripts. 1649-1653. Courtesy: The British Library, London]

DEPARTURE FROM AYODHYA

[The Mewar Ramayana Manuscripts. 1649-1653. Courtesy: The British Library, London.]

9

The Asoka Vatika

Hanuman climbed the boundary wall of the Asoka Vatika and looked around from the top. Vasanta had set in and the branches of trees were bent with the weight of bouquets of flowers at their tips. Hundreds of creepers climbed the trees in the mango orchards. Hanuman jumped like an arrow shot from a bow and landed amidst the trees.

The Sights and Sounds

The large garden was surrounded by trees of the colours of gold and silver. The place echoed with the song of a variety of colourful birds, while herds of deer roamed around freely.

Hanuman listened to the cooing of the koel and the drone of the bhramaras. The deer and the birds seemed excited. Hanuman's movements disturbed birds sleeping in their nests. As the birds flew, the wind shook the trees that shed colourful flowers. Asoka Vatika lost her shine to Hanuman's trampling when he jumped from one branch to the other. The vatika resembled a young woman who has been enjoyed to the hilt by her lover, with hair dishevelled, unguents smeared, the Amrita of her lips sucked and her body bearing marks of his teeth and nails.

Looking around, Hanuman noticed eye-catching platforms made of gold, silver and gem-studded tiles. He saw ponds full of fresh water, with jewelled steps and hillocks of coral and pearls at their bottom. Chakravaka couples rested on their banks which resounded with the calls of papeeha, hansa and sarus birds. A stream, like a beloved jumping out of her lover's lap, flowed from a hillock in the Vatika. The stooping boughs of the trees on its banks glided on its water like maids restraining their friend from deserting her lover in anger. The Kapishrestha saw an asoka tree of golden hue, rich in foliage and wrapped in creepers that spread on its branches to make several canopies. Climbing the asoka tree in no time, Hanuman thought:

'From this vantage point I can look around the huge garden and maybe catch a glimpse of Sita. Weighed by sorrow, maybe sometimes she wanders in this direction, of her sweet will. The evil Ravana's Asoka Vatika is certainly an enchanting place. Therefore, Sita, Shri Rama's queen, must frequent this site.

'Possibly, the doe-eyed Sita, beloved of Shri Rama, has withered pining for him. However, it is time for the morning prayers and Sita will definitely visit this sacred stream for her prayers. If the moon-faced beauty is alive, she will surely come to this cool bank.'

10

Hanuman Sights a Distraught Sita

Sitting on an asoka tree, Hanuman admired the beauty of the surroundings and waited for the moment when he would find Sita. Redolent with the scents emitted by diverse flowers, the garden was fragrant like the Gandhamadana Mountain.

Hanuman soon noticed a high-rising, round temple supported by a thousand pillars, as white as the Kailas Mountain. It had steps made of coral and pavilions made of gold. Dazzling the onlooker, its pointed, high dome appeared to draw a sharp line in the sky.

A Princess in Tatters

Next to the temple, Hanuman noticed a charming woman dressed in rags, sitting surrounded by fierce rakshasis. She looked emaciated and pathetic. She sobbed intermittently.

A worn out sheet of silk covered Sita's body. Dirty and shorn of any adornments, she looked like a muddy stream devoid of lotus blooms. Like Rohini [Aldebaran] harassed by Mangala [Mars] the tapasvini, reduced to a skeleton, looked crushed by grief.

Hanuman realized that this could be Sita who had grown feeble because of fasting all the time. Sorrow overwhelmed all her other emotions because she was far away from her near and dear ones. Many rakshasis surrounded her, making her feel like a doe separated from her herd and surrounded by a pack of dogs.

Looking at her large eyes, her dirty and frail body, and her helpless demeanour, Hanuman concluded logically that the woman in front of him was Sita. For him, her face was attractive as the moon, her eyebrows charming and the glow emanating from her body dispelled the darkness around her.

The lotus-eyed Sita looked charming like Rati, Kama's beloved. She sat on the ground like a tapasvini sitting in meditation. A pall of despair had dimmed her facial lustre. Her face looked like a flame of fire wrapped in smoke.

Sita was upset that she could no longer look after Shri Rama. Harassed by the rakshasis, the doe-eyed beauty seemed helpless. There was no joy on her face bathed in tears.

Is She Really Sita?

Looking at Sita who had grown lean like knowledge forgotten due to lack of practice, Hanuman had his doubts. He could not recognize her because she had not put on any auspicious marks, and applied no unguents. It took some time for Hanuman to be certain of her identity.

Looking carefully, Hanuman noticed some of the ornaments on Sita's body that had been mentioned by Shri Rama. He saw on her ear lobes lovely rings and bewitching ear pins shaped like flowers. Her bangles were studded with gems and coral. Though the ornaments had blackened, yet they tallied with the description given by Shri Rama. He was no longer in doubt that she was wearing ornaments that she had not discarded while being carried after her abduction.

Even her yellow covering, thought Hanuman, was the same as the piece of cloth thrown on the ground with her ornaments. It was dirty but its colour had not faded.

Hanuman was now certain that this fair woman was Sita, the beloved of Shri Rama. Her complexion glowed like gold. She was the one whose absence had overwhelmed Shri Rama with compassion, pity, grief and love.

Hanuman rejoiced in having the privileged darshana of Sita. Mentally, he found himself in the presence of Shri Rama and admired the latter's good fortune in having Sita as his wife.

Admiring Sita's Conduct and Charm, Hanuman Feels Sorry for her Predicament

Hanuman's eyes brimmed with tears on seeing Sita surrounded by rakshasis and in grief. In his thoughts, he moaned Sita's fate.

'She learnt her lessons at the feet of loving elders. She is Shri Rama's wife. When she has to undergo such suffering, one has to admit the irreversible dominance of Kala. However, like the divine Ganga who does not get unduly upset with the arrival of rains, confident of the valour and wisdom of Shri Rama and Lakshmana, Sita has refused to be cowed down by her misfortune.'

Looking at Sita, resplendent like the beauteous Lakshmi, Hanuman thought of Shri Rama and said to himself,

'Shri Rama killed the mighty Vali for the sake of the large-eyed Sita. Earlier Shri Rama massacred 14,000 rakshasas, including Khara, Trishira and the powerful Dooshana in the Janasthana. It is because of Sita that the unattainable kingdom of the vanaras, protected and ruled by Vali passed to the renowned Sugreeva.

'Sita, the daughter of Janaka, the virtuous king of Mithila, is a devoted wife. She appeared wrapped in the dust of a furrow, fine as the pollen of lotus, when the king was ploughing a field. She is the daughter-in-law of the valorous and gentle Dashratha who never deserted a battlefield. She is the wife of the virtuous, knowledgeable in dharma, contented and self-realized Shri Rama. Out of her love for her husband, giving up a luxurious life, she travelled to the forest without a thought of the hardships in store for her. Living on mere fruit and roots, serving her husband, Sita was happy as if she was living in a palace.

'Sita of golden limbs, of an ever smiling face, soft spoken, suffers the tortures she was never meant to suffer. She has stuck to the purity of conduct and devotion to her husband in spite of Ravana's depredations. She has not surrendered her chastity.

'A husband adorns his wife more than any ornament. That is why, away from her husband, Sita looks forlorn although she is so pretty. She is forgiving like the earth. The asoka tree with its branches bent with bouquets of flowers, add to Sita's shoka.'

Having determined the identity of Sita, Hanuman decided to wait on the tree top before presenting himself to her at an opportune moment.

11

Ravana Offers Inducements to Sita–1

As the night approached, Chandra appeared on the horizon in a crystal clear sky. For Hanuman, its light enabled Sita's darshana.

Hanuman looked at Sita whose face was as charming as the full moon. However, she was bent with grief. On looking around, Hanuman noticed a number of frightening rakshasis surrounding Sita. They carried deadly weapons, spewed angry expletives all the time, quarrelled with one another and were drunk on liquor most of the time.

Sita in Captivity

Hanuman noticed that even though Sita's hair had matted and she looked lustreless like a fallen star in the absence of suitable jewels, she was decked in her love for her husband. Away from her family, she sat as Ravana's prisoner in this far off land, separated from her husband. Sita did not deserve to be imprisoned like this, surrounded by unkind and ferocious women. Although she sat in the Asoka Vatika, she was immersed in an ocean of shoka. Hanuman noticed that her eyes were tremulous like those of a fawn. She cast suspicious glances all around like a doe. She had been reduced to a skeleton by grief.

Hanuman's happiness at finding her alive and having located her was overtaken by his grief over her pathetic condition.

Ravana Visits Asoka Vatika

It was early morning. The chanting of the Vedic mantras could be heard from the homes of Brahma Rakshasa. Ravana woke up to the playing of auspicious instruments and the chanting of pleasant songs.

As soon as he woke up, the fortunate and majestic Ravana thought of Vaidehi. He could not contain his lust.

Dressed in finery, looking magnificent, Ravana entered Asoka Vatika in a procession. The garden was full of flowers, birds and animals. Its ground was covered by fruit shed by the trees. Its golden doors were studded with gems.

Almost a hundred beauties followed the son of Pulstya as Indra is followed by the deva and the gandharva women. Some carried golden lamps; some waved fly whisks while some others held fans made of tada leaves. A few women carried water in golden flasks while some carried round cushions for the king to sit upon. Some smart looking maids carried in their right hands shining pitchers inlaid with precious stones and full of delicious drinks. An attendant carrying a canopy white as the full moon, or a swan, followed Ravana.

Like flashes of lightning accompanying clouds, several charming women were keeping company of Ravana, their husband. Their drooping eyelids reflected the revelry in Ravana's bed and harem.

With intoxicating eyes, the beloved wives of the rakshasaraja, respectfully and lovingly accompanied their master into the Asoka Vatika. He was brave, but foolish to have destroyed his discretion owing to lust. Hanuman could not ignore how, walking slowly, with only Sita on his mind, he looked majestic.

Vayunandana, Kapishrestha Hanuman noticed Ravana of unimaginable valour and unparalleled deeds, arriving at the doors of Asoka Vatika. Illuminating Ravana on all sides, several women preceded him carrying torches burning fragrant oils. He was full of lust, pride and liquor.

He was dressed in lavish garments, spotless and pure white like the froth at the top of churned milk. This was laced with strings of pearls and flowers. Hanuman saw him disentangling his garment from his bracelet.

Having ascertained that this man was indeed Ravana, Hanuman stealthily came down in order to have a close look at him.

While Hanuman, overawed by Ravana's majesty, hid himself, the king proceeded towards the beauteous Sita.

Sita's Helplessness in Ravana's Presence

When the unblemished, beautiful princess Sita looked at the rakshasaraja dressed in the most exquisite of finery and looking handsome, coming towards her, she trembled like a plantain tree shaken by a strong wind. The large eyed and extremely beautiful Janaki shrunk back, and covered herself up with her tattered sari. She was undergoing the toughest of penance.

Sita could not see any end to her suffering. Lost in the thoughts of Rama, and drowned in a pool of sorrow, she wept alone. She suffered like Rohini afflicted by a meteor. Despite being born in a virtuous family of impeccable credentials, married into a religious and reputed family of kings following appropriate rites, Sita now looked filthy like a low born woman.

To Hanuman, Janaki looked diminished in splendour, like a faith discarded. She seemed like wisdom lost forever, shattered hope, a future destroyed, a violated royal command, a city burning in a riot, a ritual violated in the course of worship, the Poornima night darkened by an eclipse, or a delicate lotus torn to pieces by a hailstorm.

Sita looked lustreless and desolate like a pond out of which the lotus, their stems and leaves have been plucked, and from where the water birds have flown out of fear. Without unguents she appeared dusky like the dark night of the Krishnapaksha. Sita was reduced to a skeleton because of fasting, grief, worry, and fear of death. Her only wealth was her penance. She prayed to God every moment that Ravana be defeated at the hands of Shri Rama and she be rescued.

Sita wept while Ravana, courting a death wish, tried to offer her blandishments.

12

Ravana Offers Inducements to Sita–2

Addressing the tapasvini Sita, humble and bereft of any joy, sitting surrounded by the rakshasis, Ravana said,

'Sita, why do you hide yourself out of fear, or wish to be invisible the moment you see me?

'O large-eyed woman, I like you. I am in love with you. Your limbs are charming and enrapture the entire world. Listen to me and oblige me.

'In this place, you have none to fear. Neither a human being nor any rakshasa can enter here without my order. It is only my prerogative and that need not scare you.

'It is our dharma as rakshasas to visit other women or abduct them forcibly. Even then, Maithili, I shall not touch you till you desire me although Kamadeva continues to torture me physically and mentally.

'Have no fear in this regard. Have faith in me and sincerely respond to my overtures. Do not let your sorrow drown you.

'It does not befit a princess like you to sleep on the ground, to keep worrying all the time, to be clad in dirty clothes and keep fasting without there being any occasion.

'Maithili, if you accept my offer, you will enjoy various garlands of flowers, unguents of sandalwood, dresses of different designs, stunning ornaments, expensive drinks, comfortable beds, thrones to sit upon, and the pleasures of dance, music and musical instruments.

'You are a rare gem among women. You must not dress in unclean clothes. Put on ornaments and beautify your limbs.

'O auspicious-looking woman, I believe that the Creator took special effort in carving every part of you because no other woman compares with you in loveliness.

'Vaidehi, there is no man who, while trying to possess the youthful and charming you, would not lose his patience. O woman with a face as lovely as the moon, my eyes stay put whenever I cast a glance.

'Maithili, be my wife. Give up your notion of loyalty to your husband. I possess so many good looking women. Come and be their superior.

'O shy woman, whatever gems I have garnered from all over the world shall be yours. I shall even hand my kingdom over to you.

'Vilasini, to please you, I shall conquer the entire earth dotted by garlands of cities and hand it over to the king Janaka.

'In this world, I do not see any other person who can face me. You will witness my valour in the battlefield where no enemy survives against me.

'Make me your own and immediately you shall be decked as a bride with sparkling jewels and other superior embellishments on your body.

'Look at my wealth and possessions. O blessed woman, what will you do with Rama dressed in tattered sheets?

'Leave aside rescuing you, Rama will not even be able to find you. Bereft of all wealth and glory, he wanders from one jungle to another. He fasts, sleeps on a bed of bare earth and I am not sure if he is alive or has been devoured by Yama.

'Your yellow silk covering is soiled, you adorn yourself with dust and are devoid of ornaments, you have withered too. Seeing you wither like that puts me off other women as well.

'Janaki, leave your grief and be the mistress of all the other well-endowed women in my palace. O beauty with raven hair, these women, the best in the world, will look after you as the apsaras serve Lakshmi in Swargaloka.

'O woman with lovely brows, come and live with me to happily enjoy the entire wealth of Kubera and of the entire universe.

'Devi, Rama is no match for me in tapasya, valour, strength, wealth, glory or fame. Give up thoughts of him and come to taste divine drinks, indulge unrestrained in all your fantasies, and live your life as you please with me. I offer you the world and all its treasures.

'My coy beloved, put on necklaces of pure gold to adorn your limbs. Come and sport with me in gardens on the ocean shore which are rich in dense, blooming trees and where the bhramaras drone all the time.'

13

Sita's Retort to Ravana

Sita, the charming tapasvini, the goddess of fidelity, trembled as she wept overwhelmed with grief. She was lost in thoughts of her husband.

The fierce Ravana's words had hurt her terribly. Humbly and sorrowfully, speaking slowly, she responded from behind a straw curtain,

'Ravana, divert your mind from me and shower your love on your own self. As an evil person cannot crave for Siddhi, you are unfit to crave for me. I shall never act against the principles of fidelity and devotion to my husband. Such conduct is condemnable.

'I was born in an illustrious family. I was married into a family of virtuous kings.'

Turning her face away from Ravana, the glorious Sita continued,

'I am a chaste woman and belong to someone else. I am, therefore, unsuitable to be your wife. O Nishachara, try to follow the dharma enjoined upon by those who are superior to you. You must protect the women who belong to others as you care for your own.

'Is Lanka without any saints? Or, you do not listen to them. Why is your conduct perverse and your thinking nothing but evil? Perhaps you, determined to ensure the annihilation of the rakshasas, do not pay heed to the wise that care for you. You probably take their wisdom to be wasteful words.

'Prosperous kingdoms and cities are destroyed when under the rule of kings who have an impure mind and who do not listen to wise counsel.

'Likewise, the wealthy Lanka, entrusted to your care, will certainly be destroyed because of your misdeeds and ignorance.

'You cannot win me over by offering your wealth or supremacy. I am as inseparable from Shri Rama as his effulgence is from the sun. Having slept with my head upon the worthy arm of Lokanatha Shri Rama, how can I rest on someone else's arm?

'It is, therefore, in your interest to restore this suffering woman to Shri Ramachandra. If you desire the safety of your city and people, and do not want to be captured and punished, you ought to befriend Shri Rama, the Purushottama.

'Rama knows his dharma. He alone is worthy of respect. If you seek his protection, he will protect you too. If you desire to live, win over his trust. With a pure heart, restore me to him and make him happy and you shall save yourself and your people.

'A Nishachara like you might escape a thunderbolt, even Kala might spare you for some time, but Raghunath in his anger will never let you live. Soon you will hear the frightening sound of Shri Rama's bow being pulled like the thunder of Indra's thunderbolt. Shri Rama will soon free me from your clutches.

'O despicable denizen of the night, you abducted me in the absence of Shri Rama and Lakshmana. Facing them you cannot last even for a moment. How can a dog survive when attacked by two lions?

'Whether you take shelter in Kubera's Kailas Mountain, or hide in the court of Varuna, you will certainly lose your life the moment Shri Rama's arrow strikes you. Kala has already announced your death and it shall come to you soon.'

14

Sita Continues to be under Threat

Ravana Grants Sita Two Months to Change Her Mind

Ravana had been patient with Sita for all this while but now his patience and willpower was wearing off. Impolitely, he replied,

'No woman can ignore a man's true affection and humble words for too long, and begins to like him. On the contrary, you spurn me all the more as I try to placate you with sweet words. My fondness for you restrains me like a charioteer trying to pull his horses onto the right track.

'Human lust is like that. Once a person falls in love, he is drawn by deep affection and kindness towards the object of his affection. That is why, O lovely woman who deserves to be contemptuously rejected, and who is indulging in false vairagya, I am not putting you to death.

'Maithili, you deserve to be killed for the harsh words you have spoken while responding to my love for you. However, I grant you two months' time to change your mind. Thereafter, you will surrender yourself to my desire. In case of your refusal to do so, my cooks will cut you to pieces and make a meal out of you.'

Sita, however, stood her ground and said,

'O despicable rakshasa, is there none in this city who can dissuade you from your evil designs? You cannot escape punishment for casting an evil eye on the wife of Shri Rama. Do not compare yourself with Shri Ramachandra; he is the king of elephants while you are merely a hare.

'You claim to be a brave warrior, Kubera's brother, the commander of large armies. Why then did you abduct me stealthily?'

Ravana looked at Sita contemptuously and cruelly. He stood large, dark like a cloud with long arms and a large neck. Red with anger, he seemed to be a personification of Vasanta season himself. He walked like a lion, wore heavy bracelets of gold and a red robe and garlands of red flowers. Ravana was wearing two orange-red gold rings on his ears. The king looked like an embodiment of the Kalpavriksha and of Vasanta.

Looking ferocious like a hissing snake, he addressed Vaidehi thus:

'O woman who is trailing a pauper and an unjust man, I shall destroy you like the sun destroys the twilight in the early hours of morning.'

Ordering the fierce-looking rakshasis who were guarding Sita, Ravana said,

'Jointly and severally you will persuade her to agree to my will. Try whatever measures it takes: sama, dama, bheda and danda. Frighten her into submission.'

As Ravana was ranting while looking at Sita, Mandodari, his principal queen and Dhanyamalini, a young woman came and took him into their arms. They invited him to come to the palace and make love to them. They observed that Sita was unfortunate and that she was not destined to enjoy his embraces.

The Rakshasis Threaten and
Unsuccessfully Try to Cajole Sita into Submission

After Ravana left with his wives, Sita was surrounded by several frightening rakshasi guards. Each one tried to do better than the others to break down her resistance. They said,

'Why do you not consider it a matter of pride to be the wife of Ravana who is a crown of the Pulstya dynasty?

'He has defeated hundreds of devatas and even Indra. He comes to you repeatedly despite there being so many queens and beautiful women in his harem. You do not realize your fortune is smiling upon you. He came to you leaving his magnificent palace.

'We say all this in your interest. If you do not listen, you will lose your life.'

Sita Declines and is Repeatedly Threatened

The rakshasis observed Sita's continuous denial and said,

'You will lose your life unless you forget Ramachandra. Why don't you consent to live in our king's luxurious palace which has priceless beds and all possible comforts available for any being?

'Rama has lost his kingdom and has been unsuccessful in all his efforts to find you till now.'

Sita heard their harsh words and rebukes and responded,

'Your vicious suggestions are not acceptable to me. Even if my husband is a pauper, even if he is without a kingdom, he is my master and I shall always love him and be devoted to him. I am attached to my husband like Arundhati to Vasishtha, Rohini to Chandrama, Savitri to Satyavan and Damayanti to the King Nala.'

Licking their lips in delight, the angry rakshasis started hitting a trembling Sita mercilessly. Torturing her thus, they declared her to be unfit for their king.

A weeping Vaidehi moved away and sat under the asoka tree where Hanuman was hiding. Sita could do nothing but weep helplessly. With all the ferocious rakshasis surrounding her, she trembled with fear and shrank as if to disappear into herself. She thought:

'I am away from my husband and surrounded by these cruel and merciless rakshasis. I feel like a stream whose embankments are being cut by forceful waves striking against them. They, indeed, are fortunate who can see my lotus-eyed husband. What did I do in my previous life that I am being punished in this manner?'

Sita Decides to End Her Life

A tearful Sita sat moaning her fate. With her head bent down, she appeared to be mumbling as if in a trance. Drowned in a pool of grief, she lay on the ground, turning on her sides every now and then and talking as if in a delirium. She said,

'Diverting Shri Rama and Lakshmana, the evil Ravana abducted me through deception. Harassed by the rakshasis under whose control I live, I cannot live any longer. Living away from Shri Rama, I need neither ornaments nor wealth. I hate the mere mention of Ravana. Liking him and becoming a part of his harem is not possible. The rakshasa pays no heed to my rejection and cares nothing for the reputation of his dynasty.

'Rakshasis, cut me to pieces. Roast me or just burn my body. I shall never go near your king.

'Has my fortune so declined that the truthful Shri Rama has forgotten me? If he could kill thousands of rakshasas in Dandakaranya, why does he not come to my rescue?

'It is the nature of humans to care for those around them and forget the ones who are not infront of their eyes. But Shri Rama can never be so indifferent. It is the ungrateful who forget their beloveds in their absence. Shri Rama is not such a person.

'Have the two brothers, surviving on fruit and roots, taken a vow of ahimsa? Have they laid down their arms? Or, has the deceitful Ravana murdered them?

'Under these circumstances and doubts looming large over all my thoughts, I wish to end my life. Those who have controlled their thoughts and who have shed all attachment towards the mortal world are fortunate indeed. I bow to the mahatmas who do not grieve on separation from their beloveds and are not hurt by coming into contact with the undesirables.

'I have been separated from my beloved Shri Rama and flutter in this cage built by Ravana. It is time that I courted death.'

15

Trijata's Dream

Trijata was among the rakshasis standing guard in Asoka Vatika. While Sita was being threatened with lynching, Trijata woke up from a dream. Narrating the same to her companions, she said,

'All of you must stop hurting the daughter of king Janaka; you cannot slice and eat her. I have just dreamt that the rakshasas will be destroyed and Sita will regain her ascendant position.

'I saw a palanquin made of ivory flying in the sky. It was drawn by a thousand horses and carried Rama and Lakshmana dressed in white clothes, with garlands of white flowers. The palanquin arrived here.

'I saw Sita dressed in white, sitting on a white mountain surrounded by an ocean. Soon she met Shri Ramachandra who now sat on an elephant with four tusks. After sitting on her husband's lap, Janaki jumped to reach for the sun and moon and wiped their faces with her hands.

'Later, riding a chariot pulled by eight bullocks, Rama accompanied by Sita and Lakshmana, arrived here. Sitting in the Pushpak Vimana they left in the northerly direction.

'Do you know that Rama is glorious and cannot be defeated by the devatas, the asuras or the gandharvas?

'In my dream I saw Ravana dressed in red garments, with his head shaven, taking an oil bath. He was drunk and had just fallen from the Pushpak Vimana. Riding a donkey, our king travelled south. I saw him falling from the donkey and running naked abusing all and sundry. He walked into a stinking pool of muck and drowned. I saw Kumbhakarna, the king's brother, as well as his sons, in a similar situation.

'Vibhishana alone did not meet this fate. I saw him sitting under a white canopy, dressed in white clothes. He was surrounded by melodious music, dancing, blowing of conches and the beating of drums.

'I saw the city of Lanka with its gates smashed to pieces, drowned in the ocean with its chariots, elephants and horses. I saw Lanka being torched by a mighty vanara who came as a messenger of Rama.

'Remember, Rama will not tolerate your harsh treatment of his beloved wife, Janaki. Stop pestering her and ask for her forgiveness; she is generous and will surely forgive you.

'None of the omens that my dream hinted at indicates that Sita will suffer endlessly.

'Look, the bird sitting in his nest on the branch of a tree repeatedly sings in sweet tones assuring Sita of happiness. One can hear the message of 'suswagatam' in its voice. Joyously, it intimates glad tidings.'

Sita heard Trijata's narrative and assured the rakshasis of full protection in the face of an imminent calamity over Lanka.

16

Sita Wavers between Hope and Despair

Even after listening to Trijata's interpretation of her dream, Sita's mind was not at peace. She could not get over Ravana's cruel words. She felt like a baby elephant caught between a lion's paws. She wailed like a young girl left alone in a dense forest. She thought to herself:

'It is true that nobody dies before their time. That is why, even though threatened time and again, I am, though dirty and impure, still alive. Even though devoid of happiness and full of anguish, I am resilient. That is why my heart has not been shattered to pieces like a mountain hit by a thunderbolt.

'Ravana has ordered my death at the end of two months. It would, therefore, not be evil even if I commit suicide. Come what may, I cannot offer this evil person my affection. My condition is that of a thief awaiting a death sentence in jail.

'My beloved Rama, you are not aware that my death is near. All my worship, forgiveness, sleeping on bare earth, chastity and living my life according to the strict rules of dharma have gone waste like favours given to the ungrateful. Following the dharma that does not reward those who practice it, I shall lose my life.

'I wish to end my life with poison or to a sharp weapon; but who will provide me with these here?'

The sorrowing Sita decided to hang herself from a tree with her own braid. She went near a tree and stood holding its branch.

Sita Perceives Auspicious Omens

Standing under the asoka tree, the grieving, chaste and joyless Sita noticed a few auspicious omens. Her large, black and white eye, surrounded by dark brows began to flutter like the red lotus in a pond stirred by fish.

Noticing these auspicious omens, Sita was overjoyed. Like

Chandrama released from Rahu's tentacles, her face began to glow. For a brief moment, she forgot her grief and felt energized. Her mind was at peace and her heart full of joy.

17

Hanuman Approaches Sita

Hanuman was now convinced that his search for Sita, for whom thousands of vanaras had travelled in all the directions, had ended. 'Acting as my master's messenger,' he thought, 'I have discovered the enemy's strength. I have surveyed the interrelations of the rakshasas, the city of Lanka and evaluated the influence of Ravana. It is time that I assure Sita who is desirous of returning to her husband that Shri Rama will rescue her soon. If she ends her life in her grief, what shall I tell Shri Rama?'

Winning Sita's Confidence

Hanuman had other worries as well. He thought, 'Sita might think me to be Ravana if I speak in Sanskrit. She will be frightened. Therefore, I must speak to her in the dialect used by common people living in Ayodhya. Also, if I approach her as a vanara, she might get scared and shriek.

'I am in the midst of a dilemma and cannot let the assignment fail owing to it not having been executed in the right manner. It is like the futility of the darkness that vanishes when the sun rises.

'Giving a careful thought to the possibility of failure, the chances of success, in order to avoid carelessness, to make sure that his flying over the ocean would not be futile, and that Sita would listen to him without fear or agitation, the wise Hanuman decided upon a strategy.

'I shall not disturb her in any manner with my behaviour. She is always focussed on Shri Rama. Therefore, I shall narrate the events of the life of Shri Rama to her. I shall convey his message in words that she can believe in, and thus, settle her doubts.'

Hanuman Narrates the Story of Rama's Life

Hanuman, in wisely chosen words, narrated the story of Rama's life as he knew it. His voice was melodious and his narration rich in devotion. Touching upon the efforts made by Sugreeva to look for Sita, Hanuman said,

'I am one of the thousands of vanaras sent out to look for Sita. At the instance of Sampati, I have traversed the hundred yojanas over the ocean in one jump. I am on the lookout for the large eyed princess. It appears that I have found her. I see the same beauty, the same complexion and the same attributes as were described by Raghava.'

Saying these words, Hanuman fell silent.

Hearing him, Sita was amazed. The coy woman lifted her face and looked at the asoka tree. Hanuman's words had sent a shiver of delight through her body. Remembering Shri Rama, she looked in all directions. Looking all around, she gazed at Pavanaputra Hanuman, of limitless wisdom, the minister of Sugreeva, the vanara king, sitting like the sun shining on the Udayachala Mountain.

Sita could not believe her eyes when she saw, hidden among the asoka branches, the valorous Hanuman dressed in white. She saw a humble, soft-spoken vanara sitting among blooming branches. His eyes glistened like heated gold.

Sita thought to herself,

'He is a frightful vanara. I dare not even look at him.'

Thinking so, Sita almost fainted out of fear. She cried, 'Ha Rama, Ha Lakshmana.' The chaste woman sobbed and wept.

Suddenly, she found the gentle vanara humbly sitting in front of her. She did not know whether he was real or it was just a dream. Looking at him, she thought,

'It seems to be a bad dream; probably just an illusion. However, I must face it if it is real. How can I ignore him who is sitting in front of me, having a form, and narrating the events of Shri Rama's life? The vanara is talking to me. I pray to Brihaspati, the giver of language, to Indra who carries a thunderbolt, to Brahma, the self created and to Agni, that whatever this vanara has told me be nothing but the truth.'

Sita Describes Her Abduction

The glorious Hanuman, with a face red like coral, standing with folded hands touching his forehead, spoke to Sita humbly,

'Dressed in dirty yellow silks, with eyes large as the petals of a blooming lotus, Anindite, who are you? Why do you stand here supporting yourself against a tree? Why do you shed tears like dew drops slipping down a lotus leaf?

'Shobhane, who is your father? Who is your husband?

'Are you the virtuous Rohini, the brightest of stars, separated from Chandrama and fallen from the devaloka to the earth? Are you, by any chance, the auspicious, chaste Arundhati who, having angered Vasishtha, her husband, has arrived here?

'Are you mourning for your father, brother or your husband who has passed away? I do not think of you as divine because you weep, take deep breaths, and are in contact with the earth. Repeatedly you mention the name of some king. You look like a queen and a king's daughter.

'God bless you if you are Sita who was forcibly abducted by Ravana from the Janasthana. Please tell me the truth. Your divine form and tapasvini's dress indicate that you are the queen of Shri Ramachandra.'

Hanuman's words cheered Sita's spirits. She responded by admitting that she indeed was Sita. She narrated her life's events from her birth to her abduction from the Dandakaranya. She told him of the ultimatum of two months laid down by Ravana for her to accede to his demand, and of her determination to end her life.

18

Hanuman Wins over Sita's Confidence

Assuring Sita once again, Hanuman informed her about the well-being of Shri Ramachandra and conveyed Lakshmana's greetings. Sita was full of joy and her confidence in Hanuman strengthened at the mention of Rama's and Lakshmana's names.

As Hanuman moved a step nearer to Sita in order to talk in whispers, she grew suspicious. Out of fear, she sat down on the ground and said,

'It will lead to your death if you are Ravana in disguise, trying to hurt me. I have been reduced to a mere skeleton due to fasting, my unhappiness is enough suffering for me and yet you torture me thus. However, God bless you if you are indeed Shri Rama's messenger. Tell me all about my husband who has been separated from me for so long.

'It is certainly not a dream. Seeing a vanara in a dream cannot be auspicious. However, a vanara cannot be as strong as you claim to be. You must be Ravana in disguise.'

Saying so, Sita was silent.

Hanuman understood Sita's dilemma and decided to talk of Shri Rama's greatness. He assured her that Ravana would soon meet his end. He considered it fortunate that she was still alive. He said,

'Shri Rama too suffers from the pangs of separation from you. Accompanied by my king, Sugreeva, he will arrive soon and with his divine arrows bring death to the evil Ravana. Devi, do not misunderstand me. I am not what you fear and you must trust me.'

It is then that Hanuman narrated to Sita how Rama and Lakshmana had come to Sugreeva for help. He said,

'While looking for you, they befriended Sugreeva, my king, and restored his kingdom to him.

'My king, Sugreeva showed them the ornaments you had scattered on the earth and they identified them as being yours. However, we did not know your whereabouts. I recall Shri Rama fainting upon looking at your ornaments. He was deeply moved. In your absence he burns in the viraha agni just like a volcano spouting fire. He suffers sleeplessness and grief. He worries for your well-being endlessly and pines for you while wandering in fascinating forests, or near streams and waterfalls.

'It was a long struggle to trace your whereabouts. Later, Sampati, brother of Jatayu who had tried to save you from Ravana, revealed your whereabouts to us. Acting on his information, I jumped over the ocean to reach you.

'Devi, this ought to convince you that I am a messenger of Shri Rama. Do not be afraid of me.'

Hanuman apprised Sita with the details of his birth and the source of his strength. He told her how he drew his power from Pavana, the god of winds and his father.

Sita, convinced of his identity, shed tears of joy. Her face looked luminous like the moon just released from Rahu's grip.

Hanuman Hands over an Identification Ring; Sita Laments Her Pathetic Situation

'Devi', said Hanuman, 'here is a ring belonging to Shri Rama. Look at it carefully. Shri Rama himself gave it and I brought it to convince you of my identity. His name is engraved on it.'

Holding her beloved husband's ring, Sita was delighted as if she had reached Shri Rama himself. Her face reflected her joy. She appreciated Hanuman's valour and said,

'I do not take you as an ordinary vanara because you are not afraid even of Ravana. The self-realized Shri Rama has sent you. Hence, I address you my concerns.

'If Shri Rama is well, why does he not like the conflagration of pralaya, destroy the earth surrounded by the ocean?

'The two brothers are powerful enough even to punish the devatas. Why am I made to suffer so long? Perhaps, the end of my suffering is not near.

'Unfortunately, I am out of Shri Rama's sight. Has his love for me, therefore, diminished? Would he ever deliver me from this torture?

'O messenger, Shri Rama loved me more than he loved his parents and relatives. I shall live as long as I am sure of his determination to come here for my rescue.'

Hanuman replied,

'O lotus-eyed woman, Shri Rama does not know of your whereabouts and was terrified to think of any misfortune to have befallen your life. That is why I have come here in search of you, as one of the many who have been sent in various directions looking for you. When I return and inform Shri Rama of your whereabouts, he can attack with the help of the vanara and bear forces. He can still even the unassailable ocean with his arrows and build a bridge over its waters to reach Lanka. He will vanquish anyone who obstructs his path.

'Devi, you will soon behold Shri Rama's auspicious face. He is so immersed in your viraha that he hardly thinks of any other subject.'

Hearing of Shri Rama's sorrow, Sita forgot her own grief and gave up her wish to end her life.

Hanuman Invites Sita to Return with Him; She Declines

While Sita was asking Hanuman to return speedily and ask Shri Rama to attack Lanka because her time was running out, Hanuman invited her to climb on his back and fly to the mainland. However, Sita did not agree to Hanuman's offer. She said,

'O great vanara, I am aware of your strength and speed. You can fly as fast as the winds. No other vanara could have crossed the ocean to reach here. However, in my reckoning, my going with you is unjustified from any point of view. Sitting on your back, moving at such rapid speed, I can faint. I can fall into the ocean when you fly so high while crossing.

'Even when we depart, the rakshasas will be suspicious when they see a woman riding on your back. Under Ravana's orders, his valorous soldiers will chase you. Your life would be in danger when you are accompanied by me. While carrying me, you would be unarmed. How then would you protect yourself?

'If I die, then all efforts made by my husband and his brother will go waste and they will end their lives.

'I am a chaste woman and have been loyal to my husband all my life. Knowingly, I cannot accept the touch of another man. It was perforce that I came into contact with Ravana's body. At that moment I was helpless, powerless and under the control of another person.

'For me the best way out is for Shri Rama to come here, defeat Ravana and then honourably carry me home. I have seen and heard of Shri Rama's valour on the battlefield. Accompanied by Lakshmana, when at war, Shri Rama, flares like a conflagration assisted by the winds.

'Therefore, I ask you to give news of my whereabouts to Shri Rama and persuade him to attack Lanka accompanied by Lakshmana and Sugreeva. Their arrival will bring me back to life and increase my happiness multiple times.'

Hanuman Requests Sita to Give Him a Token of Identification

At this stage, Hanuman explained to Sita why he had offered to carry her away to Kishkindha. Firstly, he wanted to accomplish his mission for Shri Rama at the earliest. Secondly, he had gauged how difficult it would be for everyone to cross the ocean and thirdly, to enter Lanka with an army would be very difficult.

Hanuman requested Sita to give him some token to prove that he had met her. Delighted, Sita narrated an incident that was known only to the two of them. She said,

'Remind Shri Rama of the day when, having taken a bath in a fragrant pond, all drenched, he came and sat in my lap. This was in the northeast of the Chitrakoot Mountain that lies near the river Mandakini, where there is an abundance of water, fruit and roots. A flesh-hungry crow attacked me in order to peck at my skin. He landed several times, pecked at my skin and flew away.

'I was upset and angry. I pulled at the draw-string to tighten my skirt. While doing so, my covering slid a bit and he noticed my nudity. Shri Rama laughed and made fun of me. This made me angry as well as shy. Simultaneously, the crow descended again and pecked me deep with his sharp beak.

'I was now tired and fed up of the crow's antics. I lay in his lap and he consoled me and assuaged my anger. I fell asleep. Later, tired, he slept with his head in my lap.

'Around this time, the crow dived and pierced my breast with his beak. A stream of blood awakened Shri Rama. Angry, he looked at the crow staring at me, his claws drenched in my blood. This bird, in reality, was a son of Indra. Shri Rama decided to teach him a lesson. He took out a straw from the mat and after chanting empowering mantras, directed it at the crow like an arrow.

'After hovering over the three worlds, the crow landed at the feet of my husband and sought mercy. Shri Rama is merciful, and looking at the pitiable condition of the crow, he said,

"My Brahmastra once shot cannot go waste. However, I shall lessen its intensity and limit the damage."

'Saying so, Shri Rama destroyed the right eye of the crow while sparing his life.

'Go and tell my husband that he used the Brahmastra on a petty crow which had hurt me. How can he spare Ravana who has forcibly abducted me? Ask him to take pity on the helpless Sita and not to spare the rakshasas. Why does he not use his sharp arrows to annihilate them?

'Tell my beloved husband that I shall live only for the next two months and shall end my life before Ravana tries to kill me.'

Sita handed over to Hanuman a lovely, studded choodamani (hair ornament) that had adorned her hair till then and tied it in a piece of cloth, to be handed over to her husband. He accepted it with devotion and humility and gave his word to her of a quick return with Shri Rama.

19

Hanuman Destroys the Asoka Vatika

Promising to act according to Sita's directions, Hanuman got ready to depart. However, Sita suggested that he spend another day hidden somewhere and take rest before his departure. She acknowledged the might of Hanuman; however, she desired Shri Rama to conquer Lanka with his forces and establish his supremacy. She, of course, had her doubts whether Sugreeva's forces could cross the ocean and conquer Lanka.

Speaking humbly, Hanuman said,

'If I could come here, there can be no doubt about the other warriors reaching Lanka. The best are never sent as messengers.

'Do not grieve. Rama and Lakshmana will soon arrive and set you free from bondage. You have the support of the two brothers who are glorious like Agni and Pavana. Have patience. It is only a matter of time when I reach them with proper information.'

Hanuman Decides to Destroy the Asoka Vatika

Hanuman felt satisfied at having found Sita and conveyed Rama's message. However, there was something else he wanted to accomplish. One after the other, he pondered over the use of sama, dama, danda or bheda to subjugate the rakshasas. He thought persuasion would not yield any result with the rakshasas because their thinking and conduct was perverse. Likewise, the asuras were rich, hence dama too, would not be effective. Any effort to divide them was doomed to fail. Thus, he was left with danda as his only choice. He decided to display his strength and destroy as much of Lanka as he could.

Hanuman decided to look into the strengths and weaknesses of Lanka before he departed. Such information would be of tremendous use to Sugreeva in planning the invasion. But he needed to provoke Ravana for that.

'The Asoka Vatika,' thought Hanuman 'is a delight to the eyes. Like a conflagration destroying a dry forest, if I set the Vatika on fire, it would certainly infuriate Ravana. He would attack me with armed men, horses, chariots and soldiers carrying lances.

'In this battle, nobody can thwart me. I shall kill each one of Ravana's soldiers and return to Kishkindha.'

An angry Hanuman, moving with the force of a strong wind, uprooted several large trees and threw them hither and thither in the Asoka Vatika. He destroyed the lotus ponds and the artificial hillocks. The charming place looked devastated and ugly. The creepers looked like women disrobed. The birds cried in pain, while the pets ran helter-skelter.

Hanuman destroyed everything except the space occupied by Sita, upon which the rakshasis inquired about him. Sita did not tell them anything.

Ravana Sends Soldiers to Kill or Capture Hanuman

Running breathlessly, the guards informed Ravana of the destruction wrought in the Asoka Vatika by a vanara. The king ordered eighty thousand 'kinkar' soldiers carrying maces and hammers to go and capture the vanara.

The soldiers attacked Hanuman with lances and maces. They surrounded him and challenged him to fight. The latter identified himself as a servant of Shri Rama and a general of Sugreeva. He snatched a metal bar from one of the soldiers and started attacking and killing them one by one. None of them could stand his fury.

Learning of the death of all the kinkar soldiers, an angry Ravana sent Jambumali, a son of his foremost general, Prahasta, to vanquish the troublesome vanara.

Putting on a red uniform and garlands of red flowers, Jambumali advanced to kill Hanuman. With large eyes and a gigantic frame, he pulled at his bow string and it roared like a thunderbolt.

Jambumali struck Hanuman in his arms and at his face. He shot an arrow to strike Hanuman near his heart.

Hanuman in turn hurled a massive rock at Jambumali and then hit him with a sala tree uprooted from the ground. When these efforts were unsuccessful, the Kapishrestha took hold of an iron bar, spun it in the air a few times and attacked the asura general in his chest. Its impact was such that Jambumali's body was torn to smithereens.

Ravana's anger knew no bounds. One after the other, he sent many warriors to subdue and capture or kill Hanuman, but to no avail. None came back alive including his son, Aksha Kumar.

Indrajit Captures Hanuman and Presents Him to Ravana

A sad and angry Ravana sent for his eldest son, Indrajit, the bravest of them all, and said,

'Son, while worshipping Brahma you were blessed with several divine weapons. You are the tallest of my warriors and even Indra acknowledges your prowess. You are protected by your strength and tapasya. You know the right time to strike and are also the wisest of all men in my court.

'Think of all the damage that has been caused by the enemy. Think of the deaths of the kinkar soldiers, Jambumali, the warrior, and the sons of Prahasta and of your brother Aksha Kumar. Take a measure of your prowess and act accordingly. Plan your strategy so that the moment you take to the battlefield, the massacre of my forces comes to an end.

'Even sharp and powerful thunderbolts have failed against the intruder. I thus advise you to go alone and not be hindered with an army. The speed and capability of Maruta's son are immeasurable and he seems to be enjoying limitless power. No weapon is capable of killing that vanara who is glorious like Agni.

'Please consider all these limitations and concentrate on a strategy. It is essential for you to be alert at all times and to carry the divine weapon blessed by Brahma. You must not fail, my son.

'My affection and love for you restrain me from sending you on this expedition. However, my duty as a king and a Kshatriya compels me to do so. A warrior must advance to conquer.'

Indrajit Advances to Subdue Hanuman

Receiving his father's orders and determined to fight, Indrajit did a parikrama of the king and proceeded to fight Hanuman. He looked like a full-blown lotus and walked like the ocean in high tide. Full of joy and determination, Indrajit came out of the palace.

No enemy could withstand Indrajit and his bravery was comparable to Indra. With the swiftness of Garuda, he climbed a chariot drawn by four lions. Soon he arrived to face Hanuman who was sitting at the gates of Asoka Vatika.

Indrajit's arrival made the Kapishrestha happy. Looking at the approaching chariot, Hanuman roared and expanded his body.

The prince pulled at his bowstring that crackled like lightning. Both the warriors engaged in battle like Indra and the king of asuras, Bali. Indrajit's arrows were wasted on Hanuman who with his expanded body floated high in the ethereal realms of Pavana. Indrajit's sharp arrows with golden fins, powerful as thunderbolt, had no effect on Hanuman who escaped them with ease by simply flying away from an approaching dart.

Accepting the invincibility of the vanara, Indrajit decided to ensnare him. He called for the divine astra given by Brahma, aimed it at Hanuman and tied him up. For a moment, the latter fainted and fell down. However, he revived in no time and felt no pain. He recalled Brahma's blessing that he would be able to effortlessly free himself from such a snare whenever he willed, but decided to stay put in order to honour Brahma.

Looking for an Opportunity to Come Face to Face with Ravana

Hanuman argued: 'Being ensnared by a rakshasa looks beneficial in the pursuit of my objective. When presented to the king, I shall talk to him.'

While taking Hanuman to their king, the rakshasa guards teased the prisoner and poked him and hit him in order to hurt him. They tied him with ropes made with bark and freed Hanuman from the divine snare used by Indrajit. The latter was upset to see the divine snare made inoperative by his ignorant soldiers, but was surprised to see a humble Hanuman behaving as if he was a helpless prisoner.

In the Court of Ravana

The Kapishrestha, tied like an elephant in musth, was brought into Ravana's presence. Some of the courtiers wanted him to be killed while others wanted to know his identity, the purpose of his visit and the name of the person on whose behalf he had arrived in Lanka.

Ravana sat glorious and furious like the mid-day sun. With blood-shot eyes, he angrily looked at Hanuman. Quizzed by his ministers, Hanuman replied,

'I am a messenger of the vanara king, Sugreeva.'

Hanuman was surprised at Indrajit's conduct. However, his anger for Ravana's abduction of Sita was reflected in his eyes as he looked at the king of Lanka seated on a high throne wearing crowns made of shining gold and studded with precious pearls. The king wore ornaments unique in design, silken robes, and with his ten crowned heads, looked like the Mandarachala Mountain with glistening peaks.

His throne was made of crystal and marble, embedded with precious stones and covered by eye-catching carpets. Several young women, in expensive finery, stood behind him.

Four wise rakshasa ministers, Durdhara, Prahasta, Mahaparshva, and Nikumbha sat by the king's side. The haughty king looked glorious like the earth surrounded by the four oceans. Hanuman admired the king's magnificent presence, matchless strength and dazzling glow. Thought Hanuman,

'It is surprising to see Ravana endowed with all the traits of a good king. But for his overpowering inclination towards adharma, he could have been the protector of Devaloka along with Indra. On account of his condemnable, cruel and heartless deeds, the devatas as well as the asuras fear him. If angry, he can immerse the entire world in an ocean or annihilate the universe.'

Hanuman Explains the Purpose of His Visit; Advises Ravana to Walk the Righteous Path

Ravana flew into a rage upon seeing Hanuman. Despite all the damage caused by the latter, Ravana controlled himself and worried about the identity of this vanara.

'Can he be Nandi whom I had made fun of at Mount Kailas?' he thought.

'He had cursed me that a vanara will lead to my fall. Has he come today as a vanara to avenge his insult? Or, is he Banasura, son of Bali, in disguise?'

Ravana asked Prahasta to ask Hanuman his identity. 'Wherefrom has this evil spirit arrived? What for? Why has he laid the Pramadavana desolate and killed the rakshasas? '

Prahasta addressed Hanuman in soft words and asked him to say the truth without fear.

'We shall release you if you tell us the truth,' said he. 'Have you been sent by Indra or Kubera, Yama or Varuna? Is it Vishnu's devious scheme to harass us?'

He also emphasized that Hanuman shall be killed if he utters a lie.

Ignoring Prahasta's words, Hanuman addressed Ravana thus,

'I am not a messenger for any of the gods you mentioned. I destroyed the Vatika in order to have an audience with you. I killed your soldiers only in defence because they attacked me. I am so blessed by Brahma that neither the devatas nor the asuras can ensnare me. No weapon can bind me, no ropes hold my movement.

'I have come to you to carry out a job entrusted to me by Shri Rama. I am his messenger. Therefore, listen to me with care.

'Sugreeva, the vanara king is your brother. He has enquired about your well being.

'Lakhs of vanaras are looking for Sita outside the confines of your city. Some of them can move with the speed of Garuda; others like the wind. Nobody can stop their movement. Their king, Sugreeva, has promised to restore Sita to Shri Rama.

'I am Hanuman, the son of Pavana. I have crossed the hundred yojana wide ocean to reach Lanka in search of Sita and have found her confined in your custody.

'O wise king, you are well versed in the tenets of dharma and artha. You have garnered the fruit of tapasya over a long period. It does not behove you to detain a woman who belongs to another person.

'Evil deeds, done in violation of dharma, are fraught with serious consequences and will lead to your destruction. Wise men like you ought not to indulge in such acts.

'None can stay happy or hide having done Shri Rama a bad turn. Therefore, listen to my just and fair advice and hand over Janaki to her husband with dignity.

'I have had Sita's darshana and have thus attained what you perceived impossible. Shri Rama will look after the rest.

'Sita is drowned in a pool of sorrow and suffers endlessly in your custody, away from her husband. You are not aware that she is like a serpent with five heads and cannot be subdued by devatas or asuras by force.

'Do not lay waste all the good that you have earned through tough penance. You have forgone your immortality and Shri Rama and Sugreeva are neither devatas, nor yakshas nor asuras. How then would you save yourself from their revenge?

'Your good deeds have been subsumed by your evil deeds. Your adharma overrides your virtuous actions. For long you have enjoyed the fruit of your good deeds; it is now time to reap the fruit of your crimes.

'Think of the annihilation of the rakshasas in the Janasthana, of the killing of Vali and of the friendship between Sugreeva and Shri Rama. You decide which way lies your salvation.

'I can destroy the entire Lanka with all its forces, horses and elephants single-handed. However, that is not my mandate. Shri Rama himself will destroy those who have humiliated Sita.

'Think of Sita as the dark night which will destroy all of you. For you, she is Yama's noose. Do not put your head into it.

'Lanka with its high mansions, its wide streets will soon be burnt in the fire of Shri Rama's and Sita's anger. Do not push your kith and kin, your friends and ministers, sons and daughters and all that makes them live happily, into this conflagration.

'I am a mere messenger. Shri Rama can destroy the world and recreate it anew. He is like Vishnu, master of the three worlds. Neither the self-created Brahma, nor the three-eyed Rudra, nor the majestic Indra, can face him in battle.'

Vibhishana's Counsel of Patience to Ravana

Ravana was angered by Hanuman's words of caution and ordered the soldiers to kill him. However, his younger brother, the pious Vibhishana, advised him otherwise. He said,

'Rakshasaraja, forgive me for this interruption and hear my words. A king, who is conscious of the proprieties, does not order the killing of a messenger. Killing this vanara is against dharma and public policy and you must give up anger. You are learned in shastras and rajadharma and know the subtleties of parmartha well. If a wise man like you succumbs to anger, your study of the scriptures will be in vain.

'It is the opinion of the wise that a messenger must not be killed under any circumstances or upon provocation. He merely represents his master and is bound by his orders.

'Kindly decide on another punishment for the vanara. If he is killed, no other vanara can cross the ocean and you would have no means of information about the movement of the enemy. In his absence there would be none who can instigate the two brothers to take a stand against you which will dishearten our soldiers, who are eager to show their prowess in battle'.

Following Vibhishana's advice, Ravana decided against putting Hanuman to death.

21

Lanka Dahan

Appreciating Vibhishana's counsel, Ravana said, 'Vibhishana, you are right regarding the protection that ought to be given to a messenger. However, this vanara must be punished for the death and destruction he has caused in Lanka.

'A vanara loves his tail as it is his only ornament. Soldiers, set his tail on fire at the earliest. He should be paraded in the city and the squares with his tail on fire.'

Obeying their master's command, the guards tied old cotton sheets around Hanuman's tail. They soaked it in oil and set it on fire.

An angry Hanuman expanded his body and started hitting the guards with his burning tail. He knew he was strong enough to take on all the rakshasas single-handedly, but he decided otherwise. He tried to devise a plan so as to make the residents of Lanka aware of his prowess and might. He wished to go through the streets of Lanka and observe the fortification, but as a warrior and not as a captive.

Hanuman is Paraded as a Captive

The heartless rakshasa guards joyously began parading Hanuman in the streets of Lanka. They announced his crimes while blowing on conches and bheri. Hanuman walked behind them enjoying the sights and looking at large mansions, glowing streets and flowering lawns.

After some time, Hanuman made up his mind to teach the asuras a lesson. Assuming a diminutive form, he slipped out of the shackles that bound him. He grew large again and started jumping high and roaring in a loud voice. He even snatched a large iron rod from a guard and killed a few asuras in no time.

Lanka on Fire

Hanuman decided to offer some palaces of the high and mighty in Lanka as ahuti to Agni. Sparkling like lightning in the clouds, he started dashing in and out of Lanka's palaces. Soon, he had set the residences of several ministers such as Prahasta and Mahaparshva on fire. He did not spare the houses of Indrajit, Jambumali and Sumali too. He left untouched the mansion where Vibhishana lived but except that, Hanuman burnt a large number of mansions and houses along with whatever lay inside.

As the rakshasas hurried to save their homes and wealth, they lost all enthusiasm of punishing Hanuman. They ran in all directions to save their women and children.

Hanuman Worries about Sita's Safety

The Kapishrestha extinguished his burning tail by immersing it in the ocean and was continuously worried about Sita's safety. He feared Ravana punishing Sita for the havoc he had caused and chastised himself for his hurried decision. He thought,

'I am a fool to have set Lanka on fire without thinking of Sita's fate. I have committed a great sin under the influence of overwhelming anger. In case she is punished for this act of mine, Shri Rama will not live. I have defeated the very purpose for which I came here and have behaved irresponsibly.'

At the same time, Hanuman heard some asuras talking of the miraculous escape of the prisoner while the city of Lanka was burning. Hearing them, Hanuman regained his confidence and happiness.

Reaching Asoka Vatika, Hanuman met Sita and assured her that Shri Rama and Lakshmana would soon invade Lanka and release her from captivity. He told her that Ravana would be killed at the hands of Shri Rama and that she would be a witness to the event.

Hanuman Returns to His Waiting Companions

Hanuman had completed his assignment successfully. It was time to return to his companions who patiently waited for him on the other side of the ocean. He reached the top of the Arishtha Mountain which was touched by auspicious sunbeams. At this scenic place, Hanuman stood ready for another jump across the ocean. He expanded his body and leapt, moving with the force of a mighty wind. He moved as if swallowing the vast expanse of the sky, scratching the moon's orbit with his nails, wrapping the stellar and solar universe in his arms and dragging the masses of clouds in his wake. Looking glorious, Hanuman effortlessly moved through white, red, orange, blue and purple clouds massed in the sky.

Reaching the Mahendra Mountain as a victor, Hanuman announced his arrival with the roar of a lion. Angada and Jambavan, hearing his roar, welcomed him with joy, sure of his success. Many of the vanaras danced with glee and some others made a seat of branches for him to rest.

Looking at the anticipation in everyone's demeanour, the brave Hanuman addressed his companions thus,

'I was successful in locating the whereabouts of Devi Sita; she is being held in Asoka Vatika as a prisoner. She is being guarded by fierce rakshasis and continually tortured to give in to Ravana's wishes. She is impatient to meet Shri Ramachandra. She has grown lean and has lost her charm after separation from her beloved Shri Rama.'

The words, 'I had her darshana,' fell like drops of Amrita into the ears of the vanara warriors standing around Hanuman and listening to him in rapt attention. They felt that their lives had been saved. Addressing Hanuman, Angada said,

'Kapishrestha, none compares with you in valour and courage. You have traversed the vast ocean twice and in finding Sita have given us a lease of life. We are fortunate in that you could meet the illustrious Sita. It will lessen Shri Rama's sorrow.'

Sitting gloriously on the Mahendra Mountain, Hanuman narrated the entire story of his journey to Lanka, his meeting with Sita and subsequent arrest by Indrajit. He described the meeting between Ravana and Sita during the king's visit to Asoka Vatika and of Sita's declining health and sorrow. He emphasized Sita's desire for Shri Rama to invade Lanka and free her of her captivity. He talked of the exchange of Shri Rama's ring and Sita's choodamani and about his setting fire to Lanka.

To an audience listening with rapt attention, Hanuman exhorted further action. He said,

'It will not be wise for us to invade Lanka on our own. That is not our mandate from Sugreeva. We had been asked to trace Sita's whereabouts but not to mount an invasion. Shri Rama had sworn to rescue Sita and bring her back in the presence of our warriors and he should be the one to do so. Let us go and report our findings to Shri Rama and ask him to take further action.'

22

Hanuman Arrives at Kishkindha to Brief Rama

While Angada and his companions began their journey towards Kishkindha, Rama's sorrow knew no bounds at not having got any information of Sita yet. Seeing Rama grieving thus, Sugreeva said,

'Dear brother, be patient. There is no doubt that my warriors have been able to trace Devi Sita. Otherwise, they would not have taken more time than they were assigned to accomplish the task. Grieve no more, my lord.'

Shortly, the vanaras led by Angada and Hanuman approached Kishkindha and hurried to Rama to convey the fortunate flow of events. Bowing his head at Rama's feet, Hanuman told him that Devi Sita, living a chaste life, was alive and unharmed.

'I met her, my master', he said.

Rama and Lakshmana were overjoyed to hear these words. Tears of joy adorned Rama's eyes. He took Hanuman into his arms as he thanked Sugreeva for his help.

Hanuman Describes His Meeting with Sita

The audience assembled at the scenic Prashravana Mountain listened with rapt attention as Hanuman narrated the incidents in Lanka and his meeting with Sita. He said,

'Devi Sita is detained in the custody of fierce rakshasis who threaten her all the time. She is deeply attached to Shri Rama and thinks of him at all times. Ravana has allowed her two months to surrender. At the moment, Vaidehi is physically unharmed but at the end of those months, Ravana has ordered the rakshasis to kill her.'

Rama was anxious to know more details and solicitously enquired about his beloved. He said,

'Where has she been kept in captivity? Does she still love me? Tell me in detail all about Vaidehi.'

Thinking of Sita, Hanuman bowed towards south paying obeisance to her. He narrated all the events in Lanka in detail. Handing over the identification gem to Rama, Hanuman said,

'Desirous of sighting Sita, I crossed the ocean, a hundred yojanas wide. Situated in the south is Lanka where the vile Ravana rules. I had her darshan in the Pramadavana where she was sitting surrounded by frightful rakshasis. She is suffering while she ought to be spending her time in your pleasant company. She has decided to end her life if you do not rescue her in two months.

'My lord, Sita thinks of you all the time. I found her with great effort. I gained her confidence by narrating the glorious tale of the Ikshavaku dynasty. She was happy to learn of your safety.

'She continues to be chaste and has turned down all advances made by Ravana. To make sure that you believe me, she told me of the incident of a crow harassing her at Chitrakoot. She handed me this gem as proof of her identity. She desired that I give this choodamani to you when my king Sugreeva is nearby.

'Sita sits imprisoned in Ravana's pleasure garden. Like a frightened doe she casts glances of suspicion and doubt all around. Raghava, I have narrated to you whatever had transpired. The time has come to cross the ocean with our entire might.'

Rama is Moved to Tears

A weeping Rama embraced Hanuman, and Lakshmana also wept upon hearing of Sita's pain. Looking at Sita's hair ornament, Rama said to Sugreeva,

'Friend, my heart bleeds looking at this gem. At the time of our marriage, my father in law, the king Janaka had gifted this piece to her; its lustre has been lost ever since it parted from Sita. This gem had come out of the ocean and was worshipped by devatas. Beholding it thus, I feel as if I am in Sita's presence.

'Lakshmana, nothing can be worse than my looking at this gem without its being worn by Sita.

'Hanuman, kindly repeat Sita's words; they revive me like the drops of cold water sprinkled on my face. Show me the way to the land where my Sita sits in captivity.'

Hanuman then narrated to Rama how Sita had declined to sit on his back when he had offered to cross the ocean carrying her. She had said, 'Mahakapi, of my own volition I cannot come into contact with another male's body other than that of Shri Rama. That is against my dharma. I was helpless when Ravana touched my limbs. It was my fate. Go where the two brothers are and tell them to release me from my predicament. Tell them how I am being terrorized all the time. I wish you a safe journey.

'It will enhance Shri Rama's prestige if he comes to conquer Lanka and kills Ravana. He must not try to take me away stealthily as Ravana had done.'

YUDDHAKANDAM

1

Sugreeva's Forces March to the Land's End

Rama Acknowledges Hanuman's Accomplishment

Rama was all praise for the effort put in and the success achieved by Hanuman and all others who had gone south in search of Sita. Expressing his appreciation he said,

'Hanuman has accomplished a great task. I cannot imagine anyone else doing this job. He has maintained his dignity, completed the task assigned to him, and has fully satisfied his king. Tracing the whereabouts of Vaidehi, looking at her in person, he has protected dharma and the honour of the Ikshavaku dynasty.

'I feel humble that I cannot reward Hanuman for bringing such happy tidings. However, I shall take him in my arms because that is all I can give.'

Saying so, an emotionally overwhelmed Rama took Hanuman into a warm embrace. Later, he continued,

'Friends, we have succeeded in tracing Sita but crossing the vast expanse of the ocean appears to me to be a daunting task. I feel disheartened thinking of how the vanaras will cross the ocean. Remember, Sita too had raised this doubt while talking to Hanuman. Is there a way out of this dilemma?'

Sugreeva Cheers up Rama

It was Sugreeva's turn to cheer up his dejected friend. Assuring Rama of all that could possibly be done, he said,

'O mighty warrior, you ought not to grieve like ordinary mortals. Now that we have traced Sita's location and the enemy's land, I do not see any reason for your sorrow. We shall devise some strategy to cross the ocean and destroy the enemy.

'A person who laments all the time, gives up the desire to be victorious, and feels humble for no reason, meets with failure in all his activities.

'My commanders are brave and are eager to accomplish the task. I can see the joy on their faces when we talk of crossing the ocean and killing Ravana. I, too, am determined to complete this assignment.

'Raghava, we must think of a scheme to bridge the ocean. Once a bridge is in place, our forces will cross the ocean and our victory will be assured.

'O wise Rama, at this moment, gather all your inherent strength, your habitual courage and energy. The chivalrous mahatmas do not grieve for what has been lost or destroyed but rather look forward to what can be done. Grief is destructive.

'None can stand against you in the battlefield. The job entrusted by you to the vanaras cannot go amiss. The Kshatriyas, if soft towards their enemies, can never succeed. Their rage alone frightens the enemy.

'Using your keen intellect, please suggest a way out. How do we cross the ocean?'

Vanara Sena on the March

Addressing Hanuman, Rama said,

'The sun is at his peak and it is midday, and Vijay Muhoorta is an auspicious time for departure. Ravana cannot escape me, nor can Lanka disregard its fate of being destroyed by me. Sita's hopes will be revived when she gets the news of our departure. Today is an auspicious day, Sugreeva, we ought to depart today.

'All the omens are good. My right eyebrow throbs indicating my victory.

'Let our forces be led by the commander-in-chief Neel.'

Addressing Neel, Rama said,

'Neel, you must move with speed on a road that has an abundance of fruit and roots, dense forest with cool shade on both sides of it and a supply of cold water and honey. Beware of the asuras and their tricks such as poisoning the edible fruit and drinkable water on your route. The vanaras must search the caves and pits near the path to look for the enemy. Otherwise, the asuras might attack us from behind.

'I shall be in the centre of the forces, sitting on Hanuman's shoulder like Indra on Airavata. Kumara Angada will, likewise, carry Lakshmana.'

The forces of Sugreeva set out to conquer Lanka. A number of soldiers stood guard on all sides. Others moved as a phalanx to open the route. They drank fragrant wine and ate sweet fruit. They carried long shafts of uprooted trees on their shoulders. Senapati Neel kept his forces in control by taking rounds of each segment.

The soldiers were under strict orders not to vandalize crops or towns en-route. Following Shri Rama's orders, his forces skirted the townships and farmlands.

Auspicious Omens

Lakshmana pointed out many good omens to Rama on their onward march. He said,

'Raghava, I see many auspicious omens all around us. These indicate that you will succeed in your mission and soon kill Ravana to be reunited with Sita.

'A cool, delightful and rejuvenating breeze blows in the wake of our forces. Various animals and birds sing a welcome song. The forest reverberates with songs of joy. Even the sun shines resplendent in a cloudless sky. The pure and resplendent Saptarishis go in parikrama around Dhruva shining on their right.

'In the sky, we see the Rajarshi Trishanku, our ancestor, clearly visible in the company of the Maharishi Vasishtha. Further, the constellation Vishakha (Libra) the most auspicious of the constellations for the descendants of Ikshavaku, glows without obstruction.

'On the contrary, the constellation Moola, favouring the asuras looks dim and affected by meteors. The shooting meteors predict the downfall of the rakshasas.

'The woods overflow with pools of clear and sweet water and provide sufficient fruit in the orchards as if in greeting and welcoming our arrival.

'Arya, looking at these favourable omens you ought to be happy.'

Arrival at the Seashore

The frolicking vanaras marched together and soon arrived at the Mahendra Mountain on the seashore. The mountain was a pleasant sight with mineral-rich rocks jutting out of it. Its forest was rich and fragrant with honey; while the black bees droned, the sandalwood trees spread their fragrance. Blooming creepers of ketaki, sinduvar and vasanti spread all over, as well as the madhavi creepers.

Sitting on the top of the Mahendra Mountain, Rama looked at the vast ocean. Accompanied by Sugreeva and Lakshmana, he then descended to the shore at the base of the mountain, into a rich forest. Here the rocks had been washed by the rolling ocean waves. Addressing his worries to Sugreeva, Rama said,

'Beholding the ocean with my own eyes, my worries have multiplied, Sugreeva. The ocean is limitless. How shall we cross it?

'For the present, order all the forces to rest on the shore. No commander shall part company with his troops for any reason. The soldiers must protect themselves from the deceptive asuras' stealthy attacks.'

The Majestic Ocean

Looking at the waves lifted high by the mighty winds, the vanara forces felt exhilarated. They sat on the shore trying to see land on the other side, across the vast expanse of water, which would be Lanka. There was no island visible to the eye and all they could see was ocean waters, tumultuous and forceful.

Full of frightening crocodiles, the ocean looked awesome and fearsome. The ocean was difficult to cross and with forest all around, the means to cross it were not easily available. The playful tides raised by the winds appeared to be enjoying their rise and fall, and created a hollow feeling in Rama's heart in trying to devise a strategy to cross the ocean.

The expanse of the waterbody was immense and such that the water had become one with the sky. If the stars sparkled in the firmament, the ocean was rich in pearls. Thick clouds overcast the sky while high tides were all over the sea. The highly intelligent vanara warriors noticed that buffeted by the winds, the ocean touched the sky with its waves. Then suddenly, to their amazement, the sea became restless with its water going round and round in whirlpools with a loud roar.

2

Rama Longs for Sita

As the vanara forces settled on the beach, Rama expressed his anguish to Lakshmana. He said,

'They say that
The sorrows lessen with the passage of time.
However,
Day by day, my grief multiplies,
Because
I cannot have even a glimpse of my charming woman.

'It hurts me not that my beloved sits afar.
It hurts me not that she was abducted.
My sorrow drowns me because
The lifespan allowed her
Runs out fast.

'O breeze, you blow where sits my kanta.
Saturated with her touch,
Caress my limbs.
That alone will cool the fever of my anguish and
Bring me joy,
Like a look at the moon.

'My love had cried, 'Ha Nath,'
While being abducted.
That cry burns my body entire,
Like poison settled in the innards.

'The fire of my love,
Fuelled by the grief of her separation,
By my worrying about her, and

Its leaping flames,
Day and night,
Consume my body.

'You stay put,
Sumitranandana.
I, alone shall enter the sea and go to sleep.
Under those waters,
The fire of my longing for her
Cannot destroy me.

'I slept with the stunning Sita on the ground
All these years.
It sufficed for me who desired her all the time.
I can survive like that even now.

'The rice stalks survive
Even if the furrows are dry.
I live because
I hear that Sita lives.

'When will come the time
When defeating the enemy,
I shall cast my eyes upon
The slim, lotus-eyed Sita?
For me she is Rajyalakshmi.
For me she is the harbinger of prosperity.

'Her teeth are lovely.
Her lips are luscious and red like the bimba fruit.
Her face is like a lotus in full bloom.
Like a sick person taking his medicine,
When shall I raise her face and kiss her?

'Her breasts are round,
Heavy and firm like the tala fruit.
Close set, trembling a bit.
When will the twain
Touch me, skin to skin?

'There is none to protect
The kohl-eyed, chaste Sita who sits
Surrounded by the rakshasis,
While I, her protector, sit here simply bemoaning.

'Sita,
The daughter of the king, Janaka,
The daughter-in-law of the king, Dashratha, and
My beloved,
How does she sleep in the company of those vile women?

'She was naturally of a delicate build.
Sorrowing and fasting,
Confined in the enemy land,
Sita must have further lost her glow and weight.

'When will the time arrive
When piercing the rakshendra, Ravana's chest,
With my sharp arrows,
I shall assuage our sorrow?

'When will the chaste and truthful Sita,
Beautiful like a devakanya,
Shed tears of joy in my embrace?

'When shall I be able to suddenly put off,
Like a dirty coat,
The heavy weight of sorrow deep
Which I carry
Because of my separation from Maithili?'

The day came to an end, with the sun becoming one with the ocean and losing its intensity. Lakshmana counselled his brother to be patient and persevere.

With Sita solely occupying his mind and thought, Rama said his evening prayers.

3

Ravana Longs for Sita

Ravana's Council of War

Looking at the severe damage caused by Hanuman who had displayed Indra's bravery, Ravana felt humiliated. Addressing his ministers he said,

'We all considered Lanka to be impregnable. Yet, Hanuman, a mere vanara, entered the city, met Sita and destroyed many palaces and fortifications. He killed a number of my high ranking rakshasas and created a disruption never seen before.

'I trust your wisdom, ministers, and seek your advice as to what course of action we ought to adopt. The wise say that a sound advice offered by ministers leads to victory.

'You all are very wise and I entreat you to decide upon a line of action after careful consideration. I shall follow your considered advice, irrespective of what it may be.

'According to my information, assisted by thousands of vanaras, Rama is mounting an invasion on Lanka. In order to cross the ocean, they will either dry it or find some other means of crossing it. I ask you to offer your suggestions on how to combat this menace.'

The rakshasa ministers were, no doubt, brave in battle. However, they lacked wisdom that is required for counsel. They flattered Ravana with the tales of his heroic deeds during his battles against Kubera, the demon Maya, and the yakshas. They promised to fight to victory with lances, rods of iron, maces and thunderbolts. They said,

'Master, invading Yamaloka, you had vanquished Yama's forces that stood deep like the ocean. You conquered even death. Sometime ago, this earth was inhabited by the Kshatriyas, some of them braver than Rama. Yet, you conquered them and put them to death. Rama can never stand against you.

'We are sure that you might not have to go to battle at all; the brave Indrajit alone will annihilate the vanaras. He had single-handedly captured Indra from the midst of devata forces and brought him as a prisoner to Lanka. We, therefore, request you to assign this task to the prince, Indrajit.'

One by one, several commanders of the asura forces stood up and counselled Ravana thus for taking up the battle with Rama. Among them were Prahasta, Durmukh, Bajradanstra, Kumbhakarna's son Nikumbha, and Vajrahanu, large as a mountain. Each one claimed to be brave enough by himself to take on the vanara sena and kill all of them single-handedly.

Vibhishana Dissuades Ravana from Taking on Shri Ramachandra

From this sea of flattery, Vibhishana alone stood up to tender some sane advice to his elder brother. He said,

'Brother, in the nitishastra, the learned have laid down directions for the use of force where the policies of sama, dama and bheda have not been successful. A well thought out strike succeeds only if the enemy is careless, or is under attack by another, or when his forces have been depleted by an epidemic.

'Shri Ramachandra is neither careless nor of a feeble determination to win. He is assisted by the vanara armies. He has conquered anger and, therefore, he is invincible. Do not hope to defeat such a mighty warrior with such ease.

'Generals, you underestimate the strength of Hanuman who could reach Lanka in a single jump across the ocean. It is unwise to underestimate the strength of the enemy forces before properly analysing it. It is on the basis of proper information that such a step should be taken.

'What crime had Rama committed against our king that my brother abducted his wife from the Janasthana? He had killed Khara only after being attacked by him. Everyone has a right to defend himself with his entire might. If Sita was abducted for this reason alone, we ought to send her back as early as possible. Otherwise a grave misfortune shall befall us all. The result of this abduction and unwise act of war shall not lead to anything but strife.

'Rama is a dharmatma as well as a warrior; his enmity would lead to our end. Hand over Maithili to him before he destroys Lanka. Otherwise our brave generals will meet their end, and our country will be trampled by the vanara hordes.

'You are my elder brother and I offer you wise counsel. I speak for the good of Lanka, its people and my kin. Send Sita to her husband before Rama, in order to kill you, rains his glorious, unbreakable and invincible arrows on us.

'Dear brother, give up your anger and lust which is leading to further disruption of dharma and happiness. Take pity on us so that we can live happily with our families. Please hand over Maithili to the son of Dashratha.'

Ravana dismissed the court of council and walked into his comfortable and lavish apartment to ponder over the situation.

Early next morning Vibhishana went to his brother's inner chambers where the purohits were chanting prayers for the king's victory. He greeted his brother and began pointing out the evil omens appearing around them that indicated impending destruction.

'Looking to such omens, brother, I suggest that you send Vaidehi back to Rama,' said Vibhishana. 'It is in the interest of your people.'

Listening to Vibhishana's polite, logical, meaningful, beneficial arguments, truly relevant in the past, present and in the future, Ravana flew into a rage. He replied,

'Vibhishana, I do not foresee any danger anywhere. Rama will never possess Maithili again. The two brothers cannot win in a battle against me even if the devatas led by Indra come to their rescue.'

Saying this, Ravana bade farewell to Vibhishana.

4

Ravana is Advised to Use Force on Sita; Vibhishana Counsels Restraint

Ravana's lust for Maithili grew with Rama's approach towards the ocean. He pined for her day and night and grew weak in thought and action. His well-wishers grew contemptuous of his behaviour and condemned him. However, nothing deterred Ravana from his evil objective. Though the time for considering reconciliation as an option was over, he summoned his council again.

He began by giving directions about posting troops in defensive positions to safeguard his kingdom. Later, addressing his generals and ministers, he said,

'Members of my council, you are competent to consider all issues of dharma, artha and kama, however pleasant or unpleasant, beneficial or adverse, hurtful or endearing these might be. You have never let me down and I wish the same this time also. I desire to enjoy this immensely powerful and rich kingdom, surrounded by all of you, for a long time. Presently, the deed that has led to this battle is done and I seek your approval of what I have done.

'I abducted Rama's beloved queen, Sita from Dandakaranya, a forest under the control of the rakshasas. However, that woman never gave in to my advances and sits like a hermit in the Asoka Vatika. She, in my view, happens to be the most charming woman in the world and a mere glance at her fires my lust. I have lost all control over my desires and have become a slave to Kamadeva. I am restless in mind and body and seek your advice for further action.'

Ravana lied to his audience that Sita had asked for a year's time to consider his proposal and that he had accepted her demand. Further, he said,

'My lust has fatigued me just like a horse running a long race. I am not afraid of the enemy, especially those wild vanaras, Rama and

Lakshmana. They cannot cross the limitless ocean that is full of crocodiles, large fish, several other aquatic animals and whales.

'In the end we shall be victorious.'

Kumbhakarna Reprimands Ravana

Listening to Ravana's lamentation, Kumbhakarna was upset and angry. He stood up and said,

'Why did you not consult us when you decided to abduct Sita from Rama's ashrama? Maharaja, you have abducted another's woman through deceit and this shall be seen as improper conduct by a king as mighty as you. Evil deeds committed without thinking of consequences and remedies thereof, and acting against dharma and the shastras, cause harm like ahuti added to yagya while chanting mantras to invoke a curse upon another.

'Maharaja, without thinking of its consequences in the future, you have started a chain of grave events. Like the poisoned meal killing the one who consumes it, Rama will kill you. You should consider yourself lucky that you are still alive.

'Dear brother, you have done wrong this time. However, being a part of your family, I shall still stand by you and destroy your enemies. I shall fight Indra, Surya, Agni, Vayu, Kubera and Varuna for your sake. I shall transform into a giant with sharp, large and strong jaws and frighten the devatas with my roar. I shall sip Rama's blood; you can rest assured.

'Eat, drink and be merry. Once I have killed Rama, Sita will submit to your advances forever.'

Mahaparshva Incites Ravana to Force Sita's Submission

Keeping in mind Ravana's anger, thinking deep as was his wont, standing with folded hands, Mahaparshva addressed the king saying,

'Maharaja, he is an idiot who even after entering an inaccessible forest teeming with wild beasts and reptiles, and discovering honey that is fit to drink, does not enjoy it.

'You are invincible and there is none above you. Crush your enemies and enjoy Vaidehi. Like a wild cock, force yourself upon her and relish her body.

'Once you have achieved your objective, is there anything left to be afraid of?

'I believe in danda alone as against the policies of sama, dama and bheda advocated by the learned.'

Ravana liked Mahaparshva's observations and his advice was music to his ears. However, he expressed the fear of a curse that Brahma had pronounced on him a long time ago. He said,

'Once, noticing a luminous apsara going towards Brahma's abode in the heavens, I had forcibly ravished her. Brahma had cursed that if this be repeated by me, my head would be shattered into a hundred pieces. Hence, using force to make Vaidehi lie in my bed would be the death of me. But other than that, I am sure of my prowess.

'I can advance like the ocean and move as fast as the wind. Rama is unaware of this. He invades me in ignorance. Striking him with hundreds of thunderbolts released from my arrows, I shall reduce him to ashes. On the battlefield, even Varuna and Indra-of-the-thousand-eyes cannot vanquish me.'

Vibhishana Pleads for Restraint Again

Vibhishana was the only person in Ravana's court who had the courage to advise the king contrary to his intention and desire. In meaningful words, speaking truthfully, he said politely,

'Brother, Sita is a giant cobra who shall lead us all to our ends. Hurry and entrust Maithili to the son of Dashratha before the giant vanaras, fighting with their claws and teeth, mount an assault on Lanka.

'Rajan, Kumbhakarna, Indrajit, Mahaparshva, Mahodara, Nikumbha, Kumbha or Atikaya, none of them will survive when fighting Rama.'

Listening to Vibhishana, Prahasta, the Senapati, retorted,

'We are afraid neither of the devatas nor of the asuras. The emotion of fear is unknown to us. In the battlefield, we are not afraid of the yakshas, the giant nagas, ferocious birds or the poisonous serpents. How then can we be afraid of Rama, a mere human?'

Vibhishana replied patiently,

'Prahasta, whatever you, the Maharaja, and Kumbhakarna have spoken about Rama, is not realistic. Rama is a capable prince endowed with many qualities of the mind, body and spirit. He has the ability to accomplish any task and believes in the supremacy of dharma. Born in the Ikshavaku dynasty, he is a great warrior.

'Prahasta, you are boasting thus because you have not faced Rama and his sharp, penetrating, and invincible arrows yet. Our king is a slave of Kama and seems to be surrounded by friends like you who can accomplish nothing except the destruction of our race.

'Save your king, even if you have to pull him away by force in the interest of the rakshasas and for the benefit of the king. I advise you to hand over Maithili to Rama without any further delay.

'He alone is a true minister who after weighing the strength and weakness of the enemy, exercising his judgment, tenders sound and impartial advice.'

5

Vibhishana is Humiliated and Compelled to Seek Rama's Protection

Indrajit, Ravana's eldest son, did not like his uncle's advice to the king. He called him a coward and his talk meaningless. Addressing his father, he said,

'Father, in our family, my uncle alone is bereft of bravery. He lacks perseverance and is devoid of glory. He is scaring us into submission to two human princes whom even an insignificant rakshasa can kill. I had compelled even Indra to give up Swargaloka and seek protection on the earth. All the devatas were terrified of me. If I could subdue their pride, how am I unfit to fight the two human princes?'

Vibhishana responded saying,

'Indrajit, you are young and immature and your understanding of right and wrong is still not complete. You call yourself your father's friend but in advising him thus you are being his foremost enemy.

'Rama's arrows shine like the Brahmastra. They are ferocious like the Yama danda.'

Addressing Ravana, Vibhishana said again,

'Rajan, we can live in peace only if we hand over Sita along with riches, celestial clothes, lovely ornaments, rare gems and precious stones to Rama.'

Ravana Calls Vibhishana Traitor

Ravana had been hearing Vibhishana talk for too long and was deeply offended. He squarely rebuked Vibhishana and said,

'One might live with an enemy or with an angry, poisonous serpent but never with a friend who is in the service of the enemy. I know of the behaviour of the members of the same clan. They rejoice when another clansmen is in trouble.

'You insult me whenever you can because being the eldest I was anointed the king, because I am learned, brave and because I am running the state well.

'Friend, the world respects me for my prosperity, my status, and because I have vanquished my enemies all along. Somehow, this is not to your liking.

'You are a traitor to your family and a shame. Had it been anyone else, he would have paid with his life.'

Vibhishana's Parting Advice

Listening to such harsh words uttered by Ravana, Vibhishana was deeply grieved and could foresee the destruction of his clan. Rebuking Ravana, he said,

'Rajan, you have lost your discretion and knowingly stray from the path of dharma. I respect you like a father, however, I cannot stand your offensive language.

'Dashanana, men who have failed to conquer their desires, when they are under the influence of Kala, do not listen to sound advice although tendered in their interest.

'Rajan, a friend who talks sweet, who flatters, is easy to come by. But such a friend is rare who has the courage to speak the unpleasant truth in your interest however harsh it might sound.

'You are ensnared by Kala that brings death to everyone. I did not want you to die at the hands of Rama. Hence, I tried to deter you from your chosen path. Please forgive me if you do not approve of what I have said. After all, you are my elder brother. Protect Lanka with all the resources at your command. I shall not help you in going against dharma but wish you well while I am not here to assist you.

'Rajan, he whose time has come, never listens to friendly advice from his kin.'

Vibhishana Seeks Rama's Protection

Having left Lanka, Vibhishana arrived at Rama's camp a little while later. He was accompanied by four ferocious warriors clad in armour and carrying weapons. They floated in the sky on the northern coast of the ocean before seeing Sugreeva and identifying him thus, he said,

'I am Vibhishana, the younger brother of the evil Ravana who abducted Sita. I advised him to hand over Sita to Rama. However, like a man refusing medicine, he paid no heed to my words. Rather, he humiliated me and my counsel. Therefore, leaving my wife and children in Lanka, I have come to seek Shri Rama's protection. Please allow me to see him.'

Sugreeva was suspicious of Vibhishana's motives and informed Rama of the situation. He could be Ravana's informer who had come out to gauge their strength and weakness. He could even try to divide Rama's forces by offering them incentives. They wanted to arrest Vibhishana and put him to death immediately.

Rama listened to Sugreeva and Hanuman with patience. After a moment's thought, he said,

'I value your logical advice. A wise and capable person, when in doubt about his duty or otherwise, must freely express himself.'

Some of the vanara chiefs wanted to test Vibhishana's loyalty but Hanuman held a different set of views. He said,

'In my view, this is not an occasion to put his loyalty to test. How shall we discover his true intention unless we assign him a task? His coming here is timely. He has compared the advantages and disadvantages of his decision while shifting loyalty from his evil brother to the faultless Shri Rama. His judgment is sound and in the interest of all concerned.

'Our trying to test his loyalty would create a doubt in his mind regarding our intentions about him. He comes in peace, without any threat to our forces.

'Maharaja, it is impossible to gauge anyone's real intent. We must read between the lines, and judge him by variations, if any, in his tone and behaviour. That will reveal whether he comes in good faith or otherwise.

'I do not find any evil intent in his words. A cunning person can never arrive fearlessly the way he has. He cannot maintain calm and equanimity facing the opponent's army in such large numbers. Vibhishana's words ring true to me.

'Raghunandan, Vibhishana's arrival at this moment is timely and bodes well. His assistance will be of great help to us in achieving success.

'Vibhishana has arrived after learning of your killing Vali, Sugreeva's anointment as a king, and of your chivalry. He is fed up with Ravana's evil behaviour. We ought to make him an ally for our victory, and the safety of his people.'

Rama's Response

Rama too was thinking on the same lines as Hanuman. He gladly responded saying,

'I cannot spurn a person who has approached me as a friend. Maybe he has some shortcomings. However, the truthful are not barred from providing shelter to such a person.'

Sugreeva pointed out to the fact that Vibhishana was ultimately a rakshasa. Therefore, it mattered little whether or not he was cruel or cunning. If he could desert his brother in times of trouble, how could he be loyal to anyone else?

Rama smiled and addressed Sugreeva thus,

'Sugreeva, let me explain to you my view of Vibhishana's desertion of his brother and your seeing it as a grave flaw in his character.

'It is said that a king must be alert against an attack from two sources. One is from his own kith and kin; the second one is from the inhabitants of neighbouring countries. The pure at heart recognize their kith and kin as their well wishers. However, such a kin, however good he might be, can be dangerous for a king. Ravana suspected Vibhishana's loyalty and the latter had no choice but to defect.

'We are not his kinsmen; he need not fear us. On the contrary, he too would like to be the king for his people who are being dragged into battle on the path of adharma. He is dependent on us for achieving that end and also seems learned like many other rakshasas. We ought to accept his offer of friendship.

'Brother Sugreeva, all brothers are not like my dear Bharata and all friends are not loyal like you.'

'Do not strike an enemy who begs you for protection, humbly seeking peace and mercy. He might have been arrogant, might also be grieving. However, if he asks his opponent for shelter and forgiveness, the truthful ought to protect him even at a risk to his life.

'If such an enemy suffers and meets his end because he has been refused shelter and protection, he takes away the fruit of all the good deeds done by the person who had declined him help.

'Sugreeva, I propose to follow this principle. It is my firm determination that if anyone seeks my protection, I shall free him of fear.

'Kapishrestha, bring him in even if it is Ravana himself. I have granted him freedom from fear and reprisal.'

The Coronation of Vibhishana

Descending on the earth, Vibhishana approached Rama and touched his feet. He said,

'I seek your protection because you are the protector of the universe. I have left behind my friends and wealth in Lankapuri. You alone can look after my kingdom, life and happiness.'

Rama consoled Vibhishana. Looking at him affectionately, he asked him about the strength of the rakshasa forces. In reply, Vibhishana told him how Ravana could not be killed by anyone except a human being. He talked of Kumbhakarna, Indrajit and Prahasta.'

Rama made a promise that he would make Vibhishana the king of Lanka after killing Ravana, his progeny and generals in the ensuing battle. He declared that he would not return to Ayodhya without finishing off Ravana.

In return, Vibhishana assured Rama of all help in vanquishing Ravana's forces.

With holy water collected from the ocean, under Rama's orders, Lakshmana anointed Vibhishana as the king of Lanka.

Strengthened in will with a source as rich in information about the enemy as Vibhishana, the princes and generals decided that it was time to plan the construction of the bridge over the ocean.

6

Setubandhan

Rama Prays to the Ocean

Rama lay on a kusha mat facing the ocean with hands folded, seeking permission to make a bridge.

Rama reclined using his right arm as a pillow and thought back on how his arm used to be always covered by lovely gold ornaments while he was in Ayodhya. In the forest too, prior to Sita's abduction, she used to rest her head on Rama's right arm anointed with red sandalwood. On the battlefield, Rama's long right arm added to the enemy's grief to the delight of his companions.

Resting on his right arm, Rama had determined to seek the ocean's blessings to build a bridge for his forces to cross over to Lanka. While meditating in silence, in full control of his five senses, ritually praying to the ocean for permission, he entered a state of deep sleep.

Three nights and three days passed in meditation. While the righteous Rama devotedly prayed to the ocean, the latter did not make an appearance before him.

At the end of three nights, an angry Rama expressing his thoughts to Lakshmana, said,

'The ocean does not respond to my prayers despite my true dedication. It takes my calm demeanour, forgiveness, simplicity and pleasant speech as marks of my weakness.

'Lakshmana, I shall kill all the animals in the ocean with my arrows and shall also dry the waters that shelter the coral, conches, mother of pearls and the fish. Once the ocean is dry, the vanaras can walk their way to Lanka.

'Although the ocean has been called imperturbable, today Rama's arrows will upset him, shake him and destroy his boundaries.'

An angry Rama lifted his bow and arrow and shot several arrows like Indra's thunderbolts into the ocean. The inhabitants of the ocean were caught in the turmoil created by the arrows and the ocean itself heaved with high tides. An opaque cloud of fog formed over the water and tides rose as high as the Vindhyachala Mountains. They carried crocodiles, large fish and whales in their wake.

When Rama lifted his arrow to strike at the ocean once again, Lakshmana, advising restraint, jumped and caught hold of his bow. He said,

'Brother, you are the bravest of men on the earth. You will achieve your objective even without destroying the ocean. Great men like you ought not to yield to anger. Think of an alternative plan which spares the lives of all the living creatures in the ocean.'

Mahasagara Appears, Pays Obeisance to Rama and Advises Him to Build a Bridge

As Rama threatened to dry the ocean and create a desert, turbulence was created in the waters, sky, rivers, ponds and in all the directions. The mountains shook to their roots and the sky appeared to burst. A heavy hailstorm followed thunder and lightning. Stormy winds blew uprooting the trees and volcanoes erupted, spewing rocks and fire and molten lava.

A frightened ocean rolled over his boundaries, almost one yojana towards where Rama stood with an arrow mounted on his bow. The warrior, the destroyer of his enemies, did not take even one step backwards.

Suddenly Sagara incarnate stepped out of the water like Divakara rising from behind the Meru Mountain. Dressed in red clothes, with garlands of red flowers around his neck, he looked splendid. His eyes were lovely like a lotus in full bloom. On his head lay a crown of flowers and his body was adorned with rare gems.

Mahasagara wore a single string of white pearls with a large gem looking like the Kaustubha stone, placed in the centre. He was surrounded by frolicking waves while the winds blew around him and the clouds hovered above his head.

With folded hands, Mahasagara bowed to Rama and said,

'O gentle Raghava, the earth, the sky, water and light always behave according to their inherent nature, never departing from their defined path.

'The same is true of me. I am limitless and bottomless. None can cross me. If someone does so, it will be in violation of my established nature. However, I shall guide you so that you can go beyond me, over my waters.

'O prince, I shall not allow my waters inhabited by crocodiles and serpents to be violated, to be paralyzed for greed, for fear or to satisfy a want. But to be of help to you in your noble mission, I shall tell you of a way which enables you to cross over. The living beings in the water shall not bother your army and your mission shall be fulfilled.

'For vanaras to cross, please construct a bridge. Nala, a brilliant vanara, a general in your army, is the son of Vishwakarma. His father had blessed him to be an expert in architecture as the devata himself. You too, my master, are the creator and architect of this universe. Moreover, Nala is devoted to you.

'Nala will construct a bridge over my waters and I shall gladly bear it.'

Saying this, Mahasagara disappeared.

Vanaras Construct a Bridge under the Guidance of Nala

The making of the bridge started in right earnest. Thousands of vanaras, full of joy, went into the forests nearby to bring timber and rocks. They uprooted sala, ashwakarna, bamboo, kutaja, arjuna, tala, tilaka, bela, chitvana, blooming kanera, mango and asoka trees and dragged them to the seashore. Coconut and baheda trees were available in plenty and so were rocks as large as elephants.

While some vanaras were throwing rocks and trees into the ocean, another group held a rope a hundred yojanas in length for measurement. Bamboos were tied with ropes made of grass and floated to make the base for the bridge.

In five days, a hundred-yojanas-long bridge was ready. Built by Nala and his engineers, the magnificent bridge looked like the Milky Way in the sky. The vanaras jumped with glee and roared with pride having constructed this unimaginable, mighty, and unique bridge over the ocean. Soon the vanara sena had crossed the bridge to reach Lanka. Looking to the sufficiency of supplies of food and fruit, Sugreeva decided to camp his forces on the seashore. Carrying a mace in hand, accompanied by his four companions, Vibhishana stood guard over the bridge.

7

War is On

Rama Organizes His Forces;
Sees Inauspicious Omens for Both Sides

As the vanara army rested on the shores, Rama noticed many adverse omens for both the warring sides. Rama addressed Lakshmana and said,

'Our forces ought to be stationed where sufficient cold water and fruit are available in the forest. The forces will be divided into parts and placed in formations. We must be aware of any attack by the enemy.

'The omens, as I see them, indicate a terrible destruction of the world. In this battle all the generals of the asuras, vanaras and bears will be killed.

'Even the evening, glowing like red sandalwood displays deadly flares emanating from the surface of the sun. Even at night, the moonbeams are dark and red and indicate that Pralaya has arrived.

'I can see the earth hidden by rocks, lances and swords used by the asuras and the vanaras. I can see it overlaid with the muck of flesh and blood.'

All this time, Rama was thinking of Sita who was imprisoned nearby in Asoka Vatika.

Soon thereafter, Rama stationed his forces according to the guidelines laid down in the shastras. Angada and Neel were placed high in the centre, in the heart of the formation. The right hinds were protected by Rishabha while Gandhamadana was in command of the forces at the back. Jambavan, Sushena and Vegadarshi led the forces at the central core. Sugreeva commanded the army on the western side. Rama and Lakshmana led from the front like the forehead of a person.

An Unbending Lankeshwara

Inside the city, Ravana spurned all advice from his messengers as well as well-wishers to avoid war and hand over Sita to her husband. Rather, he announced that he was waiting for the moment when his arrows would tear into the Raghava brothers. He declared,

'Rama, the son of Dashratha, has not experienced the force of my arms that have the energy of the ocean and the speed of the wind. The arrows lying in my quiver are terrible like poisonous reptiles. He does not know them yet and dares to challenge me because he has never faced me on the battlefield.

'My bow is like an enchanting veena that is played with the points of my arrows. Its frightening notes arise from the deep sound produced when I stretch its string. The cries of the suffering form its higher notes. I shall play upon my fearsome veena when I enter the battlefield.

'In this war neither Indra, nor Varuna, nor my elder brother, Kubera can defeat me with the fire of their arrows.'

8

Malyavana Advices Ravana to Make Peace with Rama

An Adamant Ravana

Rama announced the invasion of Lanka with the blow of conches and the beating of kettle-drums. Listening to the tumult, Ravana, after thinking over the situation for some time, called his ministers for a consultation. Addressing them he said,

'I do not lay any blame at your door. I have listened to your emphasis on Rama's valour and his success in crossing the ocean. However, I consider all of you to be true warriors who would wreak havoc on Rama's army in the battlefield.'

Malyavana's Words of Wisdom

Listening to Ravana, Malyavana, the king's maternal grandfather, stood up to speak.

'Rajan, a king who is learned in the fourteen branches of knowledge and who follows Niti, rules for long. He is successful in vanquishing his enemies.

'A king who cuts a deal with his foes when necessary, who goes for a settlement of disputes, and who looks after the interest of his empire more than his own interests attains grandeur and prosperity.

'When a king's power wanes or it is no more than the enemy's, he should arrive at a settlement. He must not insult an enemy who is stronger or who is his equal in power. Wage a war only if you are superior in might.

'Ravana, for these reasons, I prefer a settlement with Rama. Send Sita back because it is on her account that you are being invaded.

'Bhagwan Brahma created suras and asuras and provided dharma and adharma as their points of reference. The devatas follow dharma while the rakshasas have taken to adharma. In the Satyayuga, dharma conquers adharma while during the Kaliyuga adharma suppresses dharma.

'In pursuit of a conquest of the world, travelling all over, you destroyed the forces of dharma. You embraced the forces of adharma. That is why our enemy wields a superior force over you.

'Adharma, the ravenous reptile, fed by your negligence, pride and intoxication, wants to devour us. On the other hand, dharma, supported by the devatas, enhances Rama's strength and that of his companions.

'Enslaved by lust, acting heedless of consequences, your thoughtless conduct has upset the rishis who are glorious and extremely implacable like Agni. They perform tapasya by purifying their thought and thus garner the punya of dharma, in turn adding to Rama's prowess.

'Offering ahuti to Agni, chanting mantras, and reading the Vedas, those rishis have frightened the rakshasas and scattered them like a cloud in the summer sky. They have deprived the asuras of their powers.

'By performing austerities, you were able to get a blessing against death at the hands of the devatas, asuras and the yakshas, but not against human beings. Now, here is a gathering of powerful humans, vanaras, bears, and langurs. They roar loudly and are determined fighters. I see omens indicating a destruction of the asuras in Lanka. The clouds rain blood and surround the gardens in Lanka.

'I see several other inauspicious omens. I understand that Rama is an incarnation of Vishnu. None else could have bridged the ocean so well or come so far to rescue Sita. Raghava is no ordinary man. Ravana, it will befit you and your people if you settle your dispute with him. Act in the interest of Lanka after evaluating the unusual and supernatural deeds of Rama.'

Ravana Stands by His Decision to Fight

The evil Ravana, under the influence of Kala, could not withstand Malyavana's sane and beneficial advice. Impatiently he rolled his eyes and with eyebrows raised in anger, he addressed his grandfather thus:

'Your words spoken in support of my enemy, have not reached my ears. What you consider to be in my best interest sounds harsh and inimical to me.

'The helpless Rama is just an ordinary human being who has sought the support of vanaras. What is so special about his going into a forest because his father asked him to do so? On what basis do you consider him to be powerful?

'I am the rakshasa king and their master, endowed with remarkable valour. I can strike fear even in the minds of the devatas. How then am I inferior to Rama?

'Your manner of speech indicates that you are in league with my enemy. Without such an encouragement which learned man can challenge an established and influential king like me?

'The charming Sita is like Lakshmi without a lotus. Having brought her here, away from the forest, why should I entrust her back to Rama out of fear? In a few days, I shall kill the two brothers and all the menacing vanaras.

'I will prefer embracing death rather than bowing down to a mere human. That is my nature.

'Rama's construction of a bridge over the ocean will go waste as I vow in your presence that none of them will return alive.'

Malyavana realized the futility of explaining things to Ravana and humiliated in this way by his grandson, bowed to his king and took his leave.

Meanwhile, Ravana arranged to fortify Lanka for its defence.

9

A Wrestling Bout between Sugreeva and Ravana

Rama called a council of war to think over the arrangements of his forces and the deployment of the enemy's commanders and soldiers. Vibhishana whose four ministers had just returned from the city after a reconnaissance stood up and said,

'The eastern gate of Lanka is guarded by Prahasta while Mahodara stands at the southern gate commanding his troops. At the western gate stands Indrajit in command of a large army. At the northern gate stands Ravana himself and looks disturbed. His soldiers are brave and cruel on the battlefield; however, their king adores them and worries for their fate.

'Rama, you should feel neither humbled by my narration of Ravana's prowess nor take offence and be angry with me. I do not intend frightening you. I want to incite you against the enemy. You will certainly destroy Ravana's forces placed in four formations.'

Rama ordered Neel to mount an attack at the eastern gate where stood Prahasta with his forces. He asked Angada to attack the southern gate guarded by Mahaparshva and Mahodara. Hanuman was asked to move towards the western gate. It was decided that Rama and Lakshmana would mount an attack on Ravana who stood near the northern gate. Sugreeva, Jambavan and Vibhishana were told to attack the forces guarding the centre of the city. It was further decided that the vanaras will fight without changing their form into human beings.

The army spent the night on the Suvela peak. From here, they could look at the bustling city of Lanka that looked splendid. The dark skinned rakshasas standing on the city's ramparts appeared like fences to safeguard the city. In Rama's camp, the vanaras rearing to go to war, shouted slogans of victory.

A Duel between Ravana and Sugreeva

From a high point on the peak, Rama observed Ravana sitting on a rooftop throne, looking invincible. A canopy spread on his head symbolizing victory and he was surrounded by attendants. His body was anointed with sandalwood and looked like a cloud shining in the glow of twilight.

From among the other vanara chiefs gathered around Rama, Sugreeva stood up all of a sudden. With a speed generated by anger, using all his physical and mental strength, the vanara king traversed in no time the distance from the Suvela peak to the terrace where Ravana sat on his throne.

For a moment Sugreeva looked at Ravana. Then, considering him to be weak as a straw, speaking without any fear, using harsh words, he said,

'Rakshasa, I am a friend as well as an obedient servant of Shri Rama, the master of the universe. I come with his blessings. You cannot escape death at my hands today.'

Saying so, Sugreeva jumped at Ravana, plucked his crowns and threw them on the ground.

Taken by surprise at the sudden attack, Ravana said,

'You could be called Sugreeva, the one who has a shapely neck, only till you jumped here. Soon I shall deprive you of your neck.'

Saying this, Ravana lifted Sugreeva in his arms and threw him on the floor of the roof. Bouncing like a ball, the vanararaja too lifted and threw Ravana on the floor.

Both of them were now intertwined in their struggle to kill the other. Sweat and blood flowed like a river. They clasped each other and stood immobile like two silk cotton and palash trees. Both were brave and fought fiercely using fists, palms, elbows and claws. Many a time they lifted each other high and threw the opponent on the hard floor of the roof. Catching hold of the opponent from the waist either of them bent him double, and, dexterously manoeuvring the feet, pushed him to the wall by turns as if in a wrestling bout.

Clasping each other, the two warriors fell into a hole between the moat and the rampart. They lay panting for some time in close embrace and then stood up apart. Repeatedly they tried to crush each other in a muscular clasp. Ravana and Sugreeva pushed each other with their chests like young, teething lion and tiger cubs fighting young elephants. They measured each other's strength by pressing palms against palms and fell to the ground at the same time.

At times they took oblique steps. At another, they moved right or left in a circle. If an opponent attacked, the other person slipped out of his reach. If one stood steadfast like a pole, the other went round him in a circle. At times, they ran in for a frontal attack. They attacked each other sitting on haunches and jumping short spaces like frogs. They advanced, retreated and attacked each other with kicks.

Ultimately, Ravana decided to use maya to capture Sugreeva. However, the latter guessed his intentions and jumping high into the air, escaped. He felt victorious and relaxed. He had cheated Ravana who stood transfixed gaping at the flying vanara.

Sugreeva was received with joy by his rejoicing generals. However, Rama was not pleased. Taking him into his arms, Raghava said,

'You went away without consulting me. Kings ought not to indulge in such misadventures. If any harm comes to you, of what use to me is my life or the lives of Sita, Lakshmana, Bharata, and Shatrughna?'

10

Rama Sends Angada as
an Emissary of Peace

Early next morning it was decided to move the vanara sena forward to mount a well-considered attack on Lanka. Rama carrying his bow and arrows led the forces. Vibhishana, Sugreeva, Hanuman, Jambavan, Nala, Neel and Lakshmana followed him. The vanaras, as large as elephants that could block an enemy's path, carried large rocks and large tree trunks. In a short while, they arrived at the gates of Lanka.

The city was protected by massive ramparts and seemed impregnable. However, inspired by Rama, the vanara soldiers surrounded the city and started making forays to its walls. The generals took the positions as decided earlier. The vanaras were full of enthusiasm for the imminent fight and intended using their jaws and nails as their weapons to kill. Dark as the clouds, brave as Indra, the rakshasas did not know what to make of the vanara sena. But they sensed danger owing to the ruckus created by the vanaras. Their noise shook the ramparts, gates, forests, orchards, and even the palaces and streets of Lanka.

A Fresh Initiative for Peace

Having organized his forces, ready for an attack on the enemy, Rama called a council of war to explore his options among the policies of sama, dama, danda and bheda. After deliberation, with Vibhishana's consent, keeping in mind his rajadharma, he sent for the prince Angada. Addressing him, Rama said,

'Saumya, Ravana has lost his Rajyalakshmi. He is set on the path of destruction and death. He has bid good-bye to his conscience. Fearlessly crossing the rampart, go to him and convey the following message on my behalf:

'O Rakshasaraja, you have committed a crime against the rishis, the devatas and the kings under a false sense of pride. The time has arrived to destroy your insolence born of Brahma's blessings. You cannot digest the fruit of your evil deeds that I propose to present to you.

'As a ruler, I punish those who commit a crime. You have hurt me by abducting my wife. I stand at Lanka's doors to mete punishment to you. In case you fight me, I shall soon dispatch you to Yama's abode.

'Dharmatma Vibhishana, a noble rakshasa, has accompanied me to Lanka. For sure, he will be crowned the undisputed king of Lanka.

'You are an evil person unaware of your reality. Your supporters are fools and give you wrong counsel. Living a life without dharma, you cannot enjoy power anymore.

'I have a word of advice in your interest. Perform your Shraddha, give charity to acquire benefits in the other world and cast a last loving glance at Lanka. Henceforth you live at my mercy.'

Angada Does a Hanuman in Lanka

Angada, the son of Tara, shot like Agni incarnate into the sky. Crossing the rampart in no time, he arrived at Ravana's palace where the king looking composed, held council with his courtiers. Standing near Ravana, Angada who had put on golden bracelets introduced himself and repeated Rama's wise words. He said,

'I am Vali's son, Angada and I come as Shri Rama's messenger. You might have heard of me.

'Raghava has sent a message for you:

'O cruel Ravana, come out and fight with me. I shall kill you, your ministers and your progeny, rendering the world fearless.

'If you do not bow at my feet and honourably hand over Sita, you will die at my hands and this throne will be handed over to the righteous Vibhishana.'

Hearing Angada's harsh words, Ravana flew into a rage. At his command, four of his ministers caught hold of Angada, who let them catch him. Then, like a bird, he flew though still grabbed by the four captors and landed at the roof of the palace, high like a mountain. As he jumped, the four rakshasas were shaken off and fell to the ground. Angada jumped repeatedly on the roof until he made a gaping hole into it. Then roaring like a lion, he flew back and landed next to Rama.

11

The Vanaras Attack Lanka

When Ravana observed the numbers of the vanaras that had surrounded Lanka from all sides, he wondered how all of them could be destroyed.

On the other hand, Rama as he advanced towards mounting an attack thought of Sita with a heavy heart.

'Alas, the doe-eyed Sita sorrowfully suffers in my absence in this city. She pines for me, sleeps on bare earth and has withered due to fasting.'

Thus remembering Sita all the time, Rama ordered the vanara forces to kill all the enemy rakshasas. Soon thereafter, Sugreeva's soldiers started smashing the ramparts and gates of the city. They filled the fresh water reservoirs with mud, rubble, rocks and trees. They climbed the ramparts, levelled massive gates into the ground and destroyed domes as high as the Mount Kailas. From time to time, they hailed victory to Shri Rama, to Shri Lakshmana or to their king, Sugreeva.

Looking at Rama's forces laying siege to Lanka, an angry Ravana ordered all his soldiers to their stations. The rakshasas beat drums covered with white skins with golden sticks. They blew thousands of sonorous conches and joyously advanced to fight like the ocean tides rising and advancing on doomsday.

The earth, sky and seas resounded with the elephants trumpeting, horses neighing, the wheels rolling, the rakshasas raising battle cries and the blowing of dundubhis and conches. The rakshasas used weapons like lances, axes and shining maces while the vanaras used rocks, trees, claws and teeth.

To begin with, it was a man-to-man fight. Among others, Angada took on Indrajit and Vibhishana fought one Shatrughna. Quite a few asuras started fighting duels with the vanara soldiers. Both sides bled so profusely that rivers of blood flowed. Their severed heads floated like patches of moss covered earth. Dead bodies were carried away like bundles of wood in this river of blood.

Indrajit struck Angada with his mace. The latter snatched the mace, destroyed the prince's golden chariot, and killed his charioteer and horses.

Hanuman killed Jambumali, while Nala gauged the eyes of the fierce Pratapan when the latter injured him with his arrows. Sugreeva killed an asura named Saptaparna and Lakshmana killed Viroopaksha. With arrows as deadly as a flame of fire, Rama sliced the heads of all the four rakshasas, Agniketu, Rashmiketu, Suptaghna, and Yagyakopa who had injured him with their arrows.

Another asura, Nikumbha, attacked Neel and seeing the latter grievously injured, laughed like one victorious. However, soon Neel plucking a wheel from his chariot, killed him as well as his charioteer just like Vishnu beheading the daityas with Sudarshana Chakra on a battlefield.

Kapishrestha Sushena took on Vidyunmali and smashed his chariot with a rock. Acting with alacrity, the latter alighted from the broken vehicle and stood on the ground facing Sushena with his mace held high. He hit Sushena on his chest but the latter hit him with a rock and killed him.

The battlefield was littered with lances, arrows, maces, Shaktis, broken chariots, dead and injured horses, dead musth elephants and dead or injured soldiers. The place looked frightening as packs of jackals roamed in search of prey.

12

The Battle at Night:
Indrajit Ties Rama and Lakshmana in Nagapasha

The battle continued even after sunset and, soon, a deathly night engulfed Lanka. The rakshasas had been waiting for the sun to set because their powers multiplied at night time. Dressed in golden armour, the black skinned rakshasas shone in the dark like mountains with medicinal plants glowing at night.

While the asuras bit and ate the vanara flesh, the latter jumped out of their reach and with their sharp teeth inflicted wounds on the elephants and mahouts of the enemy and smashed their chariots with rocks and tore their flags into pieces. When the asuras magically disappeared out of sight while still engaged in a fight, Rama and Lakshmana used their poisonous arrows to kill them.

Hidden in the covers of the dark night, the emboldened asuras attacked Rama with roars as loud as the ocean. In retaliation, Rama shot six asura warriors with fiery arrows while others fled and saved their lives.

Rama, the great warrior illuminated the dark night by releasing arrows shining like flames of fire. Every nook and corner was illuminated with the arrows.

Angada attacked Indrajit and injured him, also destroying the asura prince's chariot. However, the injured Indrajit, in great pain, disappeared leaving everything behind.

Angered by this humiliating defeat at the hands of a vanara, Indrajit could not stay away from the scene for long. Using boons granted to him by Brahma, he became invisible and started shooting sharp arrows. He successfully injured Rama and Lakshmana and lacerated all their limbs. His arrows shaped like cobras wrapped the Raghava brothers in a Nagapasha and made them immobile.

Rama and Lakshmana Lose Consciousness

Rama, injured and bleeding, asked ten vanara commanders including Hanuman and Angada, to trace Indrajit's whereabouts. The vanaras carrying tall tree trunks moved in ten different directions in the sky. However, their movement was stalled by Indrajit, an expert in the use of weapons, by an incessant rain of relentless arrows. The grievously injured vanaras could not see Indrajit.

Meanwhile, a hostile Indrajit continued his shower of Nagapasha arrows on Rama and Lakshmana, hitting different parts of their bodies until not a fraction of their skin remained exposed. The brothers bled profusely and looked like two palash trees in full bloom. Their pupils turned red and the bodies black like a mound of coal freshly mined.

The invisible Indrajit spoke thus to the Raghava brothers:

'Even Indra cannot see me when I become invisible during a battle. You stand nowhere in comparison. I have snared you in a net of arrows mounted with the feathers of a heron. I propose to dispatch you soon to the Yamaloka.'

Indrajit renewed his shower of arrows and roared decisively at their predicament. He aimed at critical parts of their bodies with arrows that had golden fins. The victims of those arrows became so weak that they could not lift an eyelid. Covered by Nagapasha, their bodies bled like waterfalls.

Hanuman and other vanaras surrounded the unconscious Raghava brothers and grief enveloped the vanara army.

While the Vanaras Grieve, Indrajit Celebrates

As Indrajit moved away after his shower of arrows like Indra retreating after heavy rains, Vibhishana, Sugreeva, Hanuman and other vanara warriors gathered around Rama and Lakshmana who now lay unconscious. Mired in blood, they were breathing hard and slow; none of their limbs were moving. Looking at them, the vanara generals shed tears.

Indrajit was not visible to anyone except Vibhishana, he being a rakshasa himself. He saw him addressing the rakshasas and boasting of his having killed the enemies in the battlefield. He was saying,

'Look, how I have killed the two chivalrous brothers who were responsible for killing Khara and Dooshana. Neither the devatas, nor the asuras can release them from this snare. I have destroyed the root cause of my father's sleepless nights and of the city of Lanka that was in turbulence like a river in spate during the rains. I have uprooted the source of our terror.'

Presuming Rama and Lakshmana to be dead, Indrajit retreated into Lanka to apprise his father of the good news.

On the other hand, Vibhishana assuaged the feelings of the grieving and tearful Sugreeva. He told him that the princes were not dead and would soon regain consciousness. He wanted Sugreeva to raise the morale of his forces so that they could fight against Ravana and his forces with renewd vigour later.

Ravana's joy knew no bound on hearing the news of Rama's death from his son. He showered praise on Indrajit and shedding his fear of Rama, retreated into his palace.

13

Looking at an Unconscious Rama, Sita Laments Her Fate

While the vanara commanders reorganized their forces and kept a strict vigil on the two unconscious princes, Ravana sent for Sita's guards and asked them to fly her in the Pushpak Vimana to show her the corpses of her husband and brother-in-law. He said,

'Go and tell Vaidehi that Indrajit has killed Rama and Lakshmana. Her husband, relying on whose chivalry she had refused to reciprocate my love, has been killed even before the war began. She should not wait for him now and dressed suitably in ornaments, she should present herself to be at my service.'

Sita was asked to sit in the vimana along with Trijata, her well-wisher. Firstly they gave her a bird's eye view of Lanka where flags were flying to celebrate Rama's reported death at the hands of Indrajit.

On the battlefield, Sita saw the heavily bleeding Raghava brothers lying on a bed of arrows, supposedly dead. Their armours were shattered and limbs punctured. Their bows and arrows lay discarded. They looked like statues sculpted out of arrows.

Seeing the two princes lying in a pool of blood, Sita shrieked and wailed in a mournful voice. She sobbed uncontrollably and lamented thus,

'With Shri Rama's death, all predictions of my bearing many sons have turned out to be untrue. They were liars who had foretold that I shall be the consort of a king who performed yagyas and ruled over several kingdoms.

'With Shri Rama's death, the Brahmins, learned in jyotish shastra, who had predicted that I shall be ever auspicious, have turned out to be wrong.

'My feet certainly carry the symbols indicating that I shall be a queen. My hands and feet are marked by the lotus symbol. I do not notice any indication in my limbs to even hint at misfortune or widowhood.

'The learned astrologers had predicted that I shall be anointed a queen when my husband ascends the throne. Today, their prediction has turned out to be untrue.

'The Raghava brothers were dexterous in the use of several divine weapons. Why did they not use them? An invisible Indrajit killed my protector Shri Rama and Lakshmana who is brave as Indra.

'Kala has taken over fate and it is under his control that Shri Rama and Lakshmana are lying unconscious on the battlefield.'

Hearing Sita's wails, Trijata tried to pacify her and said,

'Devi, do not grieve. Your husband must still be alive for I do not see his forces grieving. When a commander is killed on the battlefield, his disheartened forces lose direction and wander like a boat without a boatsman. Tapasvini, I do not see any such commotion in the vanara army. They have surrounded the princes to protect them. So, lovingly I tell you that the princes are alive.

'I have never told a lie to you nor will I do so today. Neither Indra, nor the devatas or the asuras can vanquish the two brothers in a battle. Look carefully at their faces; they have the glow of life. There is no distortion as in the case of a dead person.

'O Janakanandini, let go of sorrow, pain and attachment. They cannot be dead.'

'I hope it is so,' said Sita.

Garuda Bhagwan Unties the Nagapasha

While Sugreeva and the other brave vanaras sat around full of grief, Rama gained consciousness. Looking at Lakshmana lying pale and unconscious, he bemoaned their fate. He said,

'What shall I tell the mothers, Kaushalya and Kaikeyee if I return to Ayodhya without Lakshmana? How shall I console his mother Sumitra? I would not be able to convey this sad news to them; I will end my life before Kala takes Lakshmana away from me.

'Lakshmana was a source of assurance and solace to me in the darkest hours of my grief. He deserved a luxurious bed and lies on bare earth today.'

A weeping Rama asked Sugreeva to return to Kishkindha with his generals. He felt sorry that he had not been able to fulfil his promise to Vibhishana to make him the king of Lanka.

The level-headed Vibhishana did not believe that Lakshmana had died. He suggested that Hanuman should fetch medicinal plants from the Chandra and Dron Mountains situated near the Ksheerasagara, where Samudramanthan had taken place in ancient times.

Garuda Arrives; the Princes Revive

However, while these suggestions were being discussed, with blasting winds, rolling clouds and flashes of lightning, Garuda, the son of Vinata, appeared like a flame of fire. The denizens of Lanka including the mighty nagas ran helter-skelter out of fear. Even the Nagapasha ties that had ensnared Rama and Lakshmana were unravelled in no time.

Garuda humbly touched the two princes and greeted them. He wiped their faces lovingly. With Garuda's touch their wounds were healed and their skin regained its colour. They felt strong. Their memory was revived and so was their valour.

As Garuda embraced the two princes, the latter thanked him profusely and asked for his identity. Garuda replied,

'Raghava, I am your dear friend Garuda, your life breath that pervades the universe. I have arrived to help you in your distress because even Indra, the gandharvas, devatas or asuras could not have cut the Nagapasha.

'You will know the secret of my friendship when you have won this war. I am certain of your victory over Ravana's forces.'

Garuda performed a parikrama around Rama and sped away into the sky.

14

Vanara Generals Vanquish Ravana's Commanders

The Death of Dhoomraksha and Vajradanstra

With the revival of Rama and Lakshmana at the hands of Garuda, the vanara leaders roared like lions and swung their tails. They beat kettle-drums, played the mridanga, blew conches and beat their thighs and clapped to express their joy at the turn of events. Their roar spread like thunder of the midnight clouds at the end of summer.

When Ravana heard of the joyous thunder of the vanaras, he thought to himself,

'This roar coming from the enemy indicates that they have something to celebrate. Their repeated shouts have created turmoil even in the saline ocean waters.'

On enquiry, Ravana came to know of the freedom of the Raghava princes from Indrajit's Nagapasha. The information upset him and added to his worries. He thought to himself:

'I doubt the future of my army if my enemies could free themselves from the invincible Nagapasha that had been received as a boon by Indrajit.'

An angry and fuming Ravana sent for Dhoomraksha, one of his commanders, and asked him to lead a large contingent of the asuras and kill Rama along with the vanaras.

Hanuman Fights and Kills Dhoomraksha

Dhoomraksha carried several weapons himself and was surrounded by fierce rakshasa soldiers who had tied bells to their swords, maces, spears, bars of metal, snares and axes. Dhoomraksha brayed like a donkey although he sat in a grand chariot.

The vanaras rejoiced to see an enemy whom they could give a fight.

A fierce fight ensued where the opponents attacked each other with trees, spears and maces. The injured asura soldiers vomited blood. Some of them were ground to powder after being hit by rocks, some others suffered from broken bones. The vanaras snatched their swords and reduced the chariots to pieces of wood. The battlefield was soon littered with dead elephants, horses and their riders.

The vanaras used their claws to injure asuras. The asuras were not sparing in their attack. They felled several vanaras with merely a sharp and hard slap on their face or head. Dhoomraksha pierced their hearts with his spear, cut some others to pieces with his sword and pulled out the intestines of others. Laughing with a roar, he scattered the vanaras in all directions.

The battlefield was soon littered with dead bodies, discarded weapons, blood and flesh. Seeing Dhoomraksha causing havoc among the vanara soldiers, Hanuman challenged him. He moved with the speed and majesty of Pavana and smashed the asura's chariot with a huge boulder. In one strike, while Dhoomraksha jumped to save his life, Hanuman had destroyed the latter's flag, wheels, the charioteer and horses. Later he hit Dhoomraksha with a mountain rock and crushed his body to pieces.

While the asura soldiers retreated into Lanka, the vanara forces cheered Hanuman.

Vajradanstra Mounts an Attack and is Killed by Angada

In quick succession, a fuming Ravana sent another commander by the name of Vajradanstra to annihilate the vanara forces and kill Rama, Sugreeva and Lakshmana.

Vajradanstra put on armour, performed a parikrama of his chariot and then climbed it. Soon the rakshasas reached the gate where stood the vanara general and Vali's son Angada with his forces.

Both sides soon engaged each other with bows and arrows, maces and swords, and rocks and trees. As the Pralaya fires consuming human beings, Angada dispatched the rakshasas to the other world in large numbers. Soon the battlefield was scattered with the garlands, bracelets, clothes, weapons of the dead soldiers.

The rakshasas killed the vanara soldiers mercilessly and the vanaras, in turn, gave the asuras such a beating that the latter started deserting the battlefield.

Shouting at his forces and asking them not to run away, Vajradanstra ferociously attacked the vanaras killing hundreds of them with his multiple-headed arrows. The frightened vanaras looked up to Angada for succour and protection.

Angada smashed the asura general with one rock after another. Vajradanstra started vomiting blood and became unconscious.

Regaining consciousness, he attacked Angada and hit him with his mace and then with fists in a wrestling bout. Both the warriors were vomiting blood when Angada retaliated with a massive tree that still had flowers blooming on its branches. Vajradanstra fought with a large sword while protecting himself with a shield made of a bull's hide.

Both the warriors were bleeding profusely. They looked like two palash trees in bloom and were tired.

After a moment's rest, Angada regained his strength and stood up unsheathing a sharp-edged sword. His eyes burnt with anger like that of an injured snake. Soon he had beheaded the asura general. The latter's massive head lay in dust with his eyes open and turned skywards. His head had split into two with the impact of crashing to the ground.

Returning to his camp, Angada was received with acclaim as if he was Indra incarnate.

15

Akampana and Prahasta Meet their End at the Hands of Hanuman and Neel

Ravana was beside himself with anger over the death of Vajradanstra and other warriors. Addressing his senapati Prahasta who stood by his side with folded hands, he said,

'Akampana is knowledgeable in the use of arms. It is time that he led the chivalrous and ferocious rakshasas into war.

'Akampana loves battles and has always wished me success. He is capable of vanquishing the enemy, protecting his followers and leading the army. Akampana will certainly defeat Rama and Lakshmana along with Sugreeva. He shall massacre the vanaras, for sure.'

Akampana Rides a Chariot Plated with Gold

Large and dark as a cloud, Akampana rode a chariot covered in gold. He thundered as a cloud and even the devatas failed to make him tremble out of fear. That is why he was named Akampana. To the rakshasas he looked glorious like the sun.

However, the omens were not good; his left eye was twitching. His face had lost its shine and his voice faltered. The day had dawned well but as a dry wind blew, the atmosphere turned gloomy. A fearless Akampana, with shoulders as broad as those of a lion, ignoring the adverse omens, bravely moved to the battlefield.

As both the sides engaged in battle, red dust raised by the fighters covered the sky that looked fearsome. Several vanara warriors such as Kumud, Nala, Maind and Dwivid displayed acts of valour and killed the rakshasas in large numbers. This infuriated Akampana no end. He mounted a deadly attack on the vanaras and made them flee from the field.

Hanuman noticed how the vanaras were being decimated. His presence added to the enthusiasm of the vanara soldiers.

Sighting Hanuman, Akampana sent a shower of arrows to hit him. Hanuman laughed aloud and advanced towards the asura with a speed that shook the earth. He plucked a large rock and furiously spun it in his hands. Then with a roar, he threw the missile at Akampana. Using arrows with crescent heads, the asura cut the rock into pieces much before it could hit him.

An angry Hanuman plucked a tree named ashwakarna and started killing the asuras like Yamaraja. An infuriated Akampana pierced Hanuman's body with his sharp arrows, which led to blood oozing from the latter's body. Hanuman plucked another tree and struck Akampana with great force, killing him instantly.

The rakshasa soldiers ran away, while the victorious Hanuman was received in his camp with great aplomb.

At Ravana's Instance, Prahasta Advances with a Large Force

Learning of Akampana's death, Ravana was crestfallen. He sent for Prahasta who was his wellwisher and an expert in warfare. Addressing him, Ravana said,

'O brave man, skilful in warfare, the enemy forces are stationed next to the city. The people of Lanka are now agitated and worried for their families. I do not see anyone other than you who can handle this situation. This war can be won only by you, Kumbhakarna, Indrajit, Nikumbha, or me. Therefore, proceed immediately to the station where the vanaras are amassed. The moment you depart, the vanara sena will run amok out of fear.

'Once the vanaras run away, Rama and Lakshmana would be rendered helpless and will surrender to you.

'It is glorious to lose one's life in a battlefield. Dying without facing danger is undesirable. If you do not agree with my words, please share your thoughts on this.'

Listening to Ravana, Prahasta responded as if Shukracharya was advising the king Bali. He said,

'Rajan, earlier too, in your council of the wise ministers, we had thought over this situation. On a number of issues we had disagreed and criticized each other.

'It has always been my view that our well being lies in sending Sita back to her husband. If we do not do so, war is certain, which would lead to our destruction at the hands of Rama. We face the consequences of the indecision on this issue today.

'However, you have honoured me with bounty, prestige and dignity from time to time. Therefore, in this hour of need, how can I not strive for your welfare?

'I do not care to protect my wife, progeny, wealth or myself. I do not worry for their safety. Watch how I offer myself as ahuti to the flames of war!'

Prahasta, the commander-in-chief, ordered his generals to send for the bravest of rakshasa soldiers. He was sure that vultures would have enough meat to satisfy their appetite when the vanaras died at his hands.

Prahasta rode a chariot pulled by quality steeds and his charioteer was in full control of the vehicle. The large asura army looked fierce like a parade of elephants. Moving in formations, the soldiers stepped out of Lankapuri.

They were greeted by inauspicious omens: a vulture landed on Prahasta's flag and sat facing south, and his charioteer repeatedly dropped his whip.

The vanaras stood ready for an onslaught with trees and massive rocks. Their roar was frightening.

Like a moth moving towards a flame in order to court death, Prahasta, desirous of victory, advanced towards the forces commanded by Sugreeva.

From a distance Rama looked at the advancing senapati and asked Vibhishana about the giant speedily moving forward, leading a large force. Vibhishana replied,

'This rakshasa is Ravana's commander-in-chief and his name is Prahasta. He leads an army that is, in numbers, one third of Lanka's forces. His valour is wellknown among rakshasas and he is known for his skill in the use of several weapons.'

While the vanaras fought with trees and rocks, the asuras carried swords, Shaktis, spears, maces and axes to fight. Both the armies killed each other in plenty.

A River of Blood

Both the armies moved in the battlefield like a whirlpool, one following the other. They roared like an ocean in turmoil and the battlefield seemed like a river of blood and flesh. Sliced heads and torsos floated in plenty and the smaller body parts and bunches of hair appeared like grasses growing everywhere. The vultures sat like pelicans and the skeletons moved like the herons and the sarus birds.

Meanwhile, Prahasta severely injured Neel with his arrows. Neel hit him with a large sal tree and killed the horses standing in his way. As Neel cut Prahasta's bow into pieces, the asura senapati got down from his chariot and ran to attack him with a club.

Both of them were senapatis of their armies, and were fierce warriors too. They moved with speed to strike each other and were soaked in blood like two elephants running streams of musth on their temples.

Neel and Prahasta's fight was like a battle between a lion and a tiger, both desirous of being victorious.

Prahasta hit Neel's forehead with a club which led to profuse blood oozing out and drenching his body. However, Neel lifted a large rock and smashed Prahasta's head to smithereens. The asura senapati lay dead on the ground and his soldiers fled like water gushing out of a breached dam.

A victorious Neel joined Rama and Lakshmana who appreciated his valour.

16

Ravana Arrives at the Battlefield

The news of Prahasta's death made Ravana furious. But it did not take long for the anger to turn into grief. He summoned his principal commanding officers and said,

'Never underestimate an enemy simply because he is weak in your judgment. They, whom I considered to be puny, have killed my senapati and annihilated the forces accompanying him.

'I now propose to fight this great battle on my own without giving a thought to the enemy's defeat or my victory. Like a conflagration destroying a forest, with a shower of my arrows, I shall reduce the vanara sena, and Rama and Lakshmana to ashes. Today I shall quench the earth's thirst with the blood of the vanaras.'

Ravana climbed into his chariot that had the illumination of fire. The finest of steeds were harnessed to his vehicle. His attendants blew conches and played on bheri and panava. The warriors accompanying him beat their thighs and roared like lions. The court singers chanted prayers for the success of their king.

Looking at Ravana's ferocious army, Rama asked Vibhishana,

'Who is the master of this army full of elephants that look like mountains? He comes with flags flying, and leads an army of fearless soldiers carrying weapons like maces, swords and lances. Who is he?'

Ravana's Commanders and the Rakshasaraja Described by Vibhishana

Vibhishana introduced Ravana's commanders one by one. He said,

'The warrior riding an elephant, with a face copper-red like the rising sun, and who makes the elephant wrinkle his forehead with his weight, is Akampana, a cousin of Akampana killed earlier.

'The charioteer flying an emblem with the sign of a lion, whose teeth are fierce and protruding like that of an elephant, the one who waves a bow as bright as a rainbow, is Indrajit. He derives his immense power from a boon.

'The next one is Atikaya. He is an unrivalled warrior who fights dexterously. He is pulling at his bow eager to fight the enemy.

'Atikaya is followed by the brave Mahodara whose eyes are a brilliant red like the rising sun. His speech rings louder than a bell. Riding an already angry elephant, he roars to challenge his enemies.

'Pishacha follows next. He carries a shining lance and rides a horse dressed in golden ornaments. He is resplendent like a mountain top over which hovers an evening cloud. He attacks with the speed of a thunderbolt.

'The famous warrior Trishira carrying a trident that sparkles like lightning closely follows him. In speed, he outbids a thunderbolt and rides into the battlefield on a bull.

'Kumbha is concentrating on his bow that he tightens and moves several times. He has a broad chest, is handsome and dark like a cloud. His flag carries the emblem of the Nagaraja Vasuki.

'There you see Nikumbha, a powerful warrior, who walks like the ensign of the rakshasa sena. He carries a lance that shines because it is studded with gold, and a powerful thunderbolt.

'The tall warrior is Narantaka who fights even the mountain cliffs. He rides a chariot stocked with bows, swords and arrows. His vehicle shines like a fire burning with full force.

'These warriors are followed by Ravana. He has trampled the pride of the devatas under his feet on various occasions and has defeated mighty heroes. A canopy white as the moon, mounted on a slim bar protects him.

'Ravana wears multiple crowns, his ears are adorned by large earrings, his body is large and fierce-looking like the Himalayas, and he has made even Indra and Yamaraja subservient to him. He appears on the horizon like the sun.'

Rama responded:

'I can see the glory of Ravana although it is difficult to set my eyes upon him because he is brilliant like the sun. Carrying shining weapons, his commanders look large as mountains.

'Luckily, the evil king now stands in front of me. I shall not let go of this opportunity and would release on him all my anger generated by Sita's abduction.'

Ravana scattered his forces to fearlessly and enthusiastically protect the city gates and the entrances to the mansions on the main roads. He said,

'If the vanaras see all of you gathered around me, they will utilize it as an opportunity to enter the unprotected city, otherwise invincible, and play havoc with it.'

Ravana's Engagement on the Battlefield

Noticing Ravana advancing in the battlefield, Sugreeva plucked a hillock with trees and several cliffs and threw it at the Rakshasaraja. Ravana retaliated and crushed the rock to pieces with his arrows.

Ravana now mounted an arrow that was poisonous like a cobra and frightening as Yamaraja. It flew like the wind, sparkled and shone like fire and it was devastating like Indra's thunderbolt. An angry Ravana shot it at Sugreeva in order to kill him.

Ravana's arrow injured Sugreeva grievously and the vanara king shrieked in pain before fainting. Seeing Sugreeva fall, the rakshasas rejoiced. The very next moment, Ravana had injured many vanara commanders such as Gavaksha, Gavaya, Sushena, Rishabha, Jyotirmukha and Neel who had advanced to attack him in the wake of Sugreeva falling to the ground. The furious king shot dead hundreds of vanaras in no time.

Vanaras ran for succour to Rama who decided to move against his arch enemy in person. However, Lakshmana offered to go and kill the Rakshasaraja. Rama said,

'Lakshmana, go by all means but fight to be victorious. Ravana is not a mean warrior. If he gives a real fight, his fury cannot be contained by Triloka.

'Look for his weak points and take advantage of them. At the same time take care of your flaws, if any.'

Hanuman and Neel Battle Ravana

As Lakshmana proceeded to fight Ravana, he noticed the strength of his enemy's arms. He was using his bow and arrow with devastating speed and killing the vanaras in hundreds at one go. However, avoiding his arrows, Hanuman reached his chariot and raising his right hand as if to frighten him, spoke to Ravana:

'Nishachar, even though you are blessed not to be killed by the devatas, asuras, gandharvas and the yakshas, you do not enjoy any such protection from the vanaras. This uplifted right hand of mine will soon send your soul packing to the other world.'

An angry Ravana retorted,

'Vanara, strike me as hard as you can and earn yourself an everlasting glory. I shall kill you only after taking a measure of your strength.'

Hanuman replied,

'Have you forgotten that I killed your son, Aksha?'

While Hanuman was still speaking, Ravana hit the latter's chest with his fist sending Hanuman spinning and staggering a few steps. However, he soon gained his composure and slapped Ravana hard on his face. The king shook like a mountain hit by an earthquake. The bystanders rejoiced at Ravana's discomfiture.

Taking control of his body, Ravana told Hanuman,

'You are a praiseworthy rival in bravery.'

'Ravana,' said Hanuman, 'It is a shame on me that you are still alive. When I hit you with my fist thereafter, I shall dispatch you to the Yamaloka.'

A furious Ravana, his eyes red with anger, skilfully sent his right fist deep into Hanuman's chest with full force.

As Hanuman was disbalanced with pain, Ravana attacked Neel with arrows resembling serpents. Neel threw a large rock on him and Hanuman, regaining his balance, challenged Ravana for one more fight. He said,

'O Nishachara, at present you are engaged with another warrior. Hence, I shall not attack you.'

Ravana destroyed the rock thrown by Neel with seven sharp-edged arrows. This infuriated Neel like the Pralaya fires. He continued his attack on Ravana with ashwakarna, sal, mango and other tree trunks. The latter cut all the tree missiles to pieces. Further, he attacked Neel with a barrage of arrows.

Neel in turn assumed a diminutive form and climbed Ravana's flag pole. This further angered the Rakshasaraja, who was infuriated by Neel's roaring.

Soon after, a flabbergasted Ravana readied an Agni missile to fire at Neel. Warning Neel of the consequences, he said,

'Vanara, you possess great agility in addition to your unique powers of maya. If you are sure of your powers, try and save yourself from my missile.'

Thus speaking, Ravana hit senapati Neel with the Agni missile and grievously injured him in his chest. The latter fell on the ground feeling the extreme heat of the missile. However, blessed as he was by his father Agni, Neel did not die.

Looking at the unconscious Neel, Ravana riding his thundering chariot, bypassing the vanara forces, attacked Lakshmana. He stood like a flame of fire and pulled at his bowstring repeatedly creating a frightening echo.

Ravana Renders Lakshmana Unconscious; Fails to Abduct Him to Lanka

Addressing Ravana, Lakshmana said,

'Nishacharendra, I am here. You need not waste your energy fighting the vanaras.'

Pulling at his bowstring, he produced a fearful echo. Hearing him, Ravana approached the prince and angrily rebuking him said,

'Raghava, it is my good fortune that you stand facing me on the battlefield. Your challenging me will surely lead to your end; my arrows will dispatch you to the Yamaloka in no time.'

Ravana's words did not surprise Lakshmana. He said,

'Rajan, those truly powerful do not waste time in pompous speech. You are the leader of evil forces and here I stand facing you with my bow and arrows. Let's begin the fight.'

An enraged Ravana released seven arrows with pretty fins in Lakshmana's direction. However, the Raghava cut them to pieces with arrows that had sharp tips and golden fins. This attack and counter-attack continued for some time, both the warriors using the choicest of their weapons. While Ravana's arrows had tips shaped like serpents, Lakshmana used arrows with crescent and lance-like tips.

Ravana hit Lakshmana's forehead with an arrow given to him by Brahma, which generated heat like the Pralaya fires. Lakshmana was shaken to the core and his hold over his bow loosened. However, regaining composure, he sliced the bow being used by Ravana.

Meanwhile Ravana too had been injured by the arrows shot by Lakshmana and was bleeding profusely. His body was smeared with blood. To strike decisively, he picked the Shakti weapon given to him by Brahma. This weapon emitted fire, smoke, and sent a wave of terror into the vanaras who stood as spectators to this great fight. The sovereign of the rakshasas fired this flaming weapon at Lakshmana with an unstoppable force. The prince tried to thwart Ravana's weapon but to no avail. The Brahma Shakti pierced his vast chest in no time.

Lakshmana fell unconscious to the ground and Ravana tried to lift him with both his arms in order to abduct him. However, the Rakshasaraja who had the power to lift the Himalayas, and many other mountain ranges, failed to lift Lakshmana.

An unconscious Lakshmana, injured by the Brahma Shakti, meditated on Vishnu of whose divinity he was a part and who could not easily be made a part of anyone's consciousness. Ravana could not move Lakshman's body even slightly, let alone lift it.

Meanwhile Hanuman ran towards Ravana and hit him with his powerful fist. Such was the force of this strike that the king collapsed in pain. He staggered and ultimately lay flat on the ground with his mouth, eyes and ears bleeding profusely. He got up, wheeled around and sat half-dead at the back of his chariot. For a moment, he was unconscious and restless with pain. The vanaras rejoiced at his predicament.

Hanuman tried to lift Lakshmana in his arms and was able to do so owing to his devotion to Vishnu; Hanuman carried him to Rama.

The Brahma Shakti reverted to Ravana soon after. On regaining consciousness, the king readied to use his large bow and sharp arrows again.

Meditating upon Vishnu, knowing that he partook of the Lord's divinity, Lakshmana also regained his health in no time.

Rama Challenges and Makes Ravana Retreat

As Ravana started his onslaught and killed many vanaras one after the other, Rama made up his mind to fight him. Hanuman offered to take him on his back as Vishnu rides on Garuda's while killing the asuras.

In order to challenge Ravana, Rama pulled at his bowstring creating a frightening sound. Addressing the king in a loud, sonorous voice, Rama said,

'Do not move from your place, O tiger among rakshasas. Having committed a heinous crime against me, you have nowhere to escape with your life.

'You made Lakshmana unconscious by using Brahma Shakti on him in a battle. I have come to avenge that humiliation. I come as your Kala and the death of your sons and grandsons, O Rakshasaraja.'

Listening to Rama's words, Ravana was beside himself with anger. Remembering the recent incidents and the loss of so many of his kin and warriors, he attacked and grievously injured Hanuman bearing Rama on his back, with arrows carrying the fires of doom.

Looking at the injured Hanuman, Rama attacked Ravana mercilessly with his sharp arrows. In no time, he destroyed his chariot, its wheels, the flag, horses, and the charioteer. He cut Ravana's weapons such as thunderbolt, lance and sword bit by bit into tiny pieces.

Rama speedily hit Ravana's broad and powerful chest with an arrow as powerful as a vajra. The king who had never been shaken and hurt like this before, felt an acute pain when hit by Rama. He shook violently and his bow dropped to the ground.

Looking at the restless and suffering Lankesh, Rama cut his crowns shining like the sun, with a crescent-shaped arrow. Without his bow and arrows, Ravana seemed to be a serpent without poison. He lost his splendour with his crowns cut to pieces. At this point in the battle, Rama addressed him saying,

'Ravana, you have committed terrible deeds in killing a number of my prominent warriors. However, as you are exhausted, I do not intend killing you with my arrows. I am aware that you have suffered terribly in the battle. Therefore, I order you to return to Lanka and rest for a while. Come again, fully armed and in a chariot, and then witness my bravery.'

Ravana made haste to enter Lanka. His happiness and pride had been laid to ruins. His bow had been cut into pieces, horses and the charioteer killed, and the famous crown damaged. His agony was unbearable.

After the departure of Rajnicharendra, Rama and Lakshmana tended to the injured vanaras, cleaned their wounds of arrows, and dressed them.

17

Kumbhakarna, the Sleeping Giant is Awakened

Frightened by Rama's arrows and devoid of his pride, Ravana reached Lankapuri with every limb of his body sore. The memory of Rama's arrows moving with the speed of lightning and the strength of the Brahmastra, increased his worries.

Sitting on his fabulous golden throne, Ravana thus addressed the asura generals,

'My entire tapasya has gone waste because an asura like me, as brave as Mahendra, has been vanquished by a human being. Brahma's words that I would face danger from a human being have turned out to be true. I had prayed for a boon that I should not be killed by the devatas, asuras, gandharvas and yakshas. I never thought a human would be so powerful and in my pride did not include them in my prayer for a boon.

'A long time ago, the Ikshavaku king Anaranya had cursed me that one of his descendants will be the cause of my death and of my progeny too. It now looks like Rama is that descendant.

'I had been cursed similarly by Uma, Nandeeshwara, Rambha and Varuna's daughter. Their words have come true.

'Recognizing the gravity of these curses, all of you stand united and fight. Stay alert protecting the roads, stationed at the domes of the palaces and the vital gates of Lanka.

'Simultaneously, go and awaken Kumbhakarna for he sleeps for months owing to Brahma's curse. It was nine months ago that he went to sleep at the end of our consultations. Awaken him and he will wipe out the vanara sena. He will soon kill the two princes too.

'The brave Kumbhakarna is the best among the rakshasas. He is like our flag of victory. Regrettably, he continues to sleep for very long. Once he is awake, I will be confident enough and would not mind losing to Rama in the battle.'

The Awakening of Kumbhakarna

Obeying their king, the rakshasas rushed to Kumbhakarna's residence in utter bewilderment. They carried a substantial quantity of food, fragrance, garlands and liquor.

The warrior lived in a charming cave fragrant with the scent of flowers. The moment the asuras entered the massive gate of the mile-long cave, they were pushed back by the blast of Kumbhakarna's breath. With difficulty they entered the cave laden with gold and with gems on its floor. They found Kumbhakarna fast asleep.

He breathed like a serpent and his powerful exhalation sent people into a whirl. His nostrils were large and fearful and his mouth was as deep and large as Patala. He wore bracelets on his arms and a crown on his head.

The rakshasas piled meat and wine in front of the sleeping giant and pitchers full of blood were placed near him. The attendants applied sandal paste to his body and made him smell flowers, sandalwood and incense. They shouted slogans in his praise and blew white conches and raised a ruckus. They shook Kumbhakarna's limbs to wake him up, but to no avail.

Ravana's messengers struck the sleeping giant on his chest with maces, rocks, pestles and fists. The attendants started beating drums, mridanga, pitchers and kettle-drums. While the residents of Lanka were awakened by the tumult, it had no effect on Kumbhakarna.

Ultimately, it was the elephants trampling on his body that awakened Kumbhakarna. The hungry rakshasa woke up and yawned. In no time, he ate several buffalos and pigs, and quenched his thirst with blood and wine. All this time, the attendants stood with heads bowed in fear.

When fully alert and satisfied with food and drink, the amazed brother of Ravana asked the purpose of his being awakened from sleep. At the same time, he assured them of his pleasure in their way of waking him up. He asked,

'What makes you awaken me so respectfully? Is the king safe? Is there a cause for fear?

'There has to be some unforeseen calamity, otherwise you would not have awakened me.

'I shall root out this cause of the king's fear. I shall tear Mahendra to pieces and extinguish any fierce fires.'

Yupaksha, Ravana's emissary, bowed with folded hands and said,

'Maharaja, no devatas dare frighten us; our source of worry is a human being. Vanaras, of the size of hills, have surrounded Lanka on all sides. Our fear has arisen from Rama whose anger at his wife Sita's abduction by Ravana is burning down the entire kingdom.

'Earlier one vanara had burnt a large part of Lanka and killed the prince Aksha. Rama, glorious like the sun, has defeated our king Ravana in a battle and told him to return to Lanka for rest. The king's life was saved with great difficulty.'

An enraged Kumbhakarna glared at Yupaksha and said,

'I shall defeat the vanara sena, Rama and Lakshmana at first and then appear in the court of my brother. I shall drink their blood and eat their meat alongside the rakshasas.'

Listening to his words, Mahodara asked Kumbhakarna to visit the king first and then devise a careful strategy to defeat the enemy.

Receiving Ravana's invitation, Kumbhakarna got up, had a bath and ordered liquor to fortify himself. Walking towards Ravana's palace, he looked like Yamaraja the destroyer himself. The earth shook below his feet as he walked like a mountain. The vanaras were subdued by the very sight of him and they ran helter-skelter. While some approached Rama for succour, a few others fell down to the ground owing to the tremors.

Vibhishana Describes Kumbhakarna to Rama

From a distance, Rama looked at the walking giant who wore a crown. He was dark as the deep ocean and was adorned with gold bracelets. Rama asked Vibhishana to identify this massive warrior. He said,

'He stands like a solitary flag on a flag pole. The vanaras have fled by merely looking at him. I have never seen such a being ever before; kindly tell me who he is.'

Vibhishana replied,

'He is Kumbhakarna, a majestic son of Vishrava. None stands as tall as him among the rakshasas. As a child, he ate thousands of persons. When Indra hit him with his thunderbolt, Kumbhakarna attacked him on his chest with a tusk plucked from the mouth of Airavata, the former's mount. Indra was grievously injured and felt a burning sensation in his chest. He and the other devatas approached Brahma for redress.

'Brahma sent for Kumbhakarna and the rakshasas. Himself trembling at the giant's sight, Brahma cursed him and said,

'Vishrava has certainly given birth to you to destroy the world. I curse you that you will be ever asleep like a dead body.'

'Kumbhakarna immediately fell to the ground asleep. Ravana, standing, prayed to Brahma,

"O Prajapati, do not cut the golden tree that you had planted when it is about to bear fruit. He is your grandson and would wither under your curse. Kindly allow him to awaken some times."

'Brahma replied,

'He will sleep for six months and be awake for one day. On that day, this warrior will wander upon the earth and devour many persons.'

Continuing his description of Kumbhakarna, Vibhishana said,

'He now comes from his abode and since he has been woken up for battle, he would be angry and hungry. He wanders in search of food and shall eat any vanara that comes in his way. How would the fleeing vanaras stop this giant? They should be told that he is not a being to be scared of and that might render them fearless.'

Hearing this, Rama ordered Neel to fortify his defences and post the army formations to be ready to attack and occupy the gates and streets of Lanka. He ordered a piling up of rocks, trees, mountain cliffs and other weapons in sufficient numbers at strategic points.

18

Kumbhakarna Reprimands Ravana but Assures Him of Help

An intoxicated Kumbhakarna walked through the high streets of Lanka, half asleep and upset. The residents showered flowers on him from their balconies in the hope that he will make them victorious in battle. Soon after entering the magnificent palace, Kumbhakarna, like Indra looking up to Swayambhu Brahma sitting on his celestial lotus seat, looked at Ravana sitting on his throne. He found his brother quite disturbed at the turn of events.

Touching his brother's feet, Kumbhakarna asked,

'What are my orders, my brother and mighty king?'

Ravana Motivates Kumbhakarna to Fight and Kill the Vanaras

Ravana saw Kumbhakarna and could not contain his joy. Descending from the throne, he embraced and welcomed him and offered him a high seat.

His eyes glowing red with anger, the giant rakshasa asked the king,

'Why have you honoured me with a remembrance? Who is the source of your fear? Who wants to travel to the Yamaloka?

Rolling his eyes with anger, Ravana replied,

'You have been asleep for long and do not know of Rama being the source of my fear and pain. The brave Rama, accompanied by his brother Lakshmana and friend Sugreeva has crossed the ocean and together, they intend annihilation of our dynasty.

'The vanaras have rolled over our gardens and forests like an ocean. A number of our warriors have been killed by them. We have awakened you to deliver us from this fear and to destroy all of them.

'Our treasury is empty and the city teems with infants and elderly and all the young rakshasas have been dying in the battlefield. It is time for you to show your unmatched valour for the sake of your brother. You have defeated the devatas, and even the asuras, several times on the battlefield. I hold great love and respect for you and am sure that you shall be able to defeat the enemy to save Lanka and its people.'

Kumbhakarna Tenders a Homily

Listening to Ravana's lament, Kumbhakarna had a hearty laugh. He said,

'My dear brother, the problem Vibhishana and I had foreseen has now arisen. You never trusted your well-wishers nor acted upon their advice.

'You have, in a short time, reaped the fruit of your evil deeds. This denouement was certain for your act of abducting Sita and denouncing wise counsel.

'Maharaja, arrogant of your might, you ignored your unethical deeds and never thought of their consequences.

'Anyone who considers himself to be supreme and all powerful, and shifts his priorities, is ignorant of Niti and Aniti. An act done without any consideration of time and place and under adverse circumstances, invariably results in sorrow.

'A king ought to decide upon a fight against or surrender to the enemy after consultation with his ministers. He must never overlook the principles of sama, dama, danda and bheda.

'O lord of the rakshasas, a wise person must follow dharma, gather artha and enjoy kama at the right time.

'Dharma is superior in all respects to artha and kama. Therefore, when the occasion so demands, the king or his courtiers must follow dharma in preference to artha and kama. Knowledge and penance is useless if they cannot understand or follow these precepts as laid down by the wise.

'A king ought to act in his interest after consulting the ministers who are well versed in the essence of artha. He must not listen to ministers and flatterers who advise the king out of their own greed and incompetence.

'An agile king, who hastens to act without giving a thought to the consequences of his actions, reveals his weakness to the enemy like the Kroncha Mountain opening its valley to the birds. A king, who ignores the enemy and does not take steps to protect his kingdom, loses his throne.

'It was in your interest to have listened to Mandodari, your beloved wife and our younger brother, Vibhishana. But now, what has been done stands in our way as the end of the rakshasas.'

Ravana raised his eyebrows in anger and said,

'Why do you advise me like an honoured guru and a teacher? What is the benefit that accrues from your laboured speech? Now is not the time of advice; you must do what is necessary and justified at the present moment.

'It is, at present, futile to talk of the decisions that I wrongly took or the tasks that I did not accomplish. Whatever has happened is in the past and the wise do not grieve for the bygones. Think of the present imperatives and assuage my sorrow born of indiscretions.

'Go and wage a war if you love me, if you consider yourself to be a brave person, and if you consider my assignment to be your foremost duty.

'He alone is a well-wisher who, even when all is lost, selflessly obliges his kin. A real friend helps even those who, having taken the path of impropriety, are in distress.'

Listening to Ravana's sorrowful voice and such pleadings agitated Kumbhakarna and he spoke words of comfort to the distressed brother. Speaking slowly and sweetly, he said,

'Maharaja, you have always been victorious over your enemies. It is futile to grieve now; you should overcome your anger and feel comfortable. As long as I live, you should have nothing to worry about. I shall wipe out the cause of your discomfort.

'Under all circumstances I ought to talk only of your welfare. Hence my advice, tendered out of my love for my brother and my proximity to you.

'I shall do whatever is dictated by my love for you. You will soon watch how I annihilate the enemy on the battlefield. I shall kill both the Raghava brothers and shall wipe the tears of those who have lost their kith and kin in this battle.

'Your worry is needless; Rama will have to kill me before he can touch you. I await your orders to fight.

'I do not need any Shakti, any weapon or sharp arrows to fight the foe; I shall strangle the enemy with my palms.

'I shall not spare Hanuman who had set Lanka on fire. I shall kill Indra and swallow the ocean and crush the mountains into powder. I shall tear the world into pieces to save Lanka and its people.

'Rajan, you need not worry. You should forget your grief and entertain yourself the way you please. When I dispatch Rama to Yamaloka, Sita will surrender herself to you forever.'

19

Kumbhakarna Meets His End

Ignoring the sycophants in his court, Kumbhakarna addressed the king and said,

'Rajan, today by killing the wicked Rama, I shall destroy the root cause of your fear. A warrior displays his prowess in silence and does not indulge in self-praise.'

Turning to Mahodara, Kumbhakarna said,

'Mahodara, only the cowardly, foolish kings, overconfident of their learning, will be pleased by your flattering words. Cowards and servile self-seekers like you have invited destruction by mindlessly nodding assent to the king's utterances and deeds.

'In Lanka, none has survived except the king and flatterers like you. The treasury is empty and the forces have been decimated. To have friends like you is equivalent to having enemies.

'I now proceed to the battleground in order to vanquish the enemy and sort out the situation created by your condemnable deeds and policies in the battlefield. I wish to put this danger looming over the king to an end.'

Ravana replied to Kumbhakarna's comments with laughter and said,

'Brother, you know better than others what is involved in waging a battle. Mahodara is certainly afraid of Rama. Therefore, he does not look forward to a fight.

'Among my kith and kin, there is none who compares with you in bravery or in being my well-wisher. Rama's time has come. Go like Yamaraja and kill the Raghava princes at once.'

Kumbhakarna is Decked out for Battle

Kumbhakarna armed himself with a lance made of black metal and embellished with motifs embossed in gold. Garlanded with red flowers, it was heavy and shone like Indra's thunderbolt. The lance was dyed with the blood of the enemies killed earlier and it emitted sparks of fire. Holding it aloft, Kumbhakarna declared,

'I shall wage the battle alone. The rakshasa sena stays in its barracks.

'I am hungry and my rage knows no bounds. I shall make a meal out of all the vanaras.'

Ravana, however, advised his brother to go surrounded by warriors carrying maces and spears. He put a garland of gold studded with gems around his neck and decked Kumbhakarna in bracelets, rings, a white necklace shining like the moon, and rich ornaments.

Decked in golden armlets and medals, with ears large like pitchers, Kumbhakarna gleamed like the yagya fire. A black belt tied around his midriff made him look like the Mandarachala Mountain wrapped by Vasuki, the king of serpents, at the time of the Samudramanthan.

An armour of gold was placed around Kumbhakarna's chest which could withstand the heaviest of blows. It was impervious to weapons and sparkled like lightning. Decked in this armour, Kumbhakarna looked magnificent.

Kumbhakarna walked into the battlefield with equal magnificence. As Ravana bade farewell to the brother seeking his blessing with his head bowed before the king, conches were blown and kettle-drums beaten. Flowers were showered over the canopy covering his head.

Kumbhakarna expanded himself into a frighteningly large form. His eyes looked like the giant wheels of a chariot. He was surrounded by roaring rakshasas whose eyes were red with anger, who were dark as mounds of coal and carried weapons like swords, maces, lances, large tree trunks, and unbreakable slings. Opening his large mouth and laughing derisively, the warrior said,

'Like the fire consuming the moths, I shall burn each of the vanara warriors. However, the vanaras have not come here of their own volition. Hence they are not worthy of being killed by me. They have not wronged us and merely follow orders. They are suitable as embellishments for our cities. The people to be punished are Rama and Lakshmana. It is they who are responsible for the siege of Lanka. I shall kill the two brothers first and then devour the entire vanara sena.'

Hearing this, the rakshasas roared and sent a wave of fear through all the warriors on the battlefield.

However, the omens were not encouraging: dark clouds appeared on the horizon, meteors shot through the sky and lightning flashed. His left eye twitched and the left arm felt a shiver.

Kumbhakarna ignored the omens and inspired by the destructive power of Yamaraja, came out of the Lanka fortifications. The vanaras were swept by winds like the clouds in the sky by merely looking at him. Aimlessly, they ran in all directions and sought the shelter of Rama. Looking at them running out of fear, Kumbhakarna joyously roared like a cloud heavy with water.

Angada Tries to Lift the Morale of the Retreating Vanara Sena

Looking at his soldiers running away in fear of Kumbhakarna, Angada addressed his generals, Nala, Neel, Gavaksha and Kumud. He said,

'Warriors, have you forgotten that you descend from a superior race? Forgetting the divine and chivalrous deeds of your ancestors, where are you running away like ordinary monkeys?

'Come back, my warriors. This rakshasa is not powerful enough to fight us. In order to terrorize you, he has expanded his body through maya. His efforts shall be futile when his maya ends and we shall destroy this terror of the rakshasas with our might. Rest assured and take heart.'

Hesitatingly, the vanaras returned and attacked the enemy with large tree trunks. They threw massive mountain rocks and flowering trees at Kumbhakarna but to no avail.

On the other hand, an enraged Kumbhakarna systematically crushed the vanaras under his feet like a conflagration reducing a vast jungle to ashes. The vanaras made their exit with speed without casting a glance in any direction. Some fell into the ocean and others flew into the sky. Some of them took the newly built bridge to reach for safety.

Angada challenged the deserters. He said,

'Stay back. We shall wage this war together. If you desert, I do not see a place on this earth where you could seek shelter from Sugreeva's anger. Your women will deride you if you run away.

'Those who run away shall be seen as cowards and will have to live with contemptuous comments forever. Therefore, shed your fear and follow the righteous path.

'If you die on the battlefield, you will be welcomed in heaven as a warrior. On the contrary, we shall attain glory if we can decimate the enemy. Believe me, Kumbhakarna cannot stay alive when he fights Shri Rama.'

Kumbhakarna Takes on the Vanara Warriors

The vanaras paid heed to Angada's words and returned to face Kumbhakarna's fury. Hitting them with his mace, the latter scattered them in all directions. He gathered dozens of them in his arms and angrily swallowed them. The rocks and trees thrown by the vanaras on Kumbhakarna had no effect on him.

Hanuman threw a rock on Kumbhakarna who was mercilessly killing the vanaras with his arrows. The latter smashed this rock with his lance and cut the tree missiles thrown at him. When Kumbhakarna readied to attack the vanaras again, Hanuman stood in his path and hit him causing grievous injury. The rakshasa warrior hit back with a lance which had a burning head and pierced Hanuman's chest. The latter was injured and vomited blood.

Seeing Hanuman injured in such a way, Neel threw a rock at Kumbhakarna which was smashed to pieces by the latter instantly. Kumbhakarna continued swallowing the vanaras alive like Garuda devours the serpents; however, the vanaras started slipping out alive out of his ears and nose.

Angada too had his share of the fight. While he threw a rock on Kumbhakarna, the latter tried to hit him with his spear. Angada moved out of his range and hit Kumbhakarna on his chest with a fist which rendered the rakshasa unconscious.

Regaining consciousness, Kumbhakarna hit Angada with his left fist and made him unconscious.

The rakshasa warrior noticed Sugreeva and ran to pierce him with his spear. The latter jumped into the sky and attacked the asura with a rock. Challenging him, Sugreeva said,

'O rakshasa, you have killed many of my warriors and swallowed many others. Leave them alone and face my wrath.'

Kumbhakarna replied,

'Vanara, you roar because you are Prajapati's grandson and the son of Rikshraja. You are a patient and valiant warrior.'

Suddenly, Sugreeva swung a cliff and threw it on Kumbhakarna. It was like a thunderbolt and hurt the rakshasa grievously on his chest.

However, it was reduced to powder on coming in contact with his expanded chest.

An angry and injured Kumbhakarna roared. He took aim and after turning his lance a few times to add to its momentum, threw it at Sugreeva, intending to kill. However, Hanuman jumped, intercepted the missile and in no time broke it into two against his knee. The vanara sena rejoiced at this spectacular deed of Hanuman.

Kumbhakarna's anger knew no bounds. Plucking a cliff from the Malaya Mountain and nearing Sugreeva, he hit him on the head. The vanara king fell unconscious and Kumbhakarna lifted the king in his arms and flew towards Lanka. He thought that with Sugreeva's abduction, Rama's army would disperse and be destroyed in no time.

However, Hanuman was not the one to allow this abduction to go unchallenged. He assured the vanara sena and asked them to stay put for a fight.

Kumbhakarna was welcomed with flowers and shouts of victory as he entered Lanka with the flailing Sugreeva in his arms. The latter too regained consciousness with all the commotion and planned his revenge with the resources at his command. He dug his nails into Kumbhakarna's ear lobes, sliced them, bit off his nose with his teeth and tore his ribs with the nails of his feet. A bleeding and angry Kumbhakarna threw Sugreeva on the ground and started trampling him. However, Sugreeva jumped swiftly and returned to his camp, in the presence of Rama.

Kumbhakarna, though bleeding profusely, soon returned to the battlefield carrying a mountainous mace in his hand. He looked ferocious, and the blood oozing out from various parts owing to Sugreeva's attack made him look frightening.

Lakshmana Takes on Kumbhakarna but Kumbhakarna Wishes to Fight Rama

Looking at the continuing devastation of the vanara army at the hands of Kumbhakarna, Lakshmana was worried and pierced him with seven arrows. However, the rakshasa made Lakshmana's weapons ineffective. This turn of events made the Raghava prince angry. Like a wind blowing away the evening clouds and making them disappear, Lakshmana hid Kumbhakarna's golden armour with a barrage of arrows. In spite of this, the asura warrior gleamed like the sun hidden by clouds.

Speaking derisively to Lakshmana, Kumbhakarna said,

'I can effortlessly conquer even Yamaraja in a battle and am ready to fight anyone who takes a stand against me. You have displayed unprecedented chivalry in fighting against me fearlessly and this is worthy of appreciation.

'Even Indra, riding the Airavata, and surrounded by the devatas, could not stand against me for long.

'Though young, you have pleased me with your chivalry. I, therefore ask for your permission to go near Raghava in order to engage him in a battle to the finish. You have impressed and satisfied me with your valour but my purpose in this battlefield is to kill Rama alone. Once he dies, the enemy forces will run away. If anyone still dares to challenge me, I shall fight him with all my devastating resources.'

Lakshmana laughed and in words soaked in derision and admiration said,

'What you say about having defeated Indra and other devatas is certainly true. I have witnessed your chivalry with my own eyes.

'Look, there stands Shri Rama, immovable like a mountain.'

After a Fierce Battle, Rama Beheads Kumbhakarna

Ignoring Lakshmana's praise, Kumbhakarna moved ahead to attack Rama. The earth shook under his feet as he moved.

Rama hit the giant near his heart several times with Raudrastra. An injured and infuriated Kumbhakarna ran to hit Rama in return. The peacock feathers attached to Rama's arrows, piercing his chest, had made him most uncomfortable. In discomfort, his mace slipped from his hand. His other weapons too slid to the earth, but nonetheless, he continued to hit and kill the vanaras with his fists.

Pierced by Rama's arrows, Kumbhakarna bled profusely. While eating the vanaras, bears and even rakshasas to satisfy his hunger, Kumbhakarna lifted a rock and threw it at Rama. The latter smashed this rock to pieces with his arrows long before it could reach him. However, this rock killed hundreds of vanaras before it landed on the ground in pieces.

Looking at this scene of destruction, Lakshmana observed to his brother,

'Rajan, this rakshasa is uncontrollable and devours warriors from his own army for his hunger. He is unable to distinguish between a friend and a foe and is continuously swallowing the warriors on both sides. I suggest that several of our vanara leaders climb on his body and sit there, so that weighed down he is unable to walk and swallow other vanaras.

Hearing Lakshmana's advice, several vanaras climbed onto Kumbhakarna, who shook them off as an enraged elephant throws away the mahout.

Rama noticed Kumbhakarna's anger and took a new bow in hand that had a sturdy string, was frightening like a serpent and was gilded at the edges and in the center. He attacked Kumbhakarna ferociously.

Ravana's brother was occupied with catching the vanaras and eating them. He was huge as a mountain and kept vomiting blood every now and then.

As Rama again pulled at his bowstring, unable to bear the thundering sound that emanated from it, Kumbhakarna ran towards him. Rama stalled him with a shout and said,

'Rakshasaraja, come forward without hesitation. I stand here to annihilate your dynasty and assure you of your nearing end.'

Realizing that he was face to face with none other than Rama himself, Kumbhakarna laughed scornfully and ran towards the prince. With a loud roar he said,

'Rama, do not commit the mistake of taking me as an equal of Kabandha, Viradha or Khara. I am neither Maricha nor Vali. I am here to kill you and shall accomplish that task. Look at this massive mace made of black iron; this has assisted me in killing various devatas and now shall be the end of you.

'Do not be ignorant of my prowess because my nose and ears have been chopped off. I suffer no pain because of this.

'You are a lion among the Ikshavakus. Let me see your valour first; strike me and I shall fight you once I gauge your power.'

Listening to Kumbhakarna, Rama hit him with several arrows as strong as the thunderbolts. However, none of them hurt or disturbed the equanimity of the enemy. Similar arrows had sliced the sala trees and killed the vanara raja Vali at an earlier time. Today, these arrows had no effect on Kumbhakarna's body. Revolving his powerful mace, he neutralized the force of these arrows.

Rama shot an arrow known as Vayavya and sliced away Kumbhakarna's right arm carrying the mace. As this arm fell to the ground, a number of soldiers were crushed underneath it.

With his remaining arm, Kumbhakarna uprooted a tada tree and ran towards Rama to attack him. Rama, recalling an arrow known as Aindrastra, took a shot and sliced his other arm as well.

As the mutilated rakshasa ran to kill Rama, the latter cut off his feet with two crescent-shaped arrows. Kumbhakarna opened his mouth like a gorge and leapt at Rama to swallow him, all the while roaring ferociously.

Rama filled Kumbhakarna's mouth with sharp arrows till it was totally blocked. The latter could not even moan and fell.

Rama shot another forceful and divine arrow that had the power of destruction of a Brahma danda and the capability to kill death itself. It shone like the sunrays and derived its strength from Surya and Agni.

Illuminating the universe, powered by the strength of Rama's arm, this missile looked ferocious like fire without smoke. It moved with an unstoppable speed and sliced off Kumbhakarna's head.

All at once, Kumbhakarna's large forehead lost its glow like the moon in mid-sky at sunrise. The momentum of the slicing arrow carried the giant's head into Lanka. Its impact demolished many houses, doors and high ramparts situated near the site where it fell.

Likewise, Kumbhakarna's torso fell into the sea and after squashing many crocodiles, reptiles, and whales, it sank to the bottom of the ocean.

While Ravana's kith and kin and the rakshasa generals and soldiers bemoaned the death of Kumbhakarna, the vanara hordes rejoiced. The latter's faces bloomed with happiness and they praised Rama's skills by hailing his victory with loud slogans.

20

Several of Ravana's Sons and Brothers are Killed on the Battlefield

Ravana Mourns Kumbhakarna's Death

Reporting the death of Kumbhakarna, the rakshasa soldiers said to their king,

'Maharaja, your brother, ferociously brave like Kala, after devouring hundreds of vanaras, was eventually slain on the battlefield. He fought gloriously for sometime but was eventually overtaken by Rama's majesty and chivalry. His mutilated torso drowned in the sea while his bleeding head lies at the gates of Lanka.'

Ravana fainted on hearing of this calamity; he had lost all his warriors to death at the hands of the opponent and it grieved him deeply. Learning of their uncle's death, Devantaka, Narantaka, Trishira and Atikaya wept inconsolably. Kumbhakarna's stepbrothers, Mahodara and Mahaparshva were full of grief.

Regaining consciousness, Ravana moaned,

'Kumbhakarna was my right arm and I am reduced to nothing without him. He was Kala himself; how could Rama have killed him on the battlefield? The vanara sena is ready to climb over the gates of Lanka, once inaccessible.

'I am no longer interested in being a ruler. Of what use is Sita to me? I do not want to live in the absence of Kumbhakarna and all others who have lost their lives for my sake.

'If I am unable to kill my brother's slayer Rama on the battlefield, I better court death. There is no use in prolonging this meaningless life otherwise.

'Mahatma Vibhishana had spoken well, and out of ignorance I ignored his wise advice. Whatever he had predicted has come true for the rakshasa clan. I banished Vibhishana who always followed dharma. Today, I suffer the consequences of my misdeeds.'

A wailing Ravana fainted again and fell to the ground.

Narantaka is Killed at the Hands of Angada

Ravana's stepbrothers and sons consoled him and tried to lift his spirits. Trishira said,

'Father, no doubt our uncle was a great warrior. However, the wise do not mourn for the dead. Moreover, you are powerful enough to subdue Rama.'

Each of his three sons who were present was keen to mount an offensive against Rama. All of them were experienced warriors and had won many a battle. Ravana embraced them, blessed them and sent them to the battlefield. He sent his stepbrothers, Mahaparshva and Mahodara, both eager to fight, to protect his sons.

While Mahodara mounted a dark elephant like Airavata and carried several weapons, Ravana's son Trishira travelled in a majestic chariot stocked with several weapons. He wore a three-ridged crown like the golden Trishul peak of the Himalayas.

Atikaya, known as an invincible warrior, rode a magnificent and sturdy chariot pulled by steeds harnessed in sturdy yokes. His chariot was stocked with swords, lances and maces.

Narantaka rode a white horse, sturdy like Ucchaishrava, large, harnessed in gold and as fast as the speed of thought. He carried a powerful barbed missile shimmering like a meteor. Devantaka held a lance studded with gold and tried to imitate Vishnu holding the Mandarachala Mountain in his palms at the time of Samudramanthan.

The glorious warrior Mahaparshva carried a mace and resembled Kubera on the battlefield.

All the giant-bodied nishacharas marched out of Lanka as the devatas had marched out of Alkapuri. They were followed by rakshasas, one more massive than the other, riding horses, elephants or chariots that roared like clouds. Ravana's sons and brothers, dressed in golden armour and wearing crowns, shone like the sun. Their gleaming white weapons looked like rows of flamingos shining under the autumn clouds. They were determined to win or lay down their lives fighting for their king.

The vanara generals saw the rakshasa sena coming on chariots, horses and elephants. They saw the enemy's massive weapons and heard the tinkling of thousands of bells. The vanaras, carrying massive rocks, ready for attack, roared loudly, happy that a battle was imminent. Many of them flew in the sky carrying large tree trunks and mountain cliffs. They were enraged at the sight of the asura soldiers trying to frighten them with their pomp.

Soon, the two sides engaged in a deafening and bloody combat. While the rakshasas rained arrows, the vanaras threw rocks, trees and mountain cliffs. Both of them roared like lions, one more ferociously than the other. Innumerable soldiers died on both sides.

In a short while, rivers of blood ran in the battlefield. Soldiers soaked in blood beheaded each other. The vanaras fought enthusiastically and they did not feel inferior to the well-equipped rakshasas. They were fighting for a holy cause as opposed the asuras who were supporting a king who had foisted an unholy war on them.

Narantaka led the attack and entered the vanara sena like a whale diving into an ocean. He killed hundreds of vanaras with his spear and piled their bodies like a pyramid. Looking at his soldiers' predicament, Sugreeva asked Angada to take on Narantaka.

Angada was large as a mountain himself and did not carry any weapon. He decided to use only his nails and teeth to defeat Narantaka who was prepared to hit him with his barbed missile powerful as a thunderbolt.

An angry Narantaka lifted his lance and threw it at Angada. However, the weapon broke into pieces against the rock-like chest of Angada.

Hitting back, Angada used his fist on the horse Narantaka was riding. He split the horse's head into two, making the animal fall dead on the ground.

Narantaka could not bear this and hit the forehead of Angada with his fist, leading to severe bleeding. Angada fainted at being hit thus, but revived soon. Once again he hit Narantaka on his chest and broke his ribs. The rakshasa warrior spat fire and fell down dead as if crushed by a mountain.

The Duels

Seeing his brother Narantaka being killed, an infuriated Devantaka attacked Angada with a spear. Trishira and Mahodara also joined him in the attack. Angada retaliated by hurling a tree at Devantaka. Trishira struck down this missile with an arrow as fierce as poisonous snakes.

In this ferocious give and take, Mahodara hit Angada with an iron club as powerful as a thunderbolt. At this point in time, Angada was surrounded by the three rakshasa brothers who attacked him simultaneously. The brave Angada did not feel upset in the least. He was invincible and could move fast to attack or to avoid being hit by the enemy. He hit Mahodara's elephant with his fist and killed him. He then plucked a tusk from the dead elephant and struck Devantaka with it. The injured Devantaka shook like a falling tree and blood spurted from his body.

Noticing that Angada was surrounded by the three rakshasas, Hanuman and Neel ran to his rescue. Neel threw a rock on Trishira but the latter thwarted it. Encouraged by this success, Devantaka attacked Hanuman with a lance.

Hanuman was alert and swiftly jumped to avoid the lance while simultaneously hitting Devantaka with a fist on his forehead splitting it in the centre. The rakshasa died instantaneously.

Meanwhile Neel was attacked by Trishira with several arrows. Riding an elephant, Mahodara too rained arrows on Neel. A grievously injured Neel became unconscious and fell down.

The vanara chief soon revived and hitting Mahodara with a tree, felled him.

Trishira was furious at the sight of his brothers and uncle dying. He hit Hanuman with sharp arrows which were countered by the latter using rocks. Trishira cut these rocks to pieces in no time.

An enraged Hanuman jumped into the sky, reached Trishira's chariot and clawed his horses with his nails like an angry lion tearing an elephant apart.

Trishira hurled a Shakti in Hanuman's direction. The latter caught hold of it and broke it into pieces. Trishira then attacked Hanuman with a sword and injured him in his chest. The injured Pavana putra boxed him in his chest and made him unconscious. His sword slipped from his hold and upon revival, Hanuman caught hold of his crowned head and beheaded him with the same sword.

Mahaparshva witnessed this brutal massacre of some of the most heroic warriors of his clan. Agitated, he advanced with a mace and hit

Rishabha who had blocked his path and injured him. The latter hit him with a blow on his chest with his fist. Mahaparshva fainted and his mace fell from his grip. Rishabha picked it up and killed the rakshasa when he revived.

Atikaya Falls to Lakshmana's Arrows

Atikaya had lost his brothers and uncles on the battlefield. This infuriated him no end. He had been blessed by Brahma to live long and was confident of his valour. He was as large as a mountain and was a scourge to the devatas. Riding a chariot that glittered with the light of a hundred suns shining together, he attacked the vanaras ferociously.

Atikaya, the Magnificent

Atikaya wore a crown and rings of gold on his ears and continuously pulled at his bowstring to let the enemy know of his presence.

The frightened vanaras at first thought that Kumbhakarna had come alive. They approached Rama for help.

Rama looked at the approaching warrior and asked Vibhishana about his identity. He said,

'Who is this large-built rakshasa riding a chariot pulled by a thousand horses? His eyes glow like those of a lion. Like Mahadeva surrounded by ghosts, he carries sharp trishuls, spears and javelins. He flies a flag with the symbol of Rahu. His arrows scatter light in all directions.

'He has put a garland around his golden bow. Pulling at his bowstring, he makes a thundering sound. His chariot is driven by four charioteers and is well stocked with arrows, quivers and bowstrings.

'Kindly identify this rakshasa who has frightened the brave vanaras.'

Vibhishana replied,

'He is a son of Ravana, as strong as his father. He takes care of the elderly, is learned in the Vedas and is the finest among warriors. He is respected as a charioteer, swordsman, archer, and dexterous shooter. He deals with others equitably and tenders valuable advice when sought.

'Named Atikaya, he is the son of Dhanyamalini, the second queen of Ravana. Under his protection, the residents of Lanka live fearlessly.

'With a clear conscience, he performed tapasya and pleased Brahma. The latter blessed him with several celestial and powerful weapons with which he defeated many enemies.

'My lord, he is a deadly warrior and must be defeated and killed before he kills all the vanaras.'

By now, Atikaya had advanced to the centre of the vanara formations. Sugreeva's warriors such as Kumud, Dwivid, Maind, Neel, and Sharabha attacked him with mountains, cliffs and trees. With a shower of his arrows, Ravana's chivalrous son made all these onslaughts futile. He inflicted grievous injuries on the vanara generals, defeating them all in no time.

Atikaya did not hurt any warrior who did not challenge him. He declared,

'I do not intend fighting any common soldier who confronts me. Here I stand in my chariot. Let anyone who dares, who feels brave enough and is eager to battle, challenge me to a fight. I shall oblige.'

Lakshmana and Atikaya Engage Each Other

Listening to Atikaya's arrogant challenge, Lakshmana was enraged. He moved to confront him and pulled at his bowstring producing a roaring sound. A surprised Atikaya taunted him and said,

'Saumitra, you are but a young boy. It is not safe for you to play with weapons and warriors. Go back; your wish to engage me shall lead to your Kala. Why do you desire to awaken the fires of Pralaya, lying dormant and at peace at present?'

As Atikaya readied to shoot, Lakshmana addressed him in measured tones, and said,

'O evil soul, a braggart cannot be considered great by any means. Only actions can be considered chivalrous.

'You sit there well stocked with weapons of all kinds. Show me that you know how to use them. Thereafter I shall behead you with my arrows like a gust of wind bringing down a ripe tala fruit.

'Whether I am young or old, you dare not ignore me. On this battlefield, I shall be your death.'

The fight began and Atikaya started shooting arrows at Lakshmana. However, his arrows were destroyed by crescent-topped arrows released by the Raghava prince. After several hits and misses, Lakshmana pierced his forehead with an arrow tipped like a fist. The rakshasa shuddered in pain. Lakshmana hit at Atikaya's chariot and killed his charioteer and his horses. Still he could not pierce the enemy's armour.

At this stage Vayu advised Lakshmana to use the most potent Brahmastra on the rakshasa because that alone could pierce through his invincible armour. Atikaya tried to stop the blow of the Brahmastra with each one of the weapons at his disposal, but to no avail.

Soon Lakshmana's Brahmastra had beheaded Atikaya. While the severed head fell on the ground, its jewels scattered all around.

A pall of gloom enveloped Lankapuri and its residents; Ravana's grief knew no bounds.

The vanaras rejoiced over the death of one of the greatest warriors of Lanka who was considered invincible till now. They hailed Lakshmana as a conqueror while he came to Shri Ramachandra and touched his feet in obeisance.

22

Ravana Bemoans His Loss

For Ravana, it seemed like the beginning of the end. Every male in his family with the exception of Indrajit and himself had been killed. Vibhishana had deserted him to join Rama before the war commenced. Mourning the loss of his warriors, the king said,

'The impatient and unforgiving Dhoomraksha, the most valiant Akampana, Prahasta and Kumbhakarna, the most powerful of rakshasas were ever ready to wage a war. They had never been defeated.

'However, the accomplished and mighty Rama has killed these giant warriors who were masters of weaponry of all kinds, along with a large number of the rakshasa sena.

'The enemy has killed several other chivalrous rakshasas. My brave son, Indrajit, had tied the two brothers in a snare of arrows but the two brothers came out unscathed unlike any devata, asura, yaksha and gandharva. I do not know if the princes used maya or a magical charm to unfasten the deadly Nagapasha.

'All the warriors who went out to fight under my orders have been killed by the brave vanaras. I do not see any other general who can kill Rama, Lakshmana, Sugreeva, Vibhishana and the vanara sena.'

'It is certain that Rama is powerful and so are his weapons. Numberless rakshasas have met their end fighting his forces.

'I now believe that Raghunath is Bhagwan Narayana himself. He is free from sorrow and sickness. We, on the other hand, keep the massive gates of Lankapuri shut at all times owing to our fear.'

Ravana ordered his guards to keep a close watch on Asoka Vatika where Sita was imprisoned as well as on other places in Lanka. He made special arrangements for the safety of the cantonments and ammunition depots.

Taking the above precautions, a humbled Ravana, hurt by the loss of his sons, angry at the turn of events, breathing hard and sighing deep, entered his palace.

23

Indrajit Renders Rama, Lakshmana and the Vanara Sena Unconscious

Ravana sat weeping over the death of his sons Devantaka, Trishira and Atikaya. He worried about his future. Looking at his sorrowful state of mind, prince Indrajit offered him solace and courage. He said,

'Father, as long as I am alive, do not yield to grief and attachment. Nobody can stay alive on the battlefield when shot by my arrows. Have you forgotten that I had conquered even Indra?

'Today I shall pierce the bodies of Rama and Lakshmana with my arrows. I shall tear their limbs apart and end the battle.

'Today, Indra, Yama, Vishnu, Rudra, Agni, Surya, and Chandrama will witness my unparalleled valour in the battlefield.'

Ravana gave him his blessings and said,

'There is no charioteer in the universe that can stand against you, my son. You had defeated Indra. Hence, it is child's play for you to vanquish the Raghava princes who are merely human. I am sure that you will accomplish this mission.'

Soon Indrajit arrived at the battle scene riding a chariot pulled by healthy donkeys and loaded with weapons. Several brave rakshasas followed him carrying bows and arrows, and riding elephants or horses. Indrajit's arrival was announced by the blowing of conches and beating of kettle-drums.

Indrajit Worships Agni and Invokes the Brahmastra

Surrounded by his warriors, Indrajit performed a havana and worshipped Agni. He had spread his weapons around the havana kunda as if these were the kusha leaves. A goat with a black coat was kept ready for sacrifice at the conclusion of the yagya. The fire was smokeless and flames of the colour of heated gold rose high. It was as if Agni himself was present to accept the sacrificial offering.

Chanting mantras, Indrajit invoked the Brahmastra, frightening the devatas, Surya, Chandrama, the planets and the entire universe.

With his enhanced powers, at the conclusion of the yagya, Indrajit floated upward with his chariot, his charioteer, the horses and his weapons and became invisible. He was visible only to his soldiers who were attacking the vanaras with multi-headed arrows, swords, maces and goads. He boosted their morale and encouraged them to fight aggressively.

Indrajit too started killing as many vanara soldiers as he could with his mace and other weapons. Hundreds of vanaras were either killed or made unconscious due to loss of blood. Their hope of a victory appeared doomed with Indrajit's onslaught. However, the vanaras did not retreat. They had sworn loyalty to Rama and were determined to fight to the finish.

Indrajit injured Gandhamadana and hit Nala. He shot nine to eighteen arrows at one go. He hit Jambavan with ten and Neel with thirty arrows. Sugreeva, Rishabha, Angada and Dwivid were also injured and rendered inactive for some time.

Indrajit now turned his attention to Rama and Lakshmana and rained them with arrows shining like the sun. Rama warded off his arrows and said to Lakshmana,

'Indrajit, empowered by the Brahmastra, after inflicting losses on the vanara sena, is now targeting us with sharp arrows. He has hidden his giant body. It is a matter of concern. How shall we kill him when we cannot see him? I suggest that instead of retaliation and fighting aimlessly, we let his arrows make us unconscious on the battlefield. Seeing the state of the battlefield and all our warriors unconscious, he will feel victorious and go back into Lanka.'

Rama, Lakshmana, and the vanara sena, thus, lay unconscious on the battlefield.

A delighted Indrajit returned to his father's court carrying the happy tidings of his victory.

24

Hanuman Fetches Divine Medicines

Looking at the unconscious Raghava princes, the vanara chieftains were disheartened. It was Vibhishana who spoke wisely and encouraged them. He said,

'Warriors, do not be afraid. This is not a moment for despondency. The Aryaputras did not take up arms against Indrajit's use of the Brahmastra out of respect for Brahma. They are merely unconscious and their lives are not in danger.

'Brahma had bestowed this invincible weapon upon Indrajit. Honouring the Brahmastra on the battlefield, the princes permitted themselves to be hit without retaliating. Hence, none of you ought to feel dejected. There is nothing to regret.'

Hanuman suggested that they carry a torch and give succour to the injured lying unattended on the battlefield. Vibhishana accompanied him on this mission.

Moving from soldier to soldier, from general to general, most of them mutilated, they soon came near Jambavan, who, pierced by hundreds of arrows, lay lustreless like a dying flame. Vibhishana approached him and asked about his well-being. The Rikshraja Jambavan, speaking with difficulty, replied,

'Rakshasaraja, I am able to identify you through your voice. All my limbs are pierced with arrows. I cannot even open my eyelids. But kindly tell me whether Anjana's brave son, Vayuputra Hanuman is alive.'

'Rikshraja,' said Vibhishana, 'how is it that you have enquired about Hanuman even to the exclusion of Rama and Lakshmana? Arya, you have not shown such consideration and such deep affection for the Vanararaja Sugreeva, nor for the prince Angada, or for other warriors.'

Jambavan replied,

'If the brave Hanuman lives, the vanara sena lives even if truncated. If he is dead, we too are dead even if we are physically alive. Brother, if Hanuman, swift as the wind and ferocious like Agni lives, there is hope for the vanaras.'

Jambavan Asks Hanuman to Fetch Sanjivani

Hanuman stepped forward and touched Jambavan's feet. Hanuman's touch gave Jambavan a new vitality despite the severe pain that his mortal body experienced. Addressing the glorious Hanuman, Jambavan said,

'O lion among the vanaras, you alone can save the Raghavas. It is an opportune moment for you to display your chivalry.

'You raise the morale of the vanara and the bear forces. Pluck the arrows out of the bodies of Shri Rama and Lakshmana and nurse them to health.

'Flying over the ocean, travel to the Himalayas where you will locate the golden peaks of the Rishabha and the Kailas Mountains. In between, there is a mountain where luminous medicinal plants grow, emitting unmatched light. On that peak you will notice four medicinal plants named Mritasanjivani, Vishalyakarni, Suvarnakarni and Sanghani. Bring all of them and administer them to the injured.'

Hanuman was excited to hear of the medicinal plants that could bring all the vanaras and Raghava back to life and took no time to set out on his expedition. He expanded his body and pressed one foot on a hillock, ready to jump across the ocean and the landmass in order to reach the Himalayas with the speed of light.

At one go, Hanuman jumped to the Malaya Mountain scenic with cataracts, a variety of trees and creepers and lotus ponds, a place for the devatas and the gandharvas to live in. He flew with his serpentine tail raised, his back slightly bent, ears pulled inwards and his mouth open like a furnace.

Hanuman Flies to the Himalayas

Hanuman spread his serpentine arms like Garuda and flew straight to the Himalayas. Flying over land and water, he could see the ocean with its rolling waves and aquatic animals wafting in cross currents. He moved precisely and speedily towards his goal.

Reaching the Himalayas, Hanuman saw several natural cataracts running down its slopes. He saw pretty mountain caves and charming cliffs looking like piles of white clouds. Various types of trees added to the beauty of the mountain slopes. Scattered everywhere were ashramas of various devarshis. In a moment Hanuman saw the holy Kailas Mountain, Vrishabha, the mount of Shiva and the golden mountain, Rishabha.

Thereafter, he noticed the sacred cliff where grew the divine medicinal plants which glowed with an ethereal light. It was an amazing sight. As Jambavan had informed him, the plants had a fiery glow.

Hanuman climbed the peak and started his search for the four divine plants. Since all of them exuded a divine glow, and Hanuman was not able to identify the herbs he needed, he uprooted the entire cliff and flew back to the battlefield in Lanka. Carrying the glowing cliff, he looked like another sun in the sky.

Landing on the Trikuta Mountain, Hanuman was welcomed by Vibhishana. With the smell of the divine herbs, Rama and Lakshmana regained consciousness and their wounds healed. The vanara generals and soldiers too came back to their senses in no time. As the night ended, the princes and the entire army woke up as if from sleep.

Hanuman returned to plant the medicinal cliff where it had been. Upon return to the camp, he bowed to Shri Rama.

25

Lanka is Set on Fire Once Again

Knowing that the war was nearing its end, Sugreeva called a council of his commanders led by Hanuman, to announce a new strategy to cause the maximum damage to the enemy.

He said,

'Kumbhakarna has been killed, so are most of Ravana's sons. Therefore, Ravana can hardly safeguard Lankapuri at present and is open to any sort of attack. I order that fast moving and brave soldiers in our force, carrying fiery torches, mount an attack on Lanka'

Buildings Set on Fire

At nightfall, as the vanaras carrying flaming torches approached Lanka, the guards at the massive doors ran away. The vanaras enthusiastically set fire to main gateways, upper storey towers, mansions and roadside shops. Soon hundreds of buildings were on fire. Some others as high as the mountains came tumbling down.

At some places, the burning aloe and sandalwood emitted fragrance. At others, pearls, polished gemstones, diamonds and coral were reduced to ashes. The fires destroyed jute mats, silks, goat wool blankets and other woollen clothing, gold ornaments and weapons.

In the stables for horses and elephants, the fire consumed harnesses, saddles, and decorative flaps of various sizes.

In the armouries, the fire lighted by the vanaras reduced to ashes armours used by warriors, horses and elephants. In addition a variety of weapons including swords, bows, arrows, bowstrings, maces, goads, shaktis, flywhisks, and animal skins meant for seats were all destroyed in the flames.

It was evening and the rakshasas dressed in gold armours, necklaces and fine clothes were busy dining, indulging in indoor pleasures and entertaining or bring entertained. As their houses caught fire, they ran to save their lives.

Several rakshasas having imbibed an excess of liquor were intoxicated to the extent of not being able to walk. Their eyes were red and unfocussed and though they expressed anger against the enemy in their speeches, they were not in a state to fight them. As the fires spread, warriors and people from all around ran with their wives and children to save their lives. A number of the rakshasas perished in the enveloping flames.

Many buildings that had been constructed after great planning and much embellishments were razed to the ground by the conflagration. Sleeping women were awakened by the heat and wailed while trying to escape the advancing flames. Their shrieks echoed through the entire city.

As flames rose from various parts of Lanka, the caretakers freed the horses and elephants from stables. Frightened by flames, the animals ran for their life and Lanka looked like an ocean full of crocodiles running amok.

26

Indrajit Dies at the Hands of Lakshmana

Learning of the death of so many of his warriors and the destruction of the city in the fire, an angry Ravana sent for his eldest son Indrajit and said,

'My brave son, you alone can kill Rama and Lakshmana. Go and kill the chivalrous brothers either in a straight fight or by making yourself invisible. You are definitely more powerful than them and have been the only one till now to have subdued them for some time.

'You who have defeated the invincible Indra in a battle, surely have the calibre to kill these two human beings.'

Indrajit Decimates the Vanara Sena

Once again Indrajit entered the battlefield and began his ritual worship of gods. Making an offering to Agni, Indrajit, blessed with the power to become invisible whenever he wished to do so, climbed his magnificent chariot. The golden chariot was pulled by four horses and was stocked with a large bow and hundreds of arrows. Protected by the Brahmastra, riding a chariot brilliant like the sun, Indrajit looked invincible.

Pulling at his bowstring, Indrajit declared,

'Rama and Lakshmana are counterfeit tapasvis wandering in the forest. I shall kill them on the battlefield and hand over a great victory to my father.'

Saying this, Indrajit became invisible and noticed Rama and Lakshmana standing surrounded by the vanara commanders. He started shooting arrows at them like a cloud flooding the earth with rain. The Raghava brothers released arrows but did not deliberately touch Indrajit.

On the other hand, Indrajit created smoke through maya and made it difficult for the warriors on land to see him or hear the horsebeats.

Indrajit released arrows as if he was throwing rocks and ended up injuring Rama in every limb.

Rama and Lakshmana retaliated and shot at the invisible enemy. They saw several blood soaked arrows falling to the ground and with apt concentration were able to cut most of the arrows aimed at them. Indrajit moved his chariot in the sky travelling in different directions so that his exact location could not be determined. Hit by his arrows, Rama and Lakshmana stood bleeding like blooming palash trees.

Nobody could see Indrajit's face, movement, bows and arrows. Like the sun hidden behind a thick cloud, nothing about him could be ascertained. Hitting without being seen, he injured hundreds of vanaras and killed an equal number.

An angry Lakshmana declared to Rama that he would invoke the Brahmastra to kill the entire rakshasa race.

Rama cautioned him and said,

'It is not fair to kill the entire rakshasa race because one of them has misbehaved.

'One ought not to kill anyone who is not engaged in a battle, who is in hiding, who has surrendered and sought protection, who has lost his mind or the one who is running away from the battlefield. Let us attempt to kill Indrajit alone. We shall use powerful weapons to accomplish this task.

'My weapons will burn him and bring him down dead even if he goes deep into the earth, flies to Swargaloka, hides in the netherworld, or stays in the sky.'

Saying this, Rama looked around thinking of a strategy to destroy the cruel and fierce Indrajit.

Indrajit Plays a Trick: Kills a Dummy Sita

Indrajit retreated into Lanka because he could see Rama devising a strategy to end his life. However, he could not overcome his anguish at the death of the rakshasa warriors. As soon as possible, gathering a large force, he came out of the western door of the city in order to challenge Rama's might.

To weaken Rama's resolve of defeating him and to dampen the spirit of the vanara army, he created a dummy Sita who looked real and alive and placed her on his chariot. His soldiers surrounded her making frightening faces.

The vanaras were enraged at this spectacle. Led by Hanuman, they advanced carrying huge boulders.

Finding an advancing vanara sena, Indrajit lost his cool. Pulling at her hair he dragged the dummy Sita. The woman cried and said, 'Ha Rama, Ha Rama.' Indrajit beat her in full sight of the crowd. An anguished Hanuman, looking at the maltreatment of Rama's queen, charming in every limb, wept and said,

'O evil soul, are you determined to destroy yourself that you are touching her hair? You were born in a family of Brahmarshis. Today, your conduct is condemnable. Are you so heartless that you humiliate a woman? What crime has Maithili committed against you that you mercilessly cause her hurt?

'You will not live long and it is your misfortune that you stand facing me in this battle.'

As Indrajit saw Hanuman advancing with a rock to attack him, he asked his soldiers to thwart his movement. He shot hundreds of arrows to kill the vanara soldiers and to make them run for life. Addressing Hanuman, he said,

'Vanara, I shall now, in your sight, kill Vaidehi for whose sake you, Sugreeva and Rama have attacked Lanka. Later I shall kill Rama, Lakshmana, you and Sugreeva, as well as the traitor Vibhishana.

'You said that I ought not to kill a woman. For me the most sacred act of duty is that which hurts the enemy most.'

Saying this, Indrajit cut Sita into two pieces striking her at her shoulder with a sharp sword. Having done this, he said,

'Look, I have sliced Rama's beloved wife into two. Here lies Sita, the Videha princess. All your efforts at war are now futile.'

Hanuman and his soldiers were crestfallen on seeing Sita being killed. His forces battled the rakshasa sena for some time, halted their advance and returned to Rama to tell him of the tragic incident. They thought it to be futile to continue the battle. Seeing them departing, Indrajit went to the Nikumbhila Devi temple to pray for further success in the battle.

Learning of Sita's Demise Rama Becomes Desolate

Rama fainted on learning of Sita's death at the hands of Indrajit. Lakshmana revived him speaking reassuring words. But Vibhishana realized that Indrajit had not killed the real Sita, but a mere dummy. Looking at the semi conscious Rama, he said,

'Maharaja, the sad news brought to you by Hanuman is, in my view, as impossible as the ocean going dry. I am well aware of Ravana's inclination towards Sita. He will not, come what may, allow her to be killed. He has never allowed any other man an access to Sita, whether by sama, danda or bheda. How could she be exposed in a battlefield to the eyes of other men?

'Mahabaho, Indrajit created an illusion and killed a dummy Sita created through sorcery. He has succeeded in creating a doubt in the minds of the vanaras to gain his end in the battle.

'Indrajit has gone to worship in the Nikumbhila temple. Once he has successfully completed the yagya there, even the devatas will find it difficult to fight and kill him.

'O great leader, give up your dejection and prepare to reach the temple with our forces before Indrajit completes his yagya.

'Looking at you suffering like this, our soldiers have lost hope. They are full of grief. Kindly stay here in full control and depute Lakshmana to lead us. He will interrupt Indrajit's yagya, after which he can be easily killed.'

Vibhishana's Strategy to Kill Indrajit

Coming to his senses and feeling alert, Rama asked Vibhishana to repeat his suggestions. Vibhishana replied,

'O great warrior, I have stationed our forces according to your directions. I have divided the soldiers and placed them at different gates under capable commanders.

'Your worrying for no reason makes the army desolate and hampers our battle strategies. Your being unhappy is a cause for celebration for the enemy.

'If you are keen on winning Sita back and destroying the rakshasas, you have to make an effort and act with enthusiasm and hope.

'Indrajit has proceeded to the Nikumbhila temple to worship and fortify his powers with the Devi's blessings. Lakshmana assisted by a large force must attack him and interrupt his yagya in order to defeat him. This is the right moment to mount an attack and kill Indrajit, and Lakshmana can carry out this assignment befittingly.

'Brahma while blessing him at an earlier time had said,

'You will be killed by an enemy who attacks you on your way to the Nikumbhila temple.

'Indrajit's death is thus pre-ordained. Once he has been killed, the rakshasas will automatically lose this battle.'

Rama ordered Lakshmana to proceed and carry out the expedition as suggested by Vibhishana. He directed that Sugreeva's forces would accompany Lakshmana and that he would be surrounded and protected by Hanuman, Jambavan and other commanders. Further, he said,

'The Rakshasaraja Vibhishana, being well acquainted with Indrajit's maya, will follow you along with his commanders and ministers.'

Lakshmana and his forces stopped short of the Nikumbhila complex when they noticed the rakshasa sena already guarding the place. It was a sight to see. Their weapons shone against their dark bodies.

Vibhishana advised Lakshmana to order the vanara sena to attack as early as possible and pierce the vast rakshasa formations. He said that if their ranks could be broken, Indrajit would become visible among them. He added,

'You must attack him before he can complete his yagya. Shoot at him with the deadliest of arrows, as powerful as Indra's thunderbolt. Ravana's son Indrajit deserves to be killed.'

Soon the vanaras and the rakshasas engaged in battle with trees, rocks, swords, maces, spears and arrows. As soon as Indrajit became aware of this interruption in his yagya and invocation, he stood up to fight the enemy. The disruption of his prayer enraged him.

Coming from behind the darkness of the trees, Indrajit ascended a well-furnished and sturdy chariot kept ready for him. The dark complexioned son of Ravana, black like a heap of coal, his mouth and eyes red, looked like death incarnate.

Hanuman, meanwhile, had uprooted a large tree and was hitting the rakshasas mercilessly. The asuras too attacked him with showers of arrows, maces and spears.

Indrajit asked his charioteer to steer the chariot towards Hanuman. As soon as he neared him, he attacked Pavana Putra with swords, arrows and axes. He hit him grievously in the head. An annoyed Hanuman challenged Indrajit and said,

'O evil son of Ravana, if you consider yourself to be a true warrior, come and wrestle with me. You will not escape that combat alive. Fight me with your arms. If you survive, you will be considered the bravest of the rakshasas.'

Vibhishana Reprimands Indrajit

As Indrajit raised his bow and mounted an arrow to shoot at Hanuman in order to inflict a mortal blow, Vibhishana addressed Lakshmana and said,

'Saumitra, Indrajit intends to kill Hanuman. It is time for you to take the lead and kill him with your specially crafted and invincible arrows.'

Lakshmana and Vibhishana moved forward towards a dense forest. The latter pointed out to the Raghava prince the site where Indrajit propitiated his gods. A dense banyan tree stood there. Pointing in that direction, Vibhishana said,

'Everyday this brave son of Ravana comes here to make an offering to the ghosts before engaging in battle. Through this worship he gains the power to become invisible to all of us.

'You must destroy his chariot and kill his horses and charioteer with your infallible arrows before he reaches this banyan tree.'

Lakshmana challenged the invincible son of Ravana to engage in battle. 'Come and fight me, but with care,' said he.

At this moment, Indrajit noticed his uncle Vibhishana standing by the side of the Raghava prince. Using harsh words, he said,

'Rakshasa, you were born and brought up here. You are my uncle and the younger brother of my father. Why then this inimical treatment towards your son?

'You are an evil man and have not displayed a trace of affection for your kith and kin, or any attachment towards your community.

'Even a worthless relative or friend is better than a virtuous stranger as the latter can never belong to you completely. Anyone who deserts his own people for the sake of another is ultimately killed by the stranger.

'O Nishachara, it is heartless for you to have guided Lakshmana to this spot in order to kill me. Only a traitor like you could have committed such a heinous crime against his own kin.'

Replying to his nephew's diatribe, Vibhishana said,

'Rakshasa, why do you talk thus? You are unaware of my temperament and views.

'One should not be disrespectful of one's elders, irrespective of the circumstances. I might have been born in a rakshasa family, but my conduct and thinking have not been like them. I have imbibed the satva guna that is the hallmark of the virtuous.

'I am not inclined to being cruel nor am I inclined towards adharma. How can an elder brother throw out his younger brother even if they are unlike temperamentally?

'The learned say that a wicked person, who wants to usurp another's wealth or wife, ought to be avoided like a house on fire.

'The three evils of stealing another's wealth, sleeping with another's woman, and misplaced distrust in one's well-wishers, must be avoided.

'My brother has mercilessly killed several rishis, has always taken a stand against the devatas, is proud and arrogant, loses his cool frequently, and violates dharma unhesitatingly. These traits will eventually destroy him. It is for these reasons that I deserted my brother. In a short while it will be your end and that of Ravana and Lankapuri.'

'Rakshasa, you are arrogant, irresponsible, obstinate and foolish to fight on the side of wrong deeds. Kala has ensnared you and has brought you to your end. You can call me what you will but Lakshmana's arrows will not go waste.'

Lakshmana and Indrajit Face to Face

Listening to Vibhishana's words condemning his father, a fuming Indrajit moved forward to confront Lakshmana. Riding on Hanuman's back the Raghava prince looked like the sun rising over the Udayachala Mountain. Indrajit challenged his adversaries and said,

'My enemies, you shall witness my valour today. You will be the recipient of my fatal arrows piercing your bodies just as the earthlings helplessly receive the rains.

'Lakshmana, you appear to have forgotten how a few nights ago during a battle, striking you with my arrows as powerful as a thunderbolt, I had put you, your brother and several of your warriors to sleep. You seem to be courting death now and have thus, come to fight me who is fulminating like a cobra.'

An angry Lakshmana retorted fearlessly,

'Nishachara, you have declared your intention to kill your enemies. However, it is going to be a difficult task. He alone is wise who achieves his objective without loose talk.

'You are incapable of achieving your declared objective and mere words are not enough to fulfil goals in the battlefield. You have been hiding like a thief in battle till now and thus, have remained unharmed. That is not befitting conduct for a warrior.

'Today I stand to face your arrows and answer with mine. Show me your valour and add some credibility to your words.'

Without losing any more time, Indrajit started shooting from his bow. His arrows struck Lakshmana like hissing serpents and injured him grievously in various parts of his body. The Raghava prince bled severely.

Indrajit moved nearer and taunted Lakshmana. He said in a roaring voice,

'Saumitra, the sharp, finned arrows shot from my bow invariably end the life of an adversary. You are sure to die today.

'I shall soon tear off your armour, break your bow and sever your head from your body.'

Lakshmana responded with great agility in battle as well as words,

'Why are you wasting words, O cruel, man-eating rakshasa? If you have the strength, show me your valour. I shall soon kill you without using any unbecoming language and without singing paeans about myself.'

Pulling the bowstring to his ear, Lakshmana speedily hit Indrajit's chest with five arrows that had lovely fins and looked like fiery serpents in motion. Piercing Indrajit's chest, the arrows reflected light like the sunbeams.

It was a fight between two lions, both fighting to win over the other.

After such exchange of arrows for some time, Vibhishana noticed that Indrajit looked frustrated. Pointing this out to Lakshmana, he said,

'Mahabaho, I can see that Indrajit is disheartened. It is time that you kill him without delay.'

Lakshmana started hitting Indrajit with his serpentine arrows which hit with the force of a thunderbolt rendering him temporarily unconscious.

When Indrajit gained consciousness, he attacked Lakshmana as well as Hanuman with powerful arrows injuring both of them. In return, Lakshmana, fighting without a trace of fear, struck his adversary's golden armour, shattering it into pieces. The shining armour lay on the floor of the chariot like a galaxy fallen from the sky. The blood soaked rakshasa warrior looked like the morning sun and attacked Lakshmana, smashing his armour.

Both the injured warriors were bleeding heavily and their bodies were dotted with marks of arrows that had pierced them. Several of their arrows and other weapons destroyed each other in the sky.

Looking at Indrajit and Lakshmana fighting each other like two elephants in musth, driven by a compelling urge for victory, Vibhishana, followed by his soldiers, the vanara commanders and the sena, came nearer.

Motivating the vanaras to fight and bring the battle to an end, Vibhishana said,

'O vanara commanders, we do not have any time to waste. Ravana's last pillar of support stands in front of you. Once he is demolished, nothing more is left of the rakshasa sena.

'With Indrajit's death shall be decided the fate of the rakshasa clan today. The warriors like Prahasta, Nikumbha, Kumbhakarna, Kumbha and Nishachar among others are all dead.

'For killing such mighty, chivalrous rakshasas, you have crossed an ocean parting the water merely with your arms. All that is left is a tiny rakshasa, the size of a cow's hoof. Finish him and tide over whatever little remains of the ocean.

'Being my brother's son, Indrajit is like a son to me. It is improper for me to hurt him and tears block my sight at the mere thought of hurting him. However, he has acted in a way to call death upon himself and Lakshmana shall finish this task.

'You should jointly attack the soldiers protecting him so that he is isolated for the Raghava prince to take care of.'

A fierce battle ensued and Hanuman put down Lakshmana and entered the fray carrying rocks and trees. Lakshmana and Indrajit fought face to face, no holds barred. They were so dexterous in their moves that an onlooker could not decipher when an arrow was pulled out of a quiver, when supported on the bow, when its hold was changed from one hand to another, when it was firmly held in a fist, pulled to the ear and released at its target.

Soon it was sunset and all that could be seen was blood all around. Lakshmana shot dead Indrajit's four black horses adorned with golden ornaments. Later, pulling a spear-headed arrow, the Raghava prince severed the rakshasa prince's charioteer's head.

Indrajit was left with just a chariot, fewer horses than required and without the guidance of a charioteer. Alone he steered his car, pulled the reins and shot at the enemy. For the onlookers it was an awe-inspiring scene.

Lakshmana hit Indrajit's hands when he extended them to rein the horses, and shot at his horses when the latter tried to shoot his arrows.

Pramathi, Sharabha, Rabhasa and Gandhamadana, vanara soldiers, jumped upon Indrajit's horses and crushed them to death. They smashed his chariot to pieces and joyously returned to Lakshmana.

A disheartened Indrajit addressed his loyal soldiers to boost their morale and said,

'It is dark all around and difficult to distinguish between a friend and a foe. Keep the vanaras engaged in battle. Meanwhile I will return to the palace and come back with a new chariot and weapons.'

Saying this, Indrajit quietly slipped out of the battlefield.

Indrajit's Fight to the Finish

A gold studded chariot was made ready for the son of Mandodari. It was stocked with bows, arrows, axes, spears and swords. The finest of steeds were yoked and a trained charioteer drove it. Riding in this chariot, Indrajit proceeded towards the battlefield in a spirit of either killing the enemy or laying his life down for his father.

His sudden and smart arrival in a fully decked chariot amazed Lakshmana, the vanaras, as well as Vibhishana.

A royal battle ensued. Lakshmana cut down several of the bows used by Indrajit. He then hit his chest and pierced a hole in it. The fearless Raghava cut down whatever arrows Indrajit shot in his direction. It was an astounding display of marksmanship.

Once again Lakshmana beheaded Indrajit's charioteer with a spear. Surprisingly, the rakshasa's horses were not frightened and they continued pulling the chariot as if nothing had happened.

Unable to pierce Lakshmana's armour, Indrajit hit him in his forehead. Suffering this injury bravely, the latter shot five arrows and hit the former's resplendent face.

As the two warriors were engaged in a fierce battle, Vibhishana killed Indrajit's four horses with his mace. The latter retaliated by shooting a Shakti which was intercepted by Lakshmana and destroyed.

Indrajit shot a weapon known as Asurastra that spewed maces, spears and swords in all directions. Lakshmana, however, destroyed it with Maheshwarastra.

Lakshmana got ready to release an arrow that could create a conflagration and had the strength to kill Indrajit. It was a strong weapon known as Aindrastra and could not be stalled on its path. Its impact was unbearable and it had the calibre to tear into several bodies at the same time. It was invincible and infallible on a battlefield.

Lakshmana placed the Aindrastra on his bow, pulled at the string and said,

'O divine astra, if Rama, the son of Dashratha, is dharmatma and devoted to truth, and if none compares with him in uprightness and bravery, go and kill the son of Ravana.'

Pulling the arrow balanced on a taut string to his ears, Lakshmana released it towards Indrajit. In no time the divine arrow had beheaded the rakshasa warrior whose glorious head slid to the ground. On the earth Indrajit's head, though soaked in blood, looked like a mound of gold.

The news of Indrajit's death spread like wildfire. Driven by the joyous vanaras, the rakshasa sena scattered all around. While some of them entered Lanka, others drowned in the ocean. They disappeared like the sunrays after sunset.

Vibhishana, Hanuman and Jambavan praised Lakshmana's valour. They greeted him hailing his victory.

Rama was immensely pleased on learning of Indrajit's death at Lakshmana's hands. Looking affectionately at his younger brother, he said,

'I am happy with you, Lakshmana. You have accomplished a difficult task. Our victory in this battle is now certain.

'With unprecedented chivalry, you have performed a noble deed. With the death of his son on the battlefield, I consider Ravana too as dead. Today I stand victorious. Killing Indrajit, you have deprived Ravana of his right arm because his son was his main source of strength.

'Vibhishana and Hanuman have also displayed unparalleled bravery. Fighting for three days and three nights, you have killed their bravest and made me feel as if no enemy survives.

'Ravana is not left with any choice but to come to the battlefield now; I shall surely kill him.'

27

Ravana Mourns His Son's Death and Threatens to Kill Sita

Ravana's ministers made sure that the news of Indrajit's death was not untrue. They visited the site of the battle to see for themselves. Only then did they communicate the sad news to their king. They said,

'Maharaja, Lakshmana with Vibhishana's active assistance, has killed Indrajit in full view of our soldiers. He who had defeated all devatas, the one who was invincible, fought a glorious battle with Lakshmana prior to departing for the other world.'

Ravana Mourns the Death of Indrajit

Ravana fainted on hearing this heart-breaking news. Regaining his consciousness after some time, emotionally disturbed, and wailing pathetically, Ravana said,

'O my son, you were a pillar of support for the rakshasa sena. How could Lakshmana overcome a warrior like you?

'Son, when angry, you could tear apart Yamaraja with your arrows or even smash the Mandarachala peaks. Killing Lakshmana on the battlefield was child's play for you.

'Today I realize the power that Yamaraja wields. He subjugated you to the laws of death.

'Without Indrajit, the three worlds and the earth with its forests, appear to me like a wilderness.

'In the inner chambers of the palace, today I shall hear the wail of the rakshasa beauties.

'You were a terror for the enemies. Where have you gone to, leaving behind your status as the Yuvaraja, your Lankapuri, your mother, the rakshasas, your wives and me?

'My warrior son, I ought to have preceded you to Yamaloka and you should have performed my shraddha. However, the order has been reversed.

'Rama, Lakshmana and Sugreeva are still alive. Why have you deserted us without plucking these thorns from my side?'

An Angry Ravana's Empty Boasts

Remembering his son's death, Ravana grew furious. In his son's absence, his worries had multiplied. He looked like the ocean with waves rolling high and large alligators surfacing at the time of Pralaya.

Anguished by his son's death, Ravana lost his cool and decided to kill Sita in order to wipe out the cause of the conflict. Ravana's eyes were bloodshot and the anger at his beloved son's death made them look fiercer. He looked like the invincible Rudra in his anger.

His angry eyes shed tears like drops of oil falling from a burning lamp. Angry like the doomsday fires, wherever Ravana looked, the rakshasas trembled in fear and hid from his view. To restore confidence in his soldiers, Ravana summoned them and said,

'I pleased Brahma with a penance lasting thousands of years. Because of his blessings I do not fear the devatas or the asuras. I possess armour gifted by Brahma himself. I have fought several battles against the devatas and this armour did not give way to any weapon. Today, when I go to the battlefield, none can stand against me. Even Indra dare not fight my prowess.

'A happy Brahma had blessed me with a massive bow and arrows during the Devasura sangram. I am determined to kill Rama and Lakshmana with the same powerful bow and arrows in the ensuing great fight, to the accompaniment of hundred of musical instruments playing auspicious music.'

Ravana Decides to Kill Sita but is Dissuaded

Aggrieved by his son's death, the cruel Ravana made up his mind to kill Sita after careful consideration. Addressing the assembled rakshasas in a plaintive tone he said,

'My son had cut a dummy Sita into pieces in order to deceive the vanaras. Today I shall kill the real woman and make Indrajit's declaration ring true. I shall assassinate Sita who is obsessed with Rama, a lowly Kshatriya.'

Emotionally upset with his son's death, carrying an unsheathed sword, Ravana advanced towards the Asoka Vatika, closely followed by his wife and ministers. Looking at him walking thus, his ministers roared like lions.

Sita was startled to look at the Rakshasaraja coming like this. She wailed and said,

'The manner in which the angry giant is advancing towards me indicates that this evil rakshasa will kill me. I love my husband and thus have spurned Ravana's repeated advances. I should have listened to Hanuman and gone riding on his back when he suggested me to do so.

'What if Shri Rama has been killed? What will happen to the mothers in Ayodhya? They will end their lives for sure.'

Suparshva Dissuades Ravana

Looking at Sita's suffering and wailing, Suparshva, a righteous man and a wise counsellor of Ravana, pushing aside the sycophants, addressed the king and said,

'Maharaja Dashagreeva, you happen to be a real brother to Kubera. How then have you, setting dharma aside, decided to kill Vaidehi?

'Living as a brahmachari, you had completed your formal education in scriptures in a gurukul. You have always followed the path of duty. How do you justify the killing of a helpless woman?

'Prithvinath, look at Maithili's divine face and proceed to the battlefield. We shall fight by your side till the end of the battle.

'You are a warrior without an equal. You are a wise and dexterous charioteer; you can kill Rama and get Maithili as a matter of right.'

Listening to a friendly and sound advice, Ravana returned to his palace and entered the courtroom with his well-wishers.

28

The Endgame Begins;
Lanka Women Mourn their Losses

Ravana Sends More Troops to Fight

Sitting on a high throne, Ravana, with folded hands, addressed his ministers and eminent generals. Breathing deep and hard like an angry lion, he said,

'Warriors, riding horses, elephants and chariots, surrounded by foot soldiers, go to the battlefield with the solitary objective of surrounding and killing Rama. Like the clouds releasing rain, you must rain arrows on that man in order to finish him.

'Otherwise, tomorrow I shall tear Rama to smithereens with my own arrows.'

The rakshasas marched out obeying Ravana's orders and engaged the vanaras with metal bars, swords, maces, arrows and axes. Soon the dust raised by the marching forces settled with the blood of warriors.

Rama Steps in

When the rakshasas proved too many for the vanara sena, Rama stepped in and with his superior archery rained deadly arrows on the enemy forces. Just as the clouds cannot reach the scorching sun, the asuras could not attack Rama who was burning them with his fiery arrows. He was invisible to them but not his arrows. He routed them like strong, invisible winds spreading a conflagration that uproots and burns the tallest of trees in a forest.

The rakshasa generals could see their soldiers, horses and elephants being killed by Rama; but could not see Rama because of his swift movement on the battlefield.

Rama was not to be seen, yet he was seen everywhere: in killing elephants here, killing brave warriors there, and animals and foot soldiers everywhere.

Raghava's Gandharva astra was a celestial weapon that cast a spell on the entire army. It tricked them into seeing thousands of Ramas on the battlefield at times, and at others, only one. They saw the golden cone of Rama's bow moving like a firebrand in circles but not the person who wielded it.

Rama looked like the embodiment of Sudarshana Chakra, annihilating his enemies on the battlefield. His navel was the central point of the Chakra and his valour like its flares. Rama's glory, wisdom, and majesty were its resplendence, while the destructive capabilities of his celestial weapons were the sharp edges of the Sudarshana Chakra.

With the destruction of their forces, chariots, elephants and horses, the surviving rakshasa soldiers took to their heels and sought the safety of Lanka.

The Women of Lanka Mourn Their Losses

The defeated army joined their women and worried for the next day. The helpless women who had lost their husbands or sons or other kin, gathered together and wailed over their misfortune. Recalling the events leading to Rama's advance on Lanka, they said,

'Why did the aged Shoorpanakha with a shrunken belly and frightening looks, approach Rama who is handsome like the Kamadeva? How dare she be so insolent and ignorant?

'Rama is powerful, always occupied with the welfare of humanity. This ugly rakshasi fell in love with him; she ought to be killed for her audacity.

'There is no comparison between the virtuous Rama, valorous and good looking, a depository of all the best qualities, and the worthless and evil faced rakshasi.

'It is for her sake that the Dashagreeva Ravana developed his enmity and abducted Rama's wife. That act will now lead to the annihilation of the entire rakshasa race.

'Ravana could not and will never be able to persuade Janaka's daughter to surrender to his desires. On the contrary, he has earned enmity with Rama.

'Rama killed Viradha with a single shot. With his flaming arrows he wiped out fourteen thousand soldiers in the Janasthana. He killed Khara, Dooshana and Trishira. Was that not enough to prove his invincibility? Rama killed Vali, the son of Indra, massive like the Meru Mountain, with one shot. That is proof enough of his strength.

'Whatever just and righteous advice Vibhishana had tendered, was for the benefit of the rakshasas. Ravana, enamoured of Janaki, did not listen to him and disregarded his own brother. Had he not done so, Lanka would not have suffered such a fate and would not have been reduced to a cremation ground.

'Ravana did not appreciate the power of Rama even when Kumbhakarna was killed, or when Lakshmana killed the brave Atikaya and when his dearest son, Indrajit met with his death.

'In every Lankan home we hear cries of mourners for their sons, brothers and husbands. In the battlefield, the brave Rama has killed thousands of warriors, elephants and horses.

'It looks as if we are being killed by Rudra, Vishnu, Indra, or Yamaraja in the guise of Rama. We have lost hope for our lives and there is no end to this fear.

'The Dashagreeva Ravana, no doubt, is chivalrous and has been bountifully blessed by Brahma. It is his arrogance and pride that has made him blind to Rama's indestructible might.

'Neither did Ravana wish to be freed from death at the hands of a human being, nor did Brahma grant it. Brahma's boon was limited to the devatas, the gandharvas and the rakshasas.

'In the entire world we do not see anyone who can protect us from the danger posed by Rama. Vibhishana did the right thing and went under the protection of the one who could have harmed him.'

The rakshasis, fearful, hopeless and defenceless, clinging to each other in close embraces, continued to wail loudly as above. Their future, as well as their family's, was uncertain.

29

An Unyielding Ravana Sends More Troops to Fight

Ravana's Arrogance and Delusion

Ravana heard the pathetic cries of the widows of Lanka, but stayed unmoved. He fretted, fumed and in his anger, bit his lips and mumbled orders to three of his remaining commanders, Mahodara, Mahaparshva, and Viroopaksha to lead their forces to fight.

The three generals stood with folded hands in their king's presence. Laughing aloud, Ravana said,

'Today I shall dispatch Rama and Lakshmana to Yamaloka with my arrows. I shall avenge the death of Khara, Kumbhakarna, Prahasta and Indrajit. My arrows will hide the sky like the clouds. The heavens, ocean and all the directions will become invisible under the shower of my arrows. Riding my chariot that runs faster than the wind, I shall annihilate the vanara sena.

'Today I shall wipe the tears of all the widows and mothers who have lost their husbands or sons. The battlefield will soon be carpeted with the vanara bodies.'

Despite the ill omens that greeted them, the rakshasa forces moved towards the battlefield with great speed. The battlefield resounded with the sound of drums, conches, mridanga and the noise of the rakshasas.

As Ravana was busy killing the vanara soldiers, Sugreeva took on Viroopaksha and after a fierce fight and bloodshed, killed the rakshasa warrior with a fatal blow on his skull.

As Viroopaksha lay dead, Mahodara took his place and challenged Sugreeva. They fought with maces, with fists and slaps. This was followed by a sword fight which ended in Sugreeva's victory and Mahodara's death.

Angada took on Mahaparshva and indulged in a fierce fight with spears. Ultimately, the vanara prince hit the enemy warrior with a fist on his chest near his heart and killed him.

Rama and Ravana Face to Face

Ravana saw his generals being killed in front of his eyes. He directed his charioteer to move his vehicle to the front. He said,

'Today I shall uproot Rama, the tree that could bear fruit through the delicate flower, Sita.'

Uttering these words in a fiery voice, Ravana sped towards Rama, the whir of his wheels echoing in the battlefield. The ground shook below its wheels. Clearing the field of the vanaras coming in his path, Ravana stood facing Rama and Lakshmana who stood like Indra and his younger brother Upendra.

Rama repeatedly pulled at his bowstring producing a sound that pierced even the centre of the earth. Ravana too produced a similar sound in response to the challenge. Standing opposite the Raghava princes, Ravana looked like Rahu obstructing the sun and the moon.

Ravana shot several powerful arrows at Rama, who cut them to pieces with his spears. Each of them was fighting to kill the other. The air was so covered by their arrows that nothing else could be seen.

Both the warriors were renowned archers, dexterous in the art of warfare. They were skilled in the use of different types of weapons. They traversed the battlefield with enthusiasm and confidence. A river of clashing arrows followed them, just like waves rolling over each other, pushed by stormy winds, at the confluence of the oceans.

Ravana hit Rama on his face and forehead mercilessly, but Rama was not perturbed. He pulled a few arrows out of his quiver, invoked the Raudrastra and released them in Ravana's direction. The arrows hit Ravana's impenetrable armour but could not pierce it.

To counter Rama's weapons, Ravana released a ferocious weapon known as Aasurastra. He released arrows with heads of tigers, lions, herons, vultures, eagles, jackals, wolves, pigs, dogs, crocodiles, and cobras. Defending himself from the Aasurastra, Rama released Agneyastra that released arrows carrying the shape and power of Agni, sun, moon, the crescent, comets, planets, stars and lightning. The Agneyastra destroyed the powerful arrows earlier released by Ravana which melted into vapours.

A Battle of Diverse and Powerful Weapons

The Rakshasaraja was angry beyond measure. He attacked Rama with various weapons such as thunderbolts, maces, hammers, axes, snares, goads, and swords. The doomsday winds appeared to be blowing. However, Rama used the Gandharvastra and destroyed all of Ravana's devastating weapons. This infuriated Ravana even more and enticed him to use the Suryastra that released brilliant, fiery discs. They resembled the sun, the planets and stars and illuminated the sky. However, these too were destroyed by Rama before they could cause any harm.

Rama made a frontal attack and grievously injured Ravana. Simultaneously, Lakshmana released seven arrows and tore the enemy king's ensign, beheaded his charioteer, and cut Ravana's bow, thick as an elephant's trunk, into pieces.

Vibhishana used his mace and struck Ravana's massive horses, dark as the clouds, and killed them.

An infuriated Ravana jumped from his chariot and fired a flaring Shakti as powerful as a thunderbolt at his brother. However, Lakshmana intercepted this Shakti and destroyed it with three arrows from his quiver. The Shakti garlanded in gold, broke into three parts and fell on the ground like lightning full of sparks.

Ravana made another effort to kill Vibhishana using another invincible Shakti. However, Lakshmana moved and stood in front of Vibhishana to Ravana's utter fury. Calling Lakshmana a foolish warrior, Ravana fired the Shakti at the Raghava prince. This Shakti had been devised by Mayasura, and with a thundering sound, it hit Lakshmana hard in his chest rendering him unconscious.

Rama, who was standing nearby, pulled the weapon out of his brother's chest and broke it into two. As Ravana kept shooting arrows at Rama all this while, taking Lakshmana close to his heart, Rama asked Hanuman and Sugreeva to cover him from further injury and declared,

'The long-awaited moment to display my prowess has arrived. It is time for the evil Dashagreeva to leave his mortal body. Like the chataka waiting for the clouds at the end of summer, I have looked forward to this moment.

'I vow with you all as my witness, that now, either Rama will live in the world, or Ravana.

'I have suffered an exile from my kingdom, life in the forests, wanderings in the Dandakaranya, Sita's abduction and a fight against the rakshasas from time to time. I have had enough and by killing Ravana on the battlefield, I shall be rid of all my sufferings.

'Ravana, because of whom I gathered such a large force, killed Vali in a battle and crowned Sugreeva, and because of whom we built a bridge on the ocean, stands in front of me. Now is the time for his end.

'O brave and fierce vanaras, you shall watch the battle between Rama and Ravana today where I shall display valour that would be talked of by gods and human beings as long as this earth survives. They will tell tales of how this battle was fought and won.'

Saying this, Rama attacked Ravana ferociously and forced him to leave the battlefield.

Lakshmana was revived with the herbs brought by Hanuman and found Rama sitting morose on his account. Although weak after being hit by a deadly arrow, Lakshmana asked his brother not to lose hope and fight the battle right to its end. He said,

'Arya, you have always been truthful and have promised Vibhishana the kingdom of Lanka after killing Ravana. The truthful fulfil their promise even in the most adverse of circumstances.

'I want to see Ravana killed before sunset. Fulfil my prayers, brother, as also your vow to Vibhishana. It is time Maithili be rescued from the clutches of rakshasas.'

30

Devatas and Munis Help Rama

Devatas and Rishis Offer Assistance

Next day, Rama stood fighting as a foot soldier while Ravana had returned riding a chariot with an ample store of weapons. The latter shot arrows like a cloudburst. Every arrow carried devastating fire.

The devatas, kinners and the gandharvas, watching this unequal fight from the heavens, were worried. To alleviate this situation, the glorious Indra sent for his charioteer, Matli and said,

'Rama, the pride of Raghukula, fights standing on the earth. Take my chariot and offer your services to him. You will render a service to the devatas by doing so and benefit them.'

Matli departed in Indra's chariot drawn by superior, green horses. Made of gold plate, this celestial chariot looked unusually splendid. Hundreds of bells had been tied to it. Decorated with varied gems, it glowed orange like the rising sun. Its steeds of a green colour were covered by golden lace and harness.

Soon after, Matli stood with folded hands in front of Rama and addressed him thus:

'O chivalrous killer of the enemies, the hundred-eyed Indra has sent this chariot for you to ride to victory. Here is Indra's invincible bow and armour glowing like Agni, with arrows that carry Surya's fire. Further, he has sent you the blessed and faultless Shakti.

'O brave king, ascend this chariot and assisted by me, kill Ravana in the same manner in which Mahendra kills the danavas.'

Rama went round the chariot, bowed to it and ascended it. A battle between the two charioteers began. It was a unique engagement, extremely exciting. Rama was knowledgeable in the use of several weapons. He destroyed Ravana's Gandharvastra with his Gandharvastra and the latter's Daivastra with a similar weapon.

An infuriated Ravana used the ferocious rakshasastra against Rama. Poisonous like Vasuki Nag, Ravana's arrows covered the entire sky in no time.

Rama countered these arrows by releasing the frightful Garudastra. Thousands of garudas moved in space countering Ravana's serpentine arrows and wiped them all out.

The Rakshasaraja targeted Matli, hurt him and also cut down Indra's ensign. He injured the green horses with a barrage of his arrows shot with such speed that for some time Rama could not manage to retaliate.

Rama's eyes reddened with anger to see Ravana gaining ground. With arched eyebrows, he looked fiercely as if he would burn the rakshasas to ashes.

Ravana readied to launch a weapon known as the Shoola. Addressing Rama, he said,

'O Rama, this Shoola is powerful like a bolt. I shall use it to kill you and your brother and dispatch you two to the land where my warriors have gone.'

As Ravana released the Shoola, the sky brightened with hundreds of flashes of lightning. An angry Raghava now used the Shakti sent by Indra to counter it. As soon it struck Ravana's Shoola, the latter, cut to pieces, fell upon the earth.

Gaining an upper hand, Rama injured Ravana's horses. He hit the rakshasa king in his forehead and near his heart. Bleeding heavily, Ravana found it difficult to breathe. His strength to hit at Rama with his weapons ebbed. He could not lift a bow and shoot the arrows.

Finding his king in a dire situation, the rakshasa charioteer sped him away from the battlefield.

Coming to his senses, Ravana rebuked his charioteer for his cowardice and said,

'Foolish charioteer, do you take me for a coward? A helpless, weak, and impatient man, devoid of valour and determination to fight the enemy? Disobeying my command, you have unilaterally dragged me out of the battlefield.

'You ought to have ascertained my plan, my intention. You have forever wiped out my glory, fame for chivalry and my subjects' faith in me.

'My enemy's valour is well known. I consider it my duty to overcome him in open battle. By removing me from the battlefield, you have made me look impotent in the enemy's eye.

'Has my enemy bribed you? You have not acted as a well-wisher, or as a friend. Your actions are those of an enemy.

'You have served me for long. You know my qualities and the traits of my character. If you still remember them, drive me into the battlefield before the enemy makes his escape.'

Agastya Muni Advises Rama to Worship Surya

As Rama stood tired and waited for Ravana to reappear, Muni Agastya arrived at the scene and approached him. He said,

'Rama, if you chant the secret Adityahridaya stotra, your victory over your enemy will be ascertained. These verses are pure, sacred and act adversely on the enemy. No other chant is more effective than this one in overcoming sorrow, worry and in ensuring success and longevity.

'Through these mantras you invoke Bhagwan Surya who radiates light and heat through millions of beams. He, who is worshipped by the devatas and the asuras alike and radiates glory to the entire world, will help you win the battle against all evil.

'All the devatas are his image and partake of him. He is a reservoir of energy and effulgence and gifts the world life, strength and inspiration with his beams. He alone spreading his rays sustains the devatas, the asuras, nay the entire universe.

'He is Brahma. He is Vishnu. He is Shiva. He is Skanda, Prajapati, Mahendra, Dhanada [Kubera], Kala, Yamaraja, Soma, Varuna, Pitarah, Vasu, Sadhya, Ashwini Kumar, Maruta and Manu. Surya is the populace. He is their life breath. He creates seasons. He radiates light.

'Surya is known by several other names: Aditya [son of Aditi]; Savita [Creator of the universe]; Surya [omnipresent]; Khaga [wanderer of the sky]; Pusha [one who sustains]; and Gabhastiman [effulgent, resplendent].

'Surya is like gold. He is Bhanu [source of light]; Hiranyareta [the seed of life and of the lifeless]; and Divakara [creator of the day]. He rides a chariot driven by green horses pulling in different directions and emanates thousands of beams. He is Mareechimaan [adorned by his beams]; Timironmathana [the destroyer of darkness]; Shambhu [the source of well being]; Twashta [provides succour to his devotees]]; Martandaka [gives life to the universe]; Anshuman [radiating beams];

and Hiranyagarbha [Brahma].

'Surya is Shishira [natural creator of happiness]; Tapana [source of heat, of energy]; Ahaskara [Creator of the day]; and Ravi [to be worshipped by all]; and Agnigarbha [a storehouse of fire].

'Surya is Shankha [a source of bliss; widespread]; Shishiranashana [alleviates cold]; Vyomanatha [master of the skies]; Tamobhedi [destroyer of darkness]; and Rigyujahsamaparagah [learned in the Riga, Sama and Yajur Vedas.]

'Surya is Ghanavrishti [the harbinger of rains]; Apana Mitra [creator of water]; Vindhyaveethiplavangamah [traversing the sky with speed]; and Aatapi [the source of heat].

'Surya radiates light through his beams. His heat can cause death. He gives heat but an exposure to his light can be insufferable.

'Surya is Kavi [the omniscient]; Vishwa [the universe]; Mahateja [the most glorious]; Rakta [of red colour]; and a source of all creation. He is the king of the planets, of the stars and of the constellations. He is Vishwabhaavana [the protector of the world] and among the tejasvis, he is preeminent. He is Dwadashatma because he manifests himself in twelve forms.'

Surya Stuti By Rama

'We bow to you in the form of the Udayachal and Pashchimgiri Mountains where you rise and set. You are the master of the constellations and of the day.

Addressing Rama, Agastya said,

'Surya alone is responsible for creation, sustenance and destruction of every being. He is the omniscient and omnipresent soul that resides in the core of all creatures and is awake when others sleep. He is the sacred fire lit during yagya as well as the fruit of the yagya.

'Rama, one who chants these verses in praise of the Sun during misfortune, in difficulty, walking a dangerous path, or when beset with fear, is protected.

'Hence, as you concentrate upon and worship the Sun, your victory shall be certain.'

Listening to the Muni, Rama overcame his grief and prepared for chanting the Adityahridaya mantras. After bathing, he did aachaman thrice for purification and chanted the sacred verses three times. It was then that he beheld Ravana back in the battlefield, facing him and decided to end the latter's life.

31

Ravana Meets His End at the Hands of Rama

Ravana entered the battlefield in a new chariot pulled by horses covered with diamond studded harness and garlands of gold. It was loaded with weapons that could kill an entire army.

Rama noticed the black horses pulling the enemy's chariot, making it look like a vimana flying in the sky and shining gloriously like the sun. The reflection of Ravana's bow on the chariot's surface glistened like a rainbow. Arrows rained from this vehicle like rain pouring from the clouds. The whir of its wheels made a fearsome sound like that of a mountain being split by a thunderbolt.

Looking at the approaching chariot, Rama pulled at his bowstring offering a challenge. Rama told Matli that from the manner in which Ravana was advancing violently, he appeared to have decided to provoke his own death. He said,

'Be alert. I intend destroying the enemy's chariot as the winds scatter a mass of clouds. You need not fear and continue to drive steadily. You are an experienced charioteer and have driven Indra himself. You know what to do; I want to concentrate on waging the battle.'

Both the warriors were soon engaged in a bitter fight and faced each other like angry lions hungry to win. For Ravana the omens were not good. The clouds drenched his chariot in a shower of blood, hurricanes jolted his vehicle, and vultures followed the king's chariot. Lankapuri was tinged in the untimely glow of a sunset as if it was on fire and meteors streaked down from the sky. Ravana's forces were perturbed at these happenings. Seeds of doubt were sown in their minds about their victory.

The rakshasa soldiers felt as if their arms had been paralyzed, as if these were restrained by an external force. Hundreds of weeping and quarrelling sarikas fell on the king's chariot.

The Battle of the Two Warriors

Rama and Ravana, riding their respective chariots, entered the most decisive phase of the battle. It was cruelly fought as each one was determined to kill the other.

The rakshasas looked at Ravana taking on Rama as if mesmerized. Their forces stood still as did the vanara sena. None raised a finger although both the sides were fully armed.

Ravana shot a number of powerful arrows at the flag flying on Rama's chariot. However, his arrows failed to reach the flag and fell on the wayside beside the chariot.

Rama reciprocated by shooting a sharp arrow, fierce as a cobra and glorious like himself, that cut Ravana's flag before disappearing into the earth.

Ravana tried to shoot at Rama's horses but they went unhurt owing to their divine origin. This disturbed Ravana and he showered Rama with arrows, maces, swords, bolts, rocks, axes, wheels, trees and spears. He was a source of unending, boundless energy. Though he did not experience any fatigue, his arrows not injuring Rama disturbed him.

The charioteers of both the warriors displayed remarkable dexterity. They chased each other, went around the other and advanced and retreated as they thought fit to gain an advantage. At one point their axles got entangled. At another, the horses faced each other like warriors ready to attack while the ensigns twisted around each other.

Ravana hit Matli with bolts to no avail. This angered Rama more than an attack on himself, and fighting ferociously, he made Ravana retreat some distance.

Ravana had several heads all adorned with large earrings and golden crowns. Rama sliced one of them with a fiery cobra arrow. The king's severed head fell on the ground but another one grew in its place instantaneously. This happened many a time and Rama found it difficult to counter the maya of the Rakshasaraja. The battle continued from the day into the night, without a breath in between.

Rama Fires the Brahmastra

It was Matli's turn to remind Rama to be aggressive. He said,

'O warrior prince, why do you rest contented with counter-attack only? His predicted time of death has arrived. Kindly use the Brahmastra against him and kill him.'

Rama pulled a glorious arrow from his quiver which hissed like a deadly cobra. Agastya Muni had given this weapon to Rama, making him invincible on the battlefield. Brahma of immeasurable glory had handed it over to Indra for his conquest of the world. The weapon was blessed with the speed of Pavana, the biting edge of Agni and of Surya's heat, the vastness of the sky, the weight of Meru and the eminence of the Mandarachala Mountain. It subsumed within it the glory of all that exists.

Rama chanted empowering mantras in order to invoke the powers of the Brahmastra, pulled the bowstring, mounted the arrow and fired it at Ravana. Like the invincible vajra thrown by Indra, and with the finality of Yamaraja's strike, the Brahmastra hit the Rakshasaraja in his chest and tore his heart apart. Having accomplished its task, the arrow, soaked in the king's blood, passed through his body, rebounded after hitting the ground and returned to Rama's quiver.

Ravana fell to the ground with his bow and arrow, lifeless. His soldiers took to their heels but were chased by the vanara sena.

While the vanaras' joy knew no bounds, the rakshasa soldiers wept at their defeat. Speedily, they retreated into Lankapuri.

The vanaras roared with joy and shouted victorious slogans about Shri Ramachandra. In the heavens, the devatas rejoiced with the earth having been cleansed of evil. A fragrant, mild breeze blew while the devatas sang Rama's glory. There was rejoicing in every direction.

Sugreeva, Hanuman, Vibhishana, Angada and Lakshmana expressed joy at Rama's victory. Rama had fulfilled his vow in killing his enemy. The glorious diadem of the Raghu dynasty looked magnificent like Indra surrounded by the devatas on the battlefield.

32

Rama Directs Vibhishana to Perform Ravana's Last Rites

Looking at his defeated brother lying dead on the ground, Vibhishana mourned and said,

'My valorous brother, you were renowned and well-versed in Niti. You always slept on silk sheets and today you lie on earth. Why?

'Your large arms, adorned in bracelets, stir no more and your crown, glorious as the sun, rolls in dust.

'My chivalrous brother, I had warned you of the imminent danger that had overtaken you owing to your passion and pride. Blinded by lust and attachment, you paid no heed and did not appreciate wise counsel.

'Blinded by arrogance, Prahasta, Indrajit, Kumbhakarna, Atikaya, Narantaka, even you and others attached no weight to my point of view. Today's happenings are a result of the same attitude.

'With the death of Ravana, the best of archers and swordsmen, the barriers imposed upon the wise that follow Niti, have been shattered. A treasury of Satva has been lost, a unique archer, who was the protector of the brave, has died. With the death of Ravana, the world has been deprived of chivalry and support. Nothing remains!

'Raghava has brought down the mighty tree of the rakshasa clan. His perseverance was like the leaves of that tree, his obstinacy its flowers, his tapasya its strength and his valour its roots.

'Ravana, the elephant in musth, having been crushed to death by the Ikshavaku lion, lies in eternal sleep on the ground. He was like a conflagration whose valour and enthusiasm was like wild flares, his powerful breath like its smoke and his chivalry, its brilliance. Rama like a cloud has extinguished the powerful fire that Ravana was.

Rama's Exhortation to Vibhishana to Do His Duty towards His Kin

Listening to Vibhishana's words of grief, Rama, drawing his attention to what had to be necessarily done at the moment, said,

'Vibhishana, Ravana did not die a coward's death on the battlefield. He displayed exemplary valour and fought chivalrously till the very end. He never feared death and was destined to die on the battlefield.

'We do not grieve over those who, desirous of victory, following the Kshatriya dharma, die on the battlefield. It is a warrior's fate to either be killed or kill his enemies. The shastras lay down that none ought to grieve over such a welcome death of the one who has lived like a Kshatriya.

'Do not grieve or worry about your brother's death and think of the last rites that need to be performed for the mighty warrior.'

Vibhishana replied,

'Ravana was an able ruler: he dispensed charity to the needy and took care of his people and servants. He enriched his friends and took revenge on his enemies.

'Ravana was an Agnihotri, a mahatapasvi. He was learned in the Vedas and also a superior warrior. The warrior who now lies lifeless deserves a worthy farewell from this world and hence, I shall now perform his last rites.'

The generous Rama consented and asked Vibhishana to perform the final rites of his brother, paving his entry into Swargaloka. He said.

'Vibhishana, no enmity should last beyond a lifetime. We have been successful in achieving our objective. In death, Ravana needs your affection. Likewise, I owe him love and respect.'

33

Mandodari Mourns Her Husband

Learning of Ravana's death at Rama's hands, the emotionally disturbed women in the king's harem came out. They rolled in dust in spite of being dissuaded by their well-wishers. Their hair was loose and they wept in grief.

Coming out of the northern door, they arrived at the frightening battlefield and looked for their deceased husband. Crying, 'Ha Aryaputra, Ha Nath,' they stumbled from place to place on the battlefield littered with grime, coagulated blood and carpeted with dead bodies.

They looked at the huge, valorous and glorious Ravana lying dead on the ground like a heap of black coal. Suddenly, sighting him lying covered by the battlefield grime, they fell on his body like creepers cut off from a tree. Some of them respectfully clung to him in a fond embrace while others touched his feet and wept.

While the grieving women wailed recounting Ravana's prowess and virtues, they could not forget what he had done to Sita. They said,

'You never listened to your friends and well-wishers. You abducted Sita and that led to your death. Thousands of rakshasas have been killed as a consequence of your misdeeds. Your actions have resulted in your lying sprawled on the battlefield, with your women submerged in a sea of sorrow.

'Keeping in mind your welfare, your dear brother Vibhishana advised you. You not only ignored him, arrogantly used harsh words against him, but also exiled him from Lanka. Mourning here, we are a witness to the results of your deeds.

'Had you agreed to send Sita back to Rama, we would not have been destroyed down to our roots and this tragedy would not have befallen us.

'Had you sent Maithili back, Vibhishana's desire would have been fulfilled, Rama would have become our friend and we would not have been widowed.

'However, you turned out to be so cruel and unbending that you forcibly kept Sita confined and brought about your downfall along with that of the entire clan of rakshasas.

'However, it was destiny's doing. In this war, destiny ordained your death and that of the vanaras and the rakshasas.

'What has been ordained to happen in this world cannot be changed with the help of wealth, desire, valour, command or force.'

Mandodari, the Queen of Lanka, Laments Her Fate

Among the wailing women was Mandodari, Ravana's senior queen who was dearest to him. Looking at her husband's body lying thus, she felt helpless and humble. In heart-rending words she bewailed her loss:

'A younger brother you were
To Maharaja Kubera,
Mahabaho Rakshasaraja.
Even Indra feared to face you
When you were angry!

'Frightened by you,
The Maharshis, the illustrious Gandharvas
And Charanas,
Ran helter-skelter.

'Today in a battle, Rama,
A mere human, has defeated you.
Don't you feel ashamed, O Rajan?
Tell me, what is the matter with you?

'You had conquered the three worlds.
You had thus added to your wealth and power.
None dared withstand your attack.
How then could a man,
A mere forest dweller, kill you?

'You were the master of a world
Inaccessible to the human beings.
You could change your form at will.
Incredible it is, therefore, that
You died at Rama's hands.

'You were always victorious in a battle.
I cannot believe that you were defeated by Rama,
Or that Rama could accomplish this deed.

'Perhaps, Kala, assuming Rama's form,
Turned up on this earth for your destruction.

'Or perhaps, O warrior,
It was Vasava [Indra] who attacked you.
However, he dared not look at you,
Eye to eye in a battle. After all,
You were mahabali, mahaveerya and
The most majestic enemy of the devatas.

'Surely, therefore, Rama is the Yogeshwara,
Paramatma and Sanatana.
He had no beginning;
He has no middle and no end.
He is mightiest of the mightiest.
He is beyond darkness.
He is Parameshwara in whom the universe exists.
He carries a conch, a chakra and a mace in his hands and
On his breast there is a mark of Shrivatsa.
Shree always stays beside him.
He is invincible.
He is eternal, everlasting, immobile and steady.
He is cool, collected and composed.
He is the master of the universe.
It is Vishnu who dwells in truth, who has
For the welfare of mankind,
Descended as a human being and
With the help of devatas born as vanaras,
Put you to death because you were an enemy of the devatas and
A terror for the world.

'My master, you had conquered the world
Because you had conquered your senses.
Out of enmity, those desires
Have now taken revenge and defeated you.

'When I had heard of your brother
Khara, well protected by his forces,
Having been killed by Rama in the Janasthana,
I had come to believe that
Rama is no ordinary human being.

'When Hanuman could enter and destroy Lanka,
A city even the devatas could not gain access to,
We were frightened of an impending tragedy.

'Repeatedly I had exhorted you,
"Prana Natha, do not create enmity with Rama."
You never listened to me.
Your death is the fruit of your obstinacy!

'Rakshasaraja, you lusted for Sita.
That led to the destruction of your magnificence,
Your riches, your body and your kith and kin.

'You had lost your wisdom.
Sita is more chaste than either Arundhati or Rohini.
She is the essence of Vasudha and of Shree.
Insulting Sita, who
Loved her husband so deeply,
You committed a grave error.

'Sita of lovely limbs and of qualities noble,
Living in a sparsely populated forest,
Was abducted by you and made to suffer.
Humiliated she was for no fault of hers.
This deed was a blot on your fair name.
You failed to satisfy your lust,
To cohabit with Maithili.
On the contrary, certain I am that
The tapasya of a chaste woman
Reduced you to ashes.

'It is amazing that
You were not destroyed
While abducting Sita.
Perhaps, it was your majesty, your awe,
Feared by Indra, Agni and other devatas that
Saved you.

'My master! It goes without doubt that
An evil deed recoils on the perpetrator.
The doer suffers in the long run.

'Virtue is its own reward.
The evil suffer for their misdeeds.
Vibhishana is happy today because
He acted judiciously and in pursuit of dharma.
You suffered because you acted sinfully.

'Your lust blinded you.
However, under the delusion of Kama,
You never believed that
There was no dearth of women
More charming than Sita, in your harem.

Maithili is in no way superior to me.
Neither in looks, in virtues, in lineage,
Nor in competence, she compares with me.
She is not even an equal.
However, in sheer ignorance
You never accepted this fact.

'In this world,
None dies without a cause.
Your death too had a cause:
The princess from Mithila.

'You invited your death because of Sita.
Relieved of her sorrow,
Maithili will now live happily with Rama.
On the contrary,
Whatever little punya I had earned
Stands exhausted.
I drown in the ocean of grief.

'Dressed in exquisite finery, ornaments and
In clothes divine,
Looking beauteous, I used to roam with you,
In a Vimana, as per my heart's desire,
On the Kailas, Mandarachala, and the Meru Mountains,
In the Chaitra Ratha forest,
In several orchards owned by the devatas, and
Over different countries.
Today, I stand alone, deprived of all pleasures because
You are no more!

'I am the queen Mandodari,
Reduced today to a commoner's status.
For a kings' might,
It is a matter of shame.

'Today, your lotus face has lost its shine.
It is streaked by the blood flowing from
Wounds inflicted by Rama's arrows.
Your forehead lies splintered.
Covered by the grime raised by your chariot.

Proud I used to be
Of Maya, the king of demons and my father;
Of the Rakshasaraja, my husband, and of
Indrajit, my son who had defeated even Indra.

'Firmly did I believe that
I was protected by persons who could crush
Their arrogant enemies,
Who were heartless, were known for chivalry, and
Who did not fear anyone.

'O gem in the crown of the rakshasas,
You were mighty.
You wielded limitless sway.
How then, could a mere human being frighten you?

'Your body was blue like polished sapphire.
You towered like a mountain cliff.
You looked resplendent with
Bracelets on your arms,
Necklaces of sapphire, and
Garlands of various flowers around your neck.
In the pleasure resorts,
You radiated a happy glow.
Your majesty multiplied on the battlefield.
You looked magnificent like a cloud
Made brilliant by sparks of lightning.

'Alas! The same body of yours
Lies dead, pierced by innumerable pointed arrows.
No longer, hence,
I can feel your glorious face, nor
Embrace you because of the jutting arrows.

'Like the skin of a porcupine bristling with thorns,
Your skin is so densely pierced by arrows that
Not even a little of it is visible.
The arrows have punctured all the tender regions.
The muscles and tendons are torn.
Lying dead, your dusky body,
Bathed in shining, glazed blood,
Looks like a mountain shattered in pieces
When struck by a bolt.

'My master!
Is it the truth or a dream?
How could you be killed by Rama?
You were the death even for Yamaraja.
How then did you submit to Rama?

You enjoyed the wealth of the three worlds.
You rattled their denizens.
You had conquered even the Lokapalas.
'You lifted the Kailas high
While Shankara was sitting there.

Making several proud warriors
Your prisoners on the battlefield,
Several times,
You had established your superiority.

'However, you harassed the entire world,
Killed several virtuous persons and
Treated your enemies with arrogance.
Even the danavas were not spared by you.
You interrupted hundreds of yagyas.
You protected only those who were close to you.

'You were responsible for
The breach of the bounds of dharma.
In a battle you used maya in order to cheat.
You habitually abducted the daughters of
The devatas, the asuras and of human beings.

'You made the enemy's women suffer.
You protected Lanka and led your people.
You gave us sexual pleasure, but
Your actions were evil.
It appears that I am made of stone because
I have survived my beloved
Brought down by Rama,
My love who was
The greatest of charioteers and majestic in form.

'I suffered gravely when my son was killed.
With your death, I consider myself dead.
Deprived of my kith and kin,
Without my husband,
Bereft of sexual enjoyment,
For years to come I shall be drowned in grief.

'Rajan, I cannot live without you.
Take me, the unfortunate one,
Along on the difficult and long path that you have chosen.

'Feeling humble and helpless,
I weep for you.
Why do you not speak to me?

'Today, I wear no veil.
I have walked from the gates of Lankapuri to reach here.
Why do you not rebuke me?

'Rajan, you ravished many a woman.
Of women who were devoted to their gurus,
Who followed Dharma, and who were chaste,
You made widows.
You humiliated them.
It is as a result of the curses of those sorrowing women that
You succumbed to the enemy and to death.

'O my king!
It has been rightly said that
A chaste woman's tears are never shed in vain.
You are a case in point.

'Having frightened the three worlds
With your valour and your majesty,
You thought of yourself as a chivalrous person.
Why then did you commit
The heinous deed of abducting another's woman?
Inveigling Rama in pursuit of the illusory golden deer,
To falsely call Lakshmana for help, and then
To abduct Sita in their absence,
Was cowardice.

'Mahabaho!
The truthful Vibhishana, my brother-in-law,
Who is aware of the past and who knows the future,
Who can wisely analyze the present,
Thinking of Maithili's abduction by you,
Sighing deep in frustration, had observed,
'It is time for the annihilation of
The premier of rakshasas.'
His words have come true.

'Dashanana!
Vibhishana's words of advice were logical and meaningful.
He had spoken with due deference to you.
His advice was well meaning and was politely given
Regrettably, you paid no heed.

'Intoxicated with the arrogance of your might,
You did not listen to my father,
To Kumbhakarna or even Maricha.
You reaped the fruit of your obstinacy.

'Wake up, my king, wake up!
You have just been humiliated by Rama.
How can you sleep over it?
For the first time today,
The sunbeams enter Lankapuri
Fearlessly.

'On the battlefield, your club of metal
Lies shattered here and there,
Broken into thousands of pieces by Rama's arrows.
It glowed like the sun
When you killed your enemies on the battlefield.
You worshipped it like Indra's thunderbolt.
Wrapped in golden mesh, it killed thousands of soldiers.

'My beloved, why do you lie
In the lap of the battlefield
As if you are sleeping in my embrace?
Why do you make me feel unwanted?
Why don't you utter even a word in response?

'Shame on me!
It seems that
I have a heart of stone that has not been shattered
In grief even at your death.'

34

Ravana's Funeral

The wailing Mandodari shed a flood of tears. Her grief knew no bounds. Suddenly she became unconscious and fell on Ravana's chest where she glistened like lightning shining in a cloud.

Her co-wives took charge of her. Wailing in grief, they lifted her and said,

'Devi, are you not aware that this world is ever changing and transient? Even a king's Rajyalakshmi deserts him when his times change.'

Mandodari could not restrain her tears and sobbed bitterly.

Vibhishana's Hesitation

Seeing Mandodari and other women waling thus, Rama asked Vibhishana to console them and arrange for his brother's funeral.

However, Vibhishana submitted in all humility,

'I do not want to perform the last rites of a brother who had forsaken the path of dharma and propriety, who was cruel, heartless, untruthful, and an abductor of someone else's woman.

'He wished nobody well. Even though a brother, Ravana was my enemy. He was my elder and therefore, deserved to be worshipped as such. However, he was unfit of my respect.

'The world might call me cruel, O Rama. But, when they learn of Ravana's misdeeds, they would approve of my thinking.'

Responding in wise, meaningful and polite words, Rama said,

'Rakshasaraja, I owe you my victory and I owe you a return of gratitude. Hence, I must advise you of what is correct and incorrect.

'This nishachara might have been untruthful and evil. However, on the battlefield he was always glorious, brave and chivalrous. I hear that even Indra and other devatas could not defeat him in a war. A mighty warrior, Ravana could make the world weep.

'An enmity ought not to last beyond death. Our purpose has been served. Now, he is as much my brother as yours. Hence, perform his last rites and cremate him.

'Dharma demands that you perform his last rites with proper ceremony at the earliest. This will earn you a good name.'

Obeying Rama, preparations for Ravana's cremation were made forthwith. Entering Lanka, Vibhishana performed the Agnihotra for the king. The rakshasas arranged for a carriage, logs of wood, sacred fires and purohits to perform yagya, logs of sandalwood, splinters of wood of different sizes, fragrant aloe, and gems, pearls and coral for the bier. Malyavana assisted Vibhishana in these preparations.

The trumpeters played on their instruments to announce the death of their king and welcome his body. The body of the Rakshasaraja Ravana was wrapped in silk and placed on a golden bier. The Rakshasa Brahmins stood around with tears in their eyes to chant appropriate mantras.

Vibhishana and other rakshasas carried the bier on their shoulders, while several others followed in procession.

Priests chanting the Vedic mantras and carrying three types of fires in pots led the mourners. The weeping harem women walked behind the body.

Reaching the cremation ground, Ravana's bier was placed on purified place. Ravana's body was placed on the pier erected by Vibhishana and other rakshasas, and cremated as per rituals. Earlier, the holy fire was started in a small pavilion erected towards the southeast of the pier. A ladle full of curds and ghee was placed on the shoulder of the deceased.

With tears flowing down his eyes, Vibhishana conducted all rituals and later, he lit the pier accompanied by the chanting of mantras. Then he had a bath and, dressed in wet clothes, offered his oblation of sesame seeds, kusha grass and water to Ravana. Consoling the wives of the king, he requested them to return to the palace. They followed his direction.

Vibhishana approached Rama with his head bowed. Although happy at his victory, Rama soon gave up the bow, arrows and the massive armour sent by Indra for his use and returned to his peaceful demeanour.

35

Vibhishana is Crowned the King of Lanka

Rama honoured Indra's charioteer, Matli, and asked him to return with his chariot to the Indraloka. He embraced Sugreeva to express his affection and gratitude. Lakshmana touched his brother's feet and expressed happiness at their victory. The vanara sena offered their respects to Rama, their commander-in-chief.

Returning to their camp, addressing the valorous and glorious Lakshmana who stood nearby, Rama said,

'Saumya, go to Lanka and crown Vibhishana the king. He is dear to me, is my devotee and has been kind to me. I desire to see him crowned the king of Lanka at the earliest.'

Obeying Rama's command, Lakshmana handed over a golden pitcher to a few vanara generals and asked them to fetch water from the ocean. This pitcher was ceremoniously placed on a high seat. With the holy water, Vibhishana was anointed Lanka's king with the chanting of Vedic mantras. Several vanaras and rakshasas followed Lakshmana in anointing the new king who sat on a luminous throne surrounded by his courtiers.

Vibhishana, the king of Lanka, visited Rama to thank him and brought with him auspicious offerings. Placing them at Rama's feet Vibhishana requested him to accept them as a token of gratitude, which Rama did to please Vibhishana.

Hanuman stood by with folded hands. Rama looked at him and asked him to enter Lankapuri with the permission of the new king and enquire Maithili of her well being.

He said,

'Tell Vaidehi that Sugreeva, Lakshmana and I are hale and hearty. Tell her that Ravana has been killed in battle and come back soon with her message.'

36

Hanuman Visits Sita with Glad Tidings

Hanuman entered Lankapuri and was warmly greeted by the nishacharas. With Vibhishana's permission, he went to the Asoka Vatika to see Sita.

Approaching her, he found her dressed in a dirty sari and sitting joyless and sullen surrounded by rakshasis.

Hanuman stood in front of Maithili in silence and bowed his head in a greeting. Sita recognized him and despite the feeling of joy, could not say anything to him.

Addressing her, as directed by Rama, he said,

'Vaidehi, Shri Rama, Lakshmana and Sugreeva inform you of their well-being. The victorious Shri Rama, having killed his enemy, has enquired about you.

'Devi! Assisted by the vanaras, Lakshmana and Vibhishana, Shri Rama has killed the mighty and majestic Ravana in a fierce battle.

'I bring you glad tidings and I want to see you happy. Shri Rama owes his great victory to your being a pativrata. Grieve no more and regain your health. Our enemy, Ravana has been killed. Lanka is under the suzerainty of Shri Rama. I bring you a message from him.

'Shri Rama says,

"Striving day and night, I made a great effort to fulfil my vow to free you of captivity. Constructing a bridge over the ocean and killing Ravana, I have kept my promise.

"Shed your fear of being a prisoner in Ravana's Vatika. Lanka's wealth and power has now been placed under Vibhishana's control. From now onwards, be assured that you are staying in your home. Be at peace and be patient."

'Devi, a joyous Vibhishana would be here anytime, keen to be blessed by your darshan.'

Sita's eyes filled with tears at the joyous news, and she could not reply out of sheer happiness. Hanuman continued,

'Why do you worry, Devi? Why don't you speak to me?'

Shedding tears of joy, Sita spoke in words soaked in happiness. She said,

'Learning of the glad tidings of my master's victory, I was lost in happy thoughts. Hence I could not utter a word.

'I want to reward you for bringing me such good news. However, I am unable to think of anything suitable to be offered.

'O Saumya vanara warrior, nothing on this earth can match what you have told me, and which can be offered to you, to my satisfaction. No offering such as gold, silver, gems or even the sovereignty over the three worlds can compensate you for this news.'

A delighted Hanuman responded,

'Ever desirous of your husband's victory, always thinking of his welfare, O chaste woman, you alone could have spoken so meaningfully and affectionately. Your words are more precious to me than any treasure or even the dominion of Swargaloka.

'When I find Shri Rama victorious and in the best of health, I feel that my effort has been well rewarded. In that success I have been gifted with something superior to the rule of Swargaloka or the possession of a vast treasury.'

Appreciating Hanuman's sentiments, Sita replied,

'Your words are meaningful and well chosen. You are sweet and a master of the eight aspects of wisdom. You alone are capable of such speech.

'You are the praiseworthy son of Pavana and a dharmatma. Without doubt, all the virtues, such as physical strength, chivalry, knowledge of the shastras, satva, dexterity in whatever you undertake to do, majesty, forgiveness, perseverance, consistency, humility and several others, reside in you.'

Hanuman expressed a desire to punish the rakshasis who had been tormenting Sita till now and asked for Sita's consent to do the same.

Sita Dissuades Hanuman from Causing any Harm to Her Tormentors

The kind-hearted and protector of the humble, Sita, thought over Hanuman's words for a few moments. Then, she said,

'O Kapishrestha, these helpless women were subject to the king's command. They did not act on their own will. They did what was ordered. How can anyone be angry with them?

'It was my misfortune, a retribution for some misdeeds of an earlier birth which led to such suffering.

'O Mahabaho, you are not going to hurt anyone. It was my luck alone that made me suffer. I could not escape my destiny. Even if Ravana's maidservants committed an offence, I forgive them.

'O son of Maruta, they used to threaten me when the rakshasa was alive. Since his death, they have not uttered a word to torment me.

'There is none in this universe who has never committed an offence. Even those who live in violence and sin deserve our sympathy.'

Hanuman replied,

'Devi, you are Shri Rama's wife. You are naturally endowed with noble qualities. Can I carry a message for him?'

Sita replied,

'I just want to see my husband who cares for his devotees and treats them as his children.'

Hanuman said,

'Devi, just as Shachi has Indra's darshan, today you will see Shri Rama who looks like a full moon. You will meet Lakshmana as well. They stand surrounded by their friends. Their enemies have been eliminated.'

Hanuman returned to Rama's camp and conveyed Sita's message.

37

Vibhishana Escorts Sita to Rama

Returning from his visit to the Asoka Vatika, Hanuman bowed to Rama and said,

'She sits in the Asoka Vatika shedding tears. But now, learning of your victory, Maithili desires to have your darshan.

'She had reposed full faith in me even when I had first visited her with your message. Believing that I enjoy the confidence of her master, she says, "I desire to look at my beloved."'

Hearing Hanuman, Rama, an ocean of piety, suddenly shut his eyes and went into deep thought. Soon his eyes were full of tears. He breathed hard, cast a glance downwards, and then looking at Vibhishana who stood glorious like a cloud, said,

'Sita has spent her time in Lanka with great difficulty, bearing and fighting all odds. Kindly make preparations for her to be dressed in glorious finery and jewels and fetch her to me as early as possible.'

Vibhishana rushed to the palace and sent a word to Sita. Later he went to her in person, bowed with folded hands and humbly said,

'Vaidehi, it is time for you to put on suitable finery and get dressed; your beloved wants to see you.'

Protected by the rakshasa soldiers on all sides, Sita rode in a chariot to Rama's camp.

Vibhishana announced the arrival of Sita to Rama who sat in meditation. On hearing of her arrival after a painful and long captivity, Rama experienced anger, joy and grief at the same time.

Addressing Vibhishana, he said,

'Saumya Rakshasaraja, I wish Vaidehi could reach me faster.'

Vibhishana asked the assembled crowds to make way for the chariot to reach Shri Rama swiftly. The Lanka soldiers ordered the vanara soldiers to move back. The movement of the vanara sena created a commotion like that of the ocean waves being wafted by strong winds.

The vanara sena felt hurt at being asked to move back as they were keen to have Janaki's darshan from close quarters. Rama, understanding their sentiments, asked the Lanka soldiers to desist from being too strict. He thought that his command for speeding up Maithili's approach had been misunderstood and said,

'Why do you insult the vanara soldiers and hurt their sentiments. Stop this unwelcome enforcement of authority. Everyone here is my kith and kin.

'The privacy of a woman is not necessarily assured by a home, clothing, an awning or the four walls. Likewise, harshly moving onlookers away too does not always provide a veil to a woman. A woman's covering is her conduct and the respect she receives from her husband.

'Sita is a victim of straitened circumstances. She has suffered a good deal of anguish in the past. I am here to receive her and her approaching me in everyone's sight is not objectionable under such circumstances.

'Vaidehi may please alight from the chariot and walk to meet me. Let every vanara have her darshan.'

Sita Approaches Rama

A thoughtful Vibhishana escorted Maithili to Rama. However, looking at Rama's angry mood, Lakshmana, Sugreeva and Hanuman were a bit perturbed. His conduct indicated an unusual indifference towards his wife. They thought that Shri Rama was somehow not happy with Sita.

Maithili walked towards Rama while Vibhishana followed her. Her face looked calm and peaceful. For her, her husband was a devata and she looked at his divine and charming face with amazement, joy, and warmth.

An unblinking Sita gazed at Rama's face that could put a rising full moon to shame in charm and majesty. She had not set her eyes on him for several months. Looking at him soothed her nerves and gave her peace of mind. She smiled, and her face glowed like the moon in a cloudless sky.

38

Sita's Agni Pareeksha

Rama Expresses His Doubts

As Maithili humbly stood in front of him, Rama told her of what was weighing on his mind. He said,

'Bhadre, defeating the enemy on the battlefield, I have obtained your release. I have done all that was within my might.

'With my enemy's death, my anger is gone and I have avenged the humiliation heaped upon me by Ravana.

'Each one present here is a witness to my bravery. Having fulfilled my vow, I feel unburdened and liberated.

'That evil rakshasa abducted you when you were alone in the ashrama. I earned blame because it was my destiny. With superhuman effort, I have wiped the blot.

'Hanuman's praiseworthy efforts in crossing the ocean and setting Lanka on fire have borne fruit. Sugreeva helped me with his vanara sena and tendered suitable advice at various crucial moments. Vibhishana deserted his evil brother and joined me to establish dharma; he has never failed in his mission.'

Listening to Rama's words, Sita's eyes brimmed with tears. She realized the effort that her husband had put in to save her.

Though Rama looked at her warmly and from a close quarter, he feared a general disapprobation. Turning to the lotus-eyed Sita, he addressed her in the presence of the vanaras assembled there. He said,

'To avenge my humiliation I have done my duty. I killed Ravana to protect my reputation. I salvaged you from Ravana's captivity just like the Rishi Agastya had conquered the Dakshin Disha.

'You ought to know that whatever I have done and whatever has been achieved with the help of these friends and with their valour, is not for your sake.

'I have done this to safeguard propriety, to destroy evil that had developed everywhere, and to wipe out the blot on my renowned dynasty.

'You have been captive for several months and there can be a doubt about your chastity and this very question bothers me beyond measure.

'Janaki, you are free to go wherever you like and I grant you my permission. All the ten directions are open to you.

'There would hardly be a respectable householder who, though a person of reputation himself, would accept a woman who has lived in another's house, just because she had lovingly lived with him earlier for long.

'Ravana abducted you and carried you in his lap. He lusted for you and would have made all efforts to persuade you. How then, Sita, can I accept you?

'The purpose of the war has been achieved with the blemish on my reputation and dynasty being washed away. My sympathies and love for you have ended and you are free to choose your path.

You can also spend the remaining years under the protection of Lakshmana or Bharata. You might stay with Shatrughna, with Vanara raja Sugreeva or under the protection of Vibhishana too. You are free to choose.

'Looking at your celestial charms, Ravana could not have resisted you for long.'

Rama's unpleasant words hurt Sita grievously. She was used to his affection and his words of endearment. And today, after meeting him after a long separation, his words grieved her. She cried and shed tears like a creeper injured by an elephant's trunk.

Sita Describes Her Helplessness

Rama's words were harsh, startling and demeaning. Vaidehi was deeply hurt and it aggravated Vaidehi's pain when thus spoken to in the presence of a massive audience. The allegations coming from her beloved master's mouth were unheard of.

Wounded by the fierce arrows of words, Sita wanted to disappear, to become invisible.

Sita collected herself, wiped her tears and addressing her husband in a voice choked with emotion, she said,

'O warrior, why do you use such harsh, unjustified and bitter words while talking to me? You talk to me like a low-born man addressing a lowly woman in unpalatable language.

'Mahabaho, I am not what you believe me to be. My character cannot be doubted as I have spent my time in Lanka thinking about you.

'Prabho, I was helpless when my body came in contact with Ravana's body. It was not my doing and it was destined to be so.

'I rule over my heart and that has always been devoted to you. However, I had no control over my limbs. I was under his domination. In that case, if he touched my body, I was helpless and powerless to retaliate.

'My master, you have always held others in high regard. Our mutual affection has grown over years of togetherness. Even then if you do not appreciate my character, I am lost forever.

'Why did you not abjure me when you had sent the brave Hanuman to visit me in Lanka? Had he told me about your repudiating me, I would have ended my life in his presence. You would not have been compelled to fight a futile war, put your life at risk and unnecessarily make your friends suffer.

'O lion among kings, your thinking is shallow because it is born out of anger. Putting aside the nobility of my character, you have thought of the behaviour of only the fallen women.

'You are very knowledgeable in the intricacies of good conduct and virtue. I am known as Janaki because I was born in Janaka's yagya bhoomi. I have been so pure that I was not born of Janaka's seed; it was the earth that gave birth to me. You have attached no weight to these aspects of my birth and doubt me wrongly.

'You married me while I was young and all these years I have been devoted to you alone. Have you forgotten my virtuous character?'

Sita's Ordeal by Fire

Sita's voice choked with emotion and grief. She could hardly continue. Weeping and distraught, she addressed Lakshmana, who sat distraught and said,

'Saumitra, get a pier ready for me. That alone is the remedy for my sorrow. I cannot live in ignominy.

'My master no longer appreciates my virtues. He has renounced me in open assembly. For me the only course open is to invoke death by fire.'

An angry Lakshmana looked at Rama to know his wish. Receiving Rama's assent and knowing his mind, he made a pier ready with his brother's consent.

Rama looked frightening like Yamaraja. None dared to dissuade him or even look at him eye to eye. He stood with his head bent as Sita went around him in parikrama. She then approached the rising flames and bowing to the devatas and Brahmins gathered around, standing with folded hands, Maithili said,

'If, even for a moment I have not strayed from my fidelity to Rama, may Agni devata, the witness to whatever happens in this world, protect me.

'My character is unblemished. Even then, Raghava doubts me. If I am totally blameless, may Agni devata protect me.

'If I have not, in mind, words or deeds, transgressed the omniscient Shri Rama, or violated his memory, may Agni devata protect me.'

With these words, Vaidehi fearlessly entered the rising flames in full view of the assembled soldiers and others. The event was witnessed by all beings, devatas, gandharvas and rishis.

The assembled women shrieked when they saw Sita entering like an offering into the sacrificial yagya fire, while the rakshasas and the vanaras howled in horror.

39

The Devatas and Brahma Chant to Affirm the Divinity of Rama

Hearing the wails of the vanaras and the rakshasas, Rama too was moved by grief. With eyes full of tears, he stood lost in thought.

The Devatas Arrive

Soon after, Kubera, the son of Vishrava; Yamaraja accompanied by the ancestors; Indra, the thousand-eyed king of the devatas; Varuna, the master of the oceans; the trinetra Mahadeva whose ensign is a bull; and the creator of the universe and the giver of the Vedas, Brahma, arrived at Lankapuri riding vimanas glistening like the sun. As they approached Rama who stood in front of them with folded hands, the devatas raised their arms and said,

'Rama, you are the Creator of the universe. You are omnipresent and omniscient. How can you ignore Sita who has jumped into the fire? Why do you not realize that you are Vishnu who is supreme among us all?

'You are Ritadhama, the supreme lord of the Vasus. You are God who created the three worlds.

'You are the eighth Rudra and the fifth Sadhya. The Ashwini Kumars are your ears and the sun and the moon, your eyes.

'O Parantapa, you are the beginning, the middle and the end of the universe. Why do you spurn Sita like an ordinary mortal?'

Rama replied,

'Devatas, I consider myself to be merely the son of Dashratha. Please tell me who I am and where I have come from?'

Vishnu Stuti

Brahma, the most knowledgeable amongst all the gods and devatas, replied,

'O truthful warrior, I shall tell you the truth.
'Bhagwan Narayana,
You are the one
Who carries a chakra, and
Who is omnipotent.
You are Varaha, with one horn,
Who salvaged Prithvi.
From their past and future enemies,
You protect the devatas.

'Raghava, you are the immortal Brahma who
Stays like truth in the beginning,
The middle and the end of the universe.
You are the ultimate Dharma of the world.
Beyond and outside you, nothing exists.
Of the world, you are the architect.
You are Shri Hari who has four arms.

'None can vanquish you.
You are Sharangadhanva,
Hrishikesha, and
The omniscient Purusha [the supreme being, God, the soul] and
Purushottama.
As Vishnu you carry the Nandaka sword.
You are Krishna, the most powerful.

'Of the devata armies, you are the commander.
Of villages, you are the headman.
You are the source of wisdom, sattva, mercy, and
Self-control, and
The creator as well as destroyer of the universe.
You appeared as Vamana.
You are Madhusudana.
You are Mahendra who sired Indra.
You are Padmanabha always at peace and
Who can put an end to any war.
The celestial maharshis have described you as
The protector of all those who seek your succour.

'You are the beginning and the end.
You are your own master.
You are the Mahavrishabha with several horns, that is,
The Vedas with numerous branches of knowledge.

'You are the shelter and the protector
Of the Siddhas and the Sadhyas.
You are the yagya and the one who performs.
You are the oblation and
You are the Omkar.
You are Paramatma, the almighty.

'None has divined your beginning or the end.
None of us knows who you are.
Yet, you are to be seen
In all the living beings, in the cows and the Brahmins.

You are manifested in all the directions,
In the mountains and the streams.
Thousands of feet you have.
Thousands of foreheads and thousands of eyes
You possess.

'You are the support of the living beings,
Of the mountains and the earth.
At Pralaya, you look like Sheshanaga
Towering above the waters.

'Rama, you are Narayana in whom are manifested
The three worlds, the devatas,
The gandharvas and the rakshasas.
You are Paramatma who resides in the core of all that is.
I, Brahma, am your heart.
Devi Saraswati is your tongue.

'All the devatas I have created are the pores in your body.
It is night when you shut your eyes and,
It is day when you open them.

'The Vedas are your consecration,
Outside you, the universe ceases to exist.
The entire Creation is your bodily manifestation.
The earth is stable because of you.

'Agni is your anger and the moon your joy.
You are Vishnu who bears the Shrivatsa mark on his chest.
As Vamana, in earlier times,
You had measured the universe in three steps.
Tying up Bali, the cruel king, you
Anointed Indra as the ruler of the three worlds.
Sita is Lakshmi incarnate while
You are an incarnation of Vishnu.
You are Krishna and you are Prajapati.

'O Dharmatma,
You were born as a human being on this earth
In order to kill Ravana.
You have accomplished
What we had prayed you to do.

'Rama, you have killed Ravana.
Kindly return to your celestial abode.
You are invincible.
Your effort can never be wasted.

'Rama, your darshan is a blessing without fail.
Blessing it is to meditate upon you.
Infallible is the one who chants your name divine!
On this earth, your devotees
Will never be let down.

'You are the most ancient!
You are Purushottama!
You are Paramatma!
Those who pray with devotion to you,
Would be blessed with fulfilment
In this world and beyond.'

40

Agni Appears with Sita in His Lap;
Rama Accepts Her with Joy

As soon as Brahma had finished his stuti, out of the pier emerged Agni with Vaidehi sitting in his fatherly lap. Moving the cinders aside, the devata who carries the havana offerings to the other world, stood with Sita by his side.

Sita is Reborn

Vaidehi glowed with the golden orange lustre of the morning sun. She was dressed in ornaments of burnished gold and a red silk sari. The flower garlands around her neck had not withered in the fire. The indescribably beautiful Sita looked more charming than when she had entered the pier.

Agni Deva, the universal witness, handed over Sita to Rama and said,

'Rama, I bring to you the unblemished Vaidehi, your wife.

'She, of a noble character, of countless virtues, has never dwelt on another man in her mind, speech, wisdom or through her sight. She has always worshipped you, the virtuous prince.

'When the arrogant Ravana, mad about his power, abducted her, she was alone and helpless in the ashrama. In your absence she could do nothing.

'Even when confined by Ravana and guarded by the fierce rakshasis, she thought of none other than you. For her, you were her only resort.

'She did not surrender to several blandishments and had to bear severe reprimands for the same. In her deepest thoughts, she thought of you and you alone and not about Ravana.

'She is pure at heart and no blemish can ever be associated with her. Kindly accept her with honour and offer her the love and respect she deserves owing to pure devotion to you.'

Rama Justifies His Conduct

Rama was overjoyed and tears of happiness could be seen in his eyes. He thought for a moment and then addressing Agni Deva, said,

'It was necessary to put Sita through this ordeal by fire in order to convince others. Perforce, the virtuous Sita had to spend a long time in Ravana's custody.

'I am aware of the fact that Maithili loves me immensely. She has always cared for me and has acted accordingly.

'I firmly believe that just as the ocean is unable to run over its shores, Ravana could not have molested the large-eyed Sita who is protected by her innate faith and glory.

'However, in order to assure the denizens of the three worlds, putting my faith in truth alone, I did not restrain Sita from entering the fire.

'Maithili cannot be tarnished because she is unyielding like a flame. Her purity is such that the evil Ravana could not have harmed her even in his thoughts.

'Even in Ravana's custody, the chaste Sita could not have been perturbed. She is as inseparable from me as light is from Surya.

'Janaka's daughter, Maithili, is chaste and pure. As an intelligent man cannot let go of name and fame, I cannot give her up.

'All the Lokapalas have spoken for my benefit. I am aware of your fondness for me. Therefore, I must obey your command.'

Saying this, Rama welcomed Sita warmly. Both of them were happy to be together after a long period of separation.

41

Rama Departs for Ayodhya

It was time for Rama to look after the injured vanara soldiers. He sought Indra's help in reviving even those who had laid down their lives. Addressing the celestial king, Rama said,

'Kindly revive all the vanaras, langurs and bears that died during the battle fighting for my sake. I want to see the vanaras happily united with their families. I pray that wherever they live, the orchards bear fruit even out of season, gardens bloom throughout the year and streams are full of sweet water at all times.

Mahendra replied happily and said,

'I grant all the boons you have requested for the welfare of the vanara sena.'

With this, it was time to depart from Lanka and go home.

Rama Desires to Leave for Ayodhya at the Earliest

The next morning, Vibhishana arrived to greet Rama and Sita and to know the future course of action.

Rama replied,

'Rajan, please provide hospitality to Sugreeva and others; I am keen to reach Bharata who is young and has suffered much on my account. Without meeting him, I do not fancy a ritual bath or royal clothes and ornaments.

'Kindly organize a fast mode of transport. If we walk all the way to Ayodhya, it might take months and the route is uneven and difficult.'

Vibhishana replied,

'Do not worry, O prince. I can make you reach Ayodhya in one day. Kubera's glorious Pushpak Vimana is at your disposal. This vimana flies according to your will, at any speed and in any direction. I have kept it ready for you and can take you to Ayodhya in no time.

'Shri Rama, if I deserve your kindness, if you believe that I have some good qualities, and if you feel some affection for me, kindly stay here for a few days with Sita and Lakshmana. I shall strive to make all comforts available. You can proceed to Ayodhya after enjoying my hospitality. Please oblige me by being my guest.

'Raghava, I am making this request out of love, affection, respect and fraternal feelings. I am your servant and wish to please you.'

In the hearing of the assembled vanaras and the rakshasas, Rama replied,

'O chivalrous king, you have served me wholeheartedly, with devotion, and as a valuable adviser in all respects. You have respected me and treated me with tremendous regard. I cannot say no to your offer. However, I pine to see my brother, Bharata, who had come all the way to Chitrakoot, asking me to return. I had not acceded to his request even when he had bowed at my feet.

'Then there are my mothers, Kaushalya, Sumitra and the venerable Kaikeyee, Guha, my friend, and the people of Ayodhya, all of whom I am eager to meet.

'Saumya Vibhishana, permit me to leave. You have honoured me enough. Friend, do not be angry with me because I insist on my departure.

'Rakshasaraja, please prepare for our departure without delay. The purpose of my visit here has been fulfilled.'

Vibhishana summoned the Pushpak Vimana. The vimana that glistened like the sun and was lined with lapis lazuli pavilions and adorned with precious stones, gold and silver, appeared.

Even Rama was amazed at the sight of the vimana and its magnificent qualities.

The Farewell

As the Pushpak Vimana, decked in flowers, stood nearby, Vibhishana asked Rama what other service he could render.

After a moment's thought, Rama replied warmly, in Lakshmana's hearing, and said,

'The vanaras assembled here have fought bravely and wisely. Please welcome them and gift them wealth and jewels.

'During the war these vanaras never deserted the battlefield. Fighting enthusiastically and fearlessly, they helped you to conquer Lanka. When you, feeling obliged, honour them, the vanara generals and soldiers will be greatly satisfied.

'If you do so, everyone would realize that Vibhishana can be charitable and dispense wealth when the occasion so demands, that he amasses wealth and jewels judiciously and fairly, that he is kind-hearted and that he has conquered his desires.

'Nareshwara, a king bereft of the qualities of charity and generosity which endear him to his subordinates, is deserted by his army at the time of a battle. They believe that he is making them court death in vain, that he is not worried in the least about their welfare and well-being.'

Vibhishana acted accordingly.

Satisfied on this score, Rama, carrying a coy, high-minded, virtuous and wise Sita in his lap ascended the Pushpak Vimana. Lakshmana, the great archer followed suit.

Rama advised Sugreeva and Vibhishana to return to their kingdoms and asked for their permission to return to Ayodhya.

However, everyone wanted to accompany Rama to Ayodhya in order to joyously wander in her gardens, to witness Rama's coronation, and to bow at Kaushalya's feet.

Rama readily agreed and asked all of them to ascend the Vimana.

With Rama's permission, Kubera's Vimana ascended into the sky and flew towards Ayodhya.

42

Rama Describes Bharatvarsha from the Vimana

As the vimana flying like a swan ascended the sky, Rama looked around and pointed out significant sights to Sita who was lovely as the moon. He said,

'Vaidehi, look at Lankapuri situated on the broad peak of the Trikuta Mountain, as pretty as Kailas. Built by Vishwakarma, does it not look magnificent?

'Look at the battlefield covered with the grime of flesh and blood. A large force of vanaras and rakshasas perished in this battle.

'O Vishalakshi, there lies the cruel Ravana in a heap of ashes. He was violent and had been blessed with immortality by Brahma. However, for your sake I had to kill him.

'There, I killed Kumbhakarna and Prahasta while Hanuman killed Dhoomraksha. Several other rakshasa generals were killed by our warriors like Angada and Sugreeva.

'It was here that Mandodari surrounded by a thousand co-wives wailed over Ravana's death and her widowhood.

'My lovely beloved, look at the spot on the ocean beach where we spent the night after crossing the ocean. There you see the bridge that we built over the saline waters. It is known as Nalasetu. It was a tough job, undertaken for you alone.

'Vaidehi, look at the endless, unassailable ocean. It is the abode of Varuna full of conches and precious pearls. How loudly does the ocean roar!

'Maithili, there you see the golden mountain, Hiranyabha that rose out of the deep to let Hanuman rest.

'Here is a large island where my forces had camped. We had worshipped Mahadeva at this site before starting the construction of the bridge.

'On this holy site you notice the large landing on the beach which being the origin of the bridge, will be known as Setubandha and would be a place of worship in the three worlds for all times to come. It is here that Rakshasaraja Vibhishana had come to see me. A pilgrimage to this teertha will be considered auspicious and purifying.

'Sita, you may now behold Sugreeva's charming country, Kishkindha, dotted with lovely orchards and thick forests. It was here that I had killed Vali.'

Looking at Kishkindha, an emotional Vaidehi politely requested Shri Rama to invite Sugreeva's wife Tara and other vanara females to accompany them to Ayodhya. Rama readily agreed. The vimana made a halt at Kishkindha and Ruma, Tara and other women joined them.

Soon the vimana was flying over Rishyamooka Mountain. Pointing this to Vaidehi, Rama said,

'This is the Rishyamooka Mountain, a treasure of precious minerals that shine like lightning in the clouds. I had come across Sugreeva and established a bond of friendship leading to Vali's death atop this.

'Here we can see the picturesque lake Pampa adorned by eye-catching, flowering gardens on its banks. It was here that I pined and wailed for you. I met the devout Shabari here and killed the demon Kabandha.

'There in the Janasthana, vilasini Sita, you notice the giant tree where the brave Jatayu was killed by Ravana while he was trying to protect you. Nearby too is the place where I had killed Khara and Dooshana and the warrior Trishira.

'Yonder you see our ashrama and the thatched cottage Lakshmana had built for us. The Rakshasaraja Ravana had forcibly abducted you from here.

'We have reached the auspicious, life-giving Godavari full of water. Nearby is situated Rishi Agastya's ashrama surrounded by a banana grove.

'Next, you can see the well-lighted ashrama of the mahatma Suteekshna and still further, that of Sharabhanga Muni once visited by Indra-of-the-thousand-eyes.

'We have arrived near the Tapas Ashrama where resides the Kulapati Muni Atri who is glorious like the sun and Agni. You had visited the devout tapasvini Anasuyia here and sought her blessings and advice.

'Now, we are approaching the Chitrakoot Mountain where Bharata had arrived asking me to return.

'Maithili, notice the Yamuna flowing yonder. Flowering and fruit-bearing orchards have been laid on her banks. We can now see the glorious Bhardwaj Ashrama.

'There you see the Ganga which cleanses people of their evil deeds; a variety of birds make song on her shores and Brahmins are busy performing holy rituals. Charming, colourful flowers bloom on her shores.

'Sita, we are passing over the place where my friend Guha lives in Shringaverpur. Now you can see the Saryu river dotted on her banks with sacrificial pillars. My ancestral capital Ayodhya is situated on its banks. Vaidehi, bow to Ayodhya where you return at the end of our exile.'

43

Homecoming

The Welcome at the Bhardwaj Ashrama

On the way to Ayodhya, Rama landed at the ashrama of Rishi Bhardwaj and bowed at his feet. He enquired of the rishi about the welfare of and the news about the people in that city. He wanted to know whether his mothers were well and whether Bharata had been taking good care of the people. Happily, the rishi replied,

'Bharata awaits your arrival patiently. He has grown a sadhu's matted hair. He carries out his official duties looking at your sandals. Everyone in your family and in your city is well.

'Last time when you had passed through, dressed in bark, accompanied by your brother and your wife, I had been deeply moved. You had been deprived of your kingdom. Moving away from the life of luxury, you looked like a devata who had descended from Swargaloka onto the earth.

'Today when you return after a great victory over your enemies, it makes me happy to see you. I am aware of your suffering in the Janasthana. Through my celestial powers I am aware of all that has happened at Panchavati, in Kishkindha and later in Lanka.

'Ask for whatever blessing you desire, O Rama. However, stay with me for an evening to enjoy my welcome and hospitality. Tomorrow, you may leave for Ayodhya.'

Rama acceded to this request. Asking for a boon, he said,

'O Maharshi, bless me so that the trees on the path to Ayodhya bear fruit even though unseasonal. Bless Ayodhya and its people.'

Rishi Bhardwaj said, 'So be it!'

The moment he uttered the blessing, the trees all along the route were laden with sweet and fragrant fruit like the trees in Swargaloka. They bore fruit without flowering. Some trees that do not bear fruit sprouted fresh flowers and leaves. The fruit and the flowers were enjoyed by the joyous vanaras accompanying Rama.

Rama Sends Hanuman as His Emissary to Nishadaraja and Bharata

Meanwhile Rama deputed Hanuman to visit Nishadaraja and Bharata in advance to apprise them of his arrival.

He said,

'Go to Ayodhya speedily and find out about the well-being of everyone in the royal palace. In Shringaverpur, call on Nishadaraja Guha and tell him that I am safe and sound. He will be delighted to learn this because he is my friend. Guha would brief you about Bharata and lead you to Ayodhya with delight.

'When you meet Bharata, tell him that Sita, Lakshmana and I have come back in good health. Tell him of all the incidents including Sita's abduction and Ravana's death. Tell him that Rama accompanied by the Rakshasaraja Vibhishana, the Vanararaja Sugreeva and other well-wishers has arrived at Prayag.

'Mark Bharata's facial reaction when he gets this information. Try to understand his feelings for me and about his consciousness of his duty towards me.

'Gather all the news in the palace and try to understand Bharata's true inclination. Try to gauge his intentions from changes in his facial expressions, his looks and his manner of speech.

'Who will not change his mind if he has an easy access to his ancestral kingdom rich in elephants, horses and chariots and in which it is possible to fulfil one's desires to his heart's content?

'If under Kaikeyee's influence and because Bharata has enjoyed being a ruler for several years, he desires to continue to rule, he may fearlessly continue to do so.

'Gather all this information and return soon.'

Hanuman assumed a human form and flying in the sky like his father Pavana, crossing the thunderous confluence of Ganga and Yamuna, he arrived at Shringaverpur and called on the Nishadaraja. Conveying the happy tidings, he said,

'Your friend, Shri Rama has arrived accompanied by Sita and Lakshmana. He wants you to know that he is unharmed. He spends the night at the Bhardwaj Ashrama near Prayag and will arrive here tomorrow.'

Having conveyed Rama's message, the enthusiastic Hanuman once again speedily took to the sky. En route, he glanced at the Parashurama teertha, Balukini river, Gomati and the dense sala forest. Flying over several small towns and villages, he soon arrived at a grove near Nandi gram. The orchard was rich in fruit and flower-bearing trees like Indra's Nandanavana and Kubera's Chaitraratha vana. Well-dressed women, accompanied by their children and grandchildren, were picnicking there, plucking and adorning themselves with flowers.

A short distance ahead of Ayodhya, Hanuman saw Bharata dressed in a hermit's sheet and the skin of a black deer, looking weak and sad. He had grown long matted hair and had lost weight because of his grief and yearning for Rama's darshan. Subsisting on fruit and roots, he lived the life of a celibate. He lived a disciplined life and followed his dharma. With a clear conscience, he glowed like a Brahmarshi. Having enthroned Shri Rama's sandals, Bharata ruled his kingdom in his brother's name.

Bharata looked after all the four varnas equitably. His praja was free of fear; his ministers, commanders and the purohits too, putting on ochre robes, diligently discharged their duties. Even his subjects, following his noble example, lived a sober, unattached life.

Hanuman Conveys the News of Rama's Arrival to Bharata

Hanuman approached Bharata with folded hands and said,

'Deva, Shri Rama of whom you have been thinking all the time, sends you his greetings and the news of his being in sound health. He has enquired of your well-being. Grieve no more; I bring you the joyous tidings that you will soon see your dear brother.

'Having killed Ravana and conquered Lanka, Shri Rama accompanied by the majestic Sita and the glorious Lakshmana and his other warrior companions, has reached Prayag.'

Hearing of this, Bharata swooned out of happiness and fell to the ground. Regaining consciousness, he stood up and warmly embraced Hanuman. His grief evaporated while his joy multiplied immensely. Addressing Hanuman, Bharata said,

'Are you a devata or a human being who has arrived in order to oblige me? Saumya, how do I reward you for this happy message?

'It is several years since my master, Shri Rama went into exile.

Today, the saying that a human being if alive will attain happiness at sometime or the other sounds true. Saumya, please narrate how Shri Rama came into contact with the vanaras and what all transpired during his years of absence.'

A dedicated Hanuman narrated the events of Rama's life as he was aware of it, in detail. Concluding the narrative, he said,

'At the moment Shri Rama is spending the night at the Bhardwaj Ashrama near Prayag. Tomorrow in the Pushya nakshatra, you will have his darshana.'

A delighted Bharata bowed with folded hands and said,

'I have attained what I had longed for since long.'

44

Ayodhya Welcomes Rama

The truthful Bharata, overflowing with joy, ordered Shatrughna,

'The unblemished priests should start the ritual worship of our family gods and offer prayers in the temples of Ayodhya with music and fragrant flowers.

'The entire public including the learned, priests, and talented musicians, queens, ministers, commanders and their forces with their wives, the trade chiefs and Brahmins, will come out of the city to look at Shri Rama.'

Shatrughna put thousands of labourers on job to level the roads, sweep the road to Nandi gram and sprinkle ice cold water on the path. The prince directed a scattering of grain and flowers, and colourful flags to be hoisted on both sides of the road.

The residents of Ayodhya were asked to decorate their homes with golden garlands, thickly set wreaths of flowers, unthreaded lotus blooms and colourful artefacts.

Hundreds of soldiers were deputed for controlling the multitudes who would come to see their Shri Rama.

Eight ministers – Dhrishti, Jayanta, Vijaya, Siddhartha, Arthasadhak, Ashok, Mantrapal and Sumanta – led the reception committee. They rode musth elephants spruced with flags and ornaments. Warriors riding smaller she-elephants tied with golden cords, large elephants, horses and chariots followed them.

Thousands of horsemen carrying flags followed suit. They were accompanied by foot soldiers carrying weapons like Shakti, Rishthi and Pasha.

Dashratha's queens led by Kaushalya, Sumitra and Kaikeyee followed in lavishly decorated chariots.

Soon the caravan arrived at Nandi gram.

Bharata Milap

The welcome cavalcade was led by Dharmatma Bharata, surrounded by purohits, senior Brahmins, chiefs of trades, vaishyas and ministers carrying garlands and sweets. As the deep sound of the conches and the bheris resounded, Bharata walked reverently carrying Rama's sandals on his head.

Bharata carried a white umbrella decorated with garlands of white flowers. Two white chowries with golden handles, fit for a king, were carried by a servant.

As Bharata advanced to receive Shri Rama, the earth shook and resounded with the sound of the horses' hooves, chariot wheels, and the sonorous music of the conches and the bheris. The roar of the elephants added to the tumult.

For one moment, Bharata doubted the veracity of Hanuman's message. However, the latter assured him of Rama's arrival. He drew his attention to the joyous tumult of the approaching vanara hordes that was now audible. He said,

'Look, they appear to be crossing the Gomati. Look at the clouds of dust rising in the sala forest. Yonder, I see the Pushpak Vimana looking like the moon from a distance. Now it shines like the morning sun. At the moment, the vimana is carrying the Raghava brothers and Devi Maithili, the Vanararaja Sugreeva and the Rakshasaraja Vibhishana.'

'Lo, Shri Rama has arrived!' shouted the assembly of men, women and children. Their joyous exclamation reached even the abode of gods.

People alighted from elephants, horses and chariots to have a glimpse of Shri Rama, still in the vimana.

Bharata was delighted and stood with folded hands, looking at Shri Rama sitting high in the Pushpak Vimana. His joy knew no bounds. Offering arghya at his elder brother's feet, he ritually worshipped him although the latter was still in the vimana. Bharata bowed with the humility of the dwijas bowing to Surya, rising from behind the Meru Mountain.

As the vimana landed, Rama asked Bharata to climb in and come near him at which the prince bowed at his feet once again. Rama lifted Bharata up and made him sit next to him.

Bharata greeted Lakshmana with an embrace; then he bowed and greeted Vaidehi. He warmly embraced Sugreeva, Jambavan, Angada and other vanara dignitaries.

Embracing Sugreeva, Bharata said, 'You are our fifth brother. A friend is the one who brings benefit to another out of love and affection. To act otherwise is the sign of an enemy.'

Consoling Vibhishana, Bharata said,

'Rakshasaraja, it is our good fortune that with your help Shri Rama accomplished a very difficult task.'

Shatrughna too paid his respects to Rama, Lakshmana and humbly placed his head at Sita's feet.

A sorrowing Kaushalya had lost her glow and seemed to have grown weak. Rama prostrated before her and took hold of her feet in his hands. He then bowed to Sumitra and Kaikeyee before moving to the family guru Vasishtha.

The people of Ayodhya acclaimed Rama's arrival, bowed with hands folded, and said in one voice,

'We welcome you, Shri Rama.'

Rama noticed that the praja welcomed him in thousands with their raised hands cupped like lotus blooms.

Transfer of Power

It was now Bharata's turn to hand over the kingdom to his elder brother.

The dharmagya prince put on Rama's sandals on his feet. Standing with folded hands, he said,

'At your feet, I return the kingdom of Ayodhya that I ruled for you. It is a day of fulfilment, of satisfaction that I have not lived my life in vain. I feel blessed. With the return of the king of Ayodhya, all my desires have been fulfilled.

'Please take an account of the treasury, gold and other wealth you left behind. With your blessings, everything has multiplied a hundred times.'

Listening to these words of brotherly love, the vanaras and Vibhishana shed tears of joy.

Rama ordered the Pushpak Vimana to return to Kubera. He then bowed at the feet of Guru Vasishtha just like Indra bows at the feet of Brihaspati. Seating him comfortably, Rama took another seat.

Once Rama was seated comfortably, Bharata stood up and addressing him said,

'Respecting my mother's wishes you had left this kingdom for me. I return to you what you had given me.

'A calf cannot pull a heavy load that a mighty bull can. Likewise, I too am unable to carry this heavy responsibility.

'You cannot turn away from your responsibility of ruling this kingdom. In case you do so, you would be as the fruitless tree that although planted and reared for its fruit, did not bear fruit though it did flower. The praja brought you up so that you could look after their protection and well-being. You cannot disappoint them.

'Raghava, the praja longs to witness your coronation. May your glory and grandeur increase like that of the mid-day sun!

'We wish that you rule this world as long as the stars shine and the earth exists.'

In due course, Rama was given a ritual bath, his matted hair was cut appropriately, he put on garlands and ornaments befitting a king, and putting on regal pitambar, sat on a high throne.

Dashratha's thoughtful queens attended to Sita's bath, dress and adornment. Bedecked as a queen, she looked resplendent.

The Procession

In Ayodhya, preparations were being made for Rama's coronation. In the meantime, Rama left for the capital in a chariot driven by Bharata while Shatrughna held an umbrella over his head and Lakshmana waved a white flywhisk.

Sugreeva followed riding a massive elephant and all the vanara generals followed him. The people of Ayodhya welcomed Rama with great happiness. They congratulated him on his return and joined the procession. Their love was warmly reciprocated by Rama who felt joyous to see his people.

Surrounded by the ministers, Brahmins, and his subjects, Rama looked glorious like the moon surrounded by sparkling stars.

The procession was led by a band that joyously played on turhi, kartal, and swastik. They sang auspicious songs. The band was followed by men carrying golden pitchers, cows, young women and servants who held trays full of sweets.

Rama told his ministers of the bravery displayed by Hanuman and other forces led by Sugreeva. He talked of his friendship with the Vanararaja and narrated how his meeting with Vibhishana had come about.

As the procession entered the city precincts, Ayodhya residents raised the flags flying over their houses higher.

Soon Rama arrived at the palace where his father had spent so many years. He bowed at the feet of his mothers and asked Bharata to make his large mansion situated in a lovely garden available to Sugreeva for his residence.

Sugreeva deputed four trusted vanaras to fly and bring water from four holy oceans in golden pitchers and return before dawn. On return, these pitchers were handed over to Guru Vasishtha.

45

The Coronation

The aged, pious Vasishtha, assisted by Brahmins, asked Ramachandra and Sita to be seated on a gem-encrusted asana. Just as the eight Vasus had anointed Indra, eight ministers—Vasishtha, Vamdeva, Jabali, Kashyap, Katyayana, Suyagya, Gautama and Vijay—used pure, fragrant water to anoint Rama and Sita.

Several other Brahmin priests, ministers, warriors and joyous traders were invited to join the abhishek ceremony. They sprinkled the holy ocean water and herbal extracts over the royal couple. The devatas watching from the sky greeted and anointed Rama as did the four Lokapalas.

A crown made of gold and studded with priceless gems was taken out of the family treasures, and ceremoniously placed on a stool inlaid with precious stones. This crown had been made by Brahma and glittered with a divine glow. Originally worn by Manu, all his descendants in the Raghukula had been crowned with the same.

Later, Vasishtha and the Brahmins placed this crown on the head of Rama. They put a few other ceremonial ornaments around his body.

Shatrughna unfolded a white canopy over the king's head while Sugreeva and Vibhishana stood behind waving flywhisks white as the moon.

On behalf of Indra, Vayu Deva offered the king Rama a resplendent garland of a hundred golden lotus flowers and a pearl necklace studded with several other gemstones.

As suited to the occasion, the Deva Gandharvas sang and apsaras danced.

As Rama ascended the throne, it seemed even nature showed its joy: the fields were full of fresh green crops, the trees bore abundant fruit and the flowers emitted fragrance.

Rama gave in charity thousands of horses, milch cows and hundreds of bulls to the Brahmins. He distributed golden coins and expensive clothes and ornaments to them.

Rama presented his friend Sugreeva a golden necklace studded with gems, brilliant like the sunrays. Angada was presented with two bracelets studded with sapphires.

Rama put the pearl necklace glistening like moonbeams, presented by Vayu, around Sita's neck. He offered her two celestial garments that would never get soiled as well as several gold ornaments.

Sita looked at her husband indicating an intention to present something to Hanuman. She took off the pearl garland and looked around at the vanaras. Appreciating her desire, Rama said,

'O fortunate one, Bhamini, please offer this necklace to anyone you desire.'

Sita, her eyes darkened with kohl, presented this necklace to Hanuman, the son of Vayu who was endowed with the virtues of speed, wisdom, fame, dexterity, humility, diplomacy, valour, and superior discretion. Putting on this pearl string, Hanuman looked magnificent like a mountain peak surrounded by moon-white clouds.

The king gave suitable presents to all the guests. In course of time the vanaras and the Rakshasaraja Vibhishana left Ayodhya for their respective kingdoms.

Ramarajya

Rama offered Lakshmana the status of the Yuvaraja and requested him to share the burden of ruling the reputed kingdom served by their ancestors. The latter declined the offer and as a result, Rama appointed Bharata as Yuvaraja.

Rama performed various yagyas like Ashwamedha several times. He was most charitable to the learned Brahmins. Under Rama's rule, the widows did not mourn their loss because they were well looked after. His praja enjoyed good health and the kingdom prospered under the wise leadership of the king.

Marauders and thieves were eliminated and since all had various means readily available, people kept away from crime. The elders did not have to cremate and mourn their children. Each one lived to a proper age.

People lived happily and followed their dharma. They looked to Rama as a role model and thus, did not harm each other.

Under Rama's rule, the trees were well looked after. They grew strong roots and bore flowers and fruit the year round. The rains were timely and so was their departure. The winds blew gently over Ayodhya and comforted the residents.

All the four varnas, brahmins, kshatriyas, vaishyas and the shudras lived in peace and harmony and without greed. They were content to perform their prescribed duties.

People did not tell lies and followed their dharma. They strove to inculcate good habits and follow a righteous path.

Assisted by his brothers Rama ruled for a long time.

UTTARAKANDAM

Translator's Note

Doubts have often been expressed about the authenticity of the Uttarakandam as a text written by Valmiki. Though at the end of the Yuddhakandam, shlokas 107 and 112 of the 128th chapter mention that this was the conclusion of the adikavya written by Maharshi Valmiki, in my humble view, the entire Uttarakandam is an interpolation. Its writing lacks the clarity and finesse of the other kandams of the adikavya. Goswami Tulsidasa chose to omit the events as narrated in this kanda completely in his *Ramcharitamanas*.

However, the Uttarakandam includes the story of Sita's banishment and the birth of Lava and Kusha. In the present times and versions of the Ramayana story that exist, this has become a part of every Hindu's understanding. Keeping this in mind, I have translated and abridged the relevant chapters for the benefit of the readers.

I have omitted the last few chapters in the Gita Press version of the Valmiki Ramayana that describe the death of the senior queens, and Rama's ascension to the Vaikuntha Dhama.

1

Raja Rama is Awakened with Music and Song

Rama's coronation was a source of delight to the people of Ayodhya. He knew the meaning of dharma and duty, and for his praja, Rama was the gem in the crown of the Kakutstha dynasty.

Music to Awaken the King

Every morning the court singers gathered in front of the palace to awaken the king with melodious lyrics and music. These musicians were as proficient in music as the Kinners. In melodious, well-modulated and sweet words, they addressed the king:

'Wake up, O king, gentle in looks, and
A source of joy to mother Kaushalya.

'Chivalrous you are as Vishnu.
Handsome you are as the Ashwinikumars.
Brihaspati's wisdom you possess while
You take care of your praja like Prajapati.

'You have Prithvi's forbearance and
The sun's brilliance.
You have imbibed the ocean's gravity and
The wind's agility and speed.

'O Naradhipa, sovereign among men,
Like Shankara, in a battle,
Unshakeable you are.
The moon alone has a pleasant face like yours.
Neither in the past there was,
Nor in future there will be,
A king like you.

'O Purushottama!
You are invincible.
Following dharma at all times,
You are occupied with your subjects' welfare.
For this very reason,
Keerti and Lakshmi are eternally yours.
For that reason,
You stand like a rock in dharma at all times,
Unchallenged in sovereignty and in the discharge of duty.'

Upon hearing such words, Rama woke up on his bed made of white sheets and resembled Narayana turning on Sheshanaga. His attendants humbly offered him water for his bath in shining utensils. Later, he offered ahuti to Agni and went to a temple consecrated by the Ikshavaku dynasty. He worshipped the devatas, his ancestors and the Brahmins. Soon he joined Vasishtha and several wise ministers waiting outside for his arrival.

In the court, Rama sat surrounded by several warriors and rulers of different countries; it resembled Indra's court like the devatas sitting around him. His brothers, Bharata, Lakshmana and Shatrughna awaited his orders like the three Vedas being always ready for the performance of a yagya.

The vanaras and Vibhishana visited Rama from time to time. Rama was surrounded by learned and wise men at all times and enjoyed his kingship over an ideal kingdom.

2

Rama and Sita Relax in the Asoka Vanika

In due course, Rama's guests including Sita's father Janaka left Ayodhya for their respective kingdoms while the Pushpak Vimana was returned to its rightful owner, Kubera.

The King's Relaxation

The king's palace had a pleasure garden named Asoka Vanika where a variety of trees bearing fruit and flowers had been planted. Among them one noticed trees like sandalwood, mango, coconuts, deodar, champa, asoka, punnag, parijata, kadamba, arjuna, mandar, and others. Priyangu, bakul, jamun and pomegranate trees added to the beauty of the Vanika.

Some of the trees flowered all the year round. Expert gardeners looked after the garden and its trees. Droning bhramaras hovered over pretty leaves and flowers. The trees were inhabited by birds like koel, papiha, and parrots, while the water bodies were adorned with flamingos and sarus cranes.

Some of the flowers were golden yellow while others shone red like a flame. The water bodies had crystal steps and glass flooring. Many coloured lotus bloomed in them and chakravaka leisurely floated. The surrounding lawns were laid with green, velvety grass.

The pavilions in the Asoka Vanika were provided with settees, cushions and pillows. There were several bowers designed with creepers.

It was to this place of joy that Rama and his consort Sita came to relax and spend time together. They often sat on a seat covered by a luxurious carpet with flower motifs. Like Indra offering sudha to Shachi, Rama would ask Sita to drink madhu from a cup held in his hands.

Soon thereafter, the attendants served them fruit and meals fit for a king.

The apsaras, nagakanyas and kinner women, dexterous in the arts of song and dance, entertained them; Rama rewarded the artists with fine clothing and jewellery.

Living the life of duty and pleasure, Rama and Sita spent the autumn and winter in happiness. In the early hours of the day, Sita worshipped in the palace temple. She looked after her mothers-in-law in the forenoon. Later, dressed in finery, she joined her husband and served him like Shachi looking after the thousand-eyed Indra in Swargaloka.

Sita is a Mother-to-be

Rama was overjoyed when he noticed that Sita was pregnant. Addressing his wife, pretty as any devakanya, he said,

'Vaidehi, soon you will give birth to a son. Vararohe, what do you desire? I shall fulfil all your wishes.'

Sita smiled and replied,

'I want to visit the holy tapovanas situated on the banks of the Ganga. I want to spend some time in the company of the tejasvi rishis who stay there subsisting on fruits and roots.'

Rama assured Sita that her desire would be fulfilled the very next day.

3

Doubts About Sita's Chastity

The same afternoon, Rama asked Bhadra, one of his friends, what were the most important issues in the minds of the people in Ayodhya. He desired to know what his people talked of socially. He asked,

'What do the members of the janapada think and say about Sita, Bharata, Lakshmana, Shatrughna, mother Kaikeyee and about me? If a king lacks character, if he acts thoughtlessly, he will be a subject of ridicule in the kingdom as well as in the ashramas. The public will find fault with his policy and behaviour.'

Rama Learns of His Subjects' Doubts Regarding Sita's Integrity of Character

Bhadra folded his hands and replied, 'Rajan, by and large, the people speak well of you. Saumya, they often talk of your victory over Ravana.'

Rama interrupted him and said,

'Tell me truthfully whatever is said about me, even if it against me. I shall continue practices that they approve of and give up those which are denounced by my praja.

'You may speak fearlessly. No harm will come to you even if you tell me of any adverse references made to me by the people.'

Bhadra folded his hands again and politely replied,

'Rajan, I narrate to you some of the comments which are made by people assembled at the town squares, in the bazaars, on the roadside, in the orchards and in the forests. I propose to tell you the pleasant as well as the unpleasant words that are spoken about you.

'They are astonished about your constructing a bridge over the ocean. They acknowledge that neither the devatas nor the danavas had performed or heard of such a glorious feat ever. The people talk admiringly of your killing Ravana and his forces and purposefully commanding an army of the vanaras and the bears.

'There is, however, one issue upon which they have a different opinion. It is regarding your bringing Sita home after killing Lankeshwara. They are unable to understand the reasons why you did not suspect her chastity. They are unable to reconcile your living with the Maharani as your wife when she had been forcibly abducted by Ravana and carried in his lap. They say that Ravana had kept her in his pleasure garden, Asoka Vatika within his palace. They question why their king does not look down upon Sita when she had spent quite a few months under the control of the Rakshasaraja. They say that they too will now have to tolerate indiscretion on the part of their wives. Yatha raja tatha praja, they assert.'

Listening to Bhadra, Rama felt disturbed and hurt. He asked the assembled friends and well-wishers for their advice, who vouched for Bhadra's comments.

Rama Consults His Brothers

Rama saw off his friends and advisers. He thought over his duty as a king and immediately sent for his three brothers.

Arriving in his presence, Bharata, Lakshmana and Shatrughna faced a Rama looking gloomy as if the moon had been eclipsed. His face was lustreless like the evening sun. The wise Rama was weeping; his lotus-like visage had withered.

The younger brothers bowed in the presence of the king. Rama addressed them and said,

'Brothers, you are all that I have. You are my prana, my life force. It is with your assistance that I rule this kingdom. You are well-versed in the Shastras and follow the rules laid therein. You are mature in your thinking and wisdom. O kings among men, I solicit your whole hearted cooperation in the task I propose to lay down before you.'

The brothers were startled. They could not anticipate what was weighing on Rama's mind so much.

Rama's throat was dry when he started talking on a subject not dear to his heart. He said,

'I want your total attention. I want to inform you of what the residents of Ayodhya say about Sita and me. Rumours are spread about Sita and her being abducted by Ravana. Some people in the praja even hate me for my not suspecting Sita's chastity and that hurts me to the core.

'I was born in the great Ikshavaku dynasty. Sita too was born in the family of the great Janaka. Lakshmana, you are aware how Sita was abducted from Dandakaranya that had no human habitation nearby, and how we punished Ravana for this evil doing.

'A doubt had arisen in my mind about Janaki while we were still in Lanka. To prove her purity and innocence, Sita had entered a bed of fire in your presence. Later, Agni himself brought her back in the presence of the devatas and declared her to be chaste and pure. Vayu, Surya, Chandrama concurred with this view in the presence of the rishis. Devaraja Indra, in the presence of the devatas and the gandharvas handed over Sita to me while still on the Lanka island.

'My conscience too believes that Sita is chaste and pure and thus, I brought her along to Ayodhya.'

Sita is Banished

'However, now the people of Ayodhya are talking of this as a scandal, denouncing my conduct and acceptance of Sita as my queen. Anyone, whose reputation is tarred like this, goes to naraka. The mahatmas care for him alone who has a good reputation.

'Dear brothers, I am willing to lay down my life to save my reputation against the onslaught of public denunciation. For this, I am willing to forsake you and even Sita.

'Look at me. I drown in the sea of sorrow. In my memory, I have never suffered more.

'Saumitra, tomorrow morning, in a chariot driven by Sumantra, take Sita with you and leave her outside the boundaries of our state.

'Across the Ganga, on the banks of the river Tamasa, is situated mahatma Valmiki's salubrious ashrama. You shall drop Sita in a forest near that ashrama and return without delay. These are orders you will obey. I have nothing more to say about Sita to anyone of you.

'Lakshmana, go now. Do not brood over what I have said and promise not to discuss anything about this subject. If you refute my decision, I shall be very unhappy.

'Sita had asked for a visit to the muni ashramas situated on the banks of the Ganga. Her wish is being granted.'

As the brothers left him to his thoughts, themselves in a state of confusion, Rama sat and wept. As the sorrowing king entered the palace, he was sighing deeply.

4

Lakshmana Drives an Unsuspecting Sita into the Forest

Sita's Journey into the Forest

Next morning, an unhappy Lakshmana asked Sumantra to fetch a chariot driven by swift horses and comfortably equipped for Sita to travel.

'I have orders to escort her to the muni ashrama,' he told the minister-cum-charioteer.

Lakshmana went to Sita to inform her of a chariot being ready for her to go to the ashrama. He said,

'You had made a request to the king for a visit to the muni ashrama. The king had assured you of its fulfilment. Devi, as per the Maharaja's orders, I shall forthwith drive you to pleasant rishi ashramas on the banks of the Ganga.'

An unknowing Sita was delighted at the news. She gathered several costly clothes, ornaments and jewels in order to gift them to the women living in the ashramas.

While being driven in the comfortable chariot, Sita saw a few bad omens. She said,

'Raghunandan, I notice a twitching in my right eye. My limbs shiver. These are not good omens.

'Saumitra, my mind is not at ease. I am afraid of the unknown and feel impatient. All of a sudden, the earth seems uninhabited. I hope your brother is well.

'I pray for the well-being of my mothers-in-law and the residents of Ayodhya.'

Listening to her and seeing her praying to the gods asking for the welfare of everyone, Lakshmana with a superficial sense of joy, nodded in agreement and said,

'May everyone be happy!'

The night was spent in an ashrama situated on the banks of the Gomati. Next morning they rode towards the Ganga that destroys all evil. Reaching those holy waters, Lakshmana broke down. His bitter weeping confused Sita beyond measure as she could not gauge the reason for his sorrow. She asked,

'Lakshmana, why do you shed tears? Reaching the banks of the Ganga is a fulfilment of my long cherished desire. In this moment of joy, why do you weep and make me sad?

'You keep company of Shri Rama all the time. Being away for just two days has made you so unhappy. Why so?

'Shri Rama is dearer to me than my life, yet I am not unhappy. What is it that makes you so unhappy? Do not behave like a child.

'Take me across the Ganga. I desire to have darshana of the rishis. I have brought clothes and ornaments for them.

'We shall spend a night in the ashrama and return to Ayodhya tomorrow. I am keen to return and look at Shri Rama.'

Lakshmana wiped his tears. The boatmen announced that a boat was ready. Accompanied by Sita, Lakshmana crossed the river to the western bank.

Lakshmana Conveys Rama's Decision to Sita

Reaching the other side of Bhagirathi, alighting from the boat, with folded hands Lakshmana stood in front of Sita and said,

'Vaidehi, I am deeply upset because the wise Shri Rama has entrusted me with an assignment that will bring me disrepute in the eyes of the public. In this situation I would have preferred death or a suffering akin to death. It is not fair that I have to discharge this condemnable duty.

'Shobhane, kindly do not blame me for these tidings and try to be happy.'

Saying this, Lakshmana collapsed with grief.

Looking at the weeping Lakshmana, beset with sorrow, Sita felt agitated. She could not make anything out of her brother-in-law's pining for death. She said,

'I am unable to comprehend the meaning of your words, Lakshmana. Tell me the truth. Is the maharaja hale and hearty? All that I notice is that you are not at peace. Kindly tell me what agitates you.'

In a choking voice, an unhappy and weeping Lakshmana said,

'The terrible rumours spread in the town regarding your chastity upset Shri Ramachandra and, having taken me into confidence, he retreated into the palace. I cannot narrate to you the evil words spoken about you by some of Ayodhya's people. Shri Rama has taken them to his heart and feels deeply hurt at the same.

'Even though you were proved innocent in my presence, the king, afraid of the calumny, has decided to banish you. Devi, do not misunderstand me. Following the king's orders and keeping in mind your desire to visit the sylvan rishi ashramas, I propose to take you to one of them.

'We have arrived at one such Brahmarshi tapovana on the banks of Ganga. It is a sacred place and ought to be a pleasure to live in. Kindly do not feel despondent.

'Janaki, in this ashrama, lives Maharshi Valmiki, a close friend of my father, the late king Dashratha. You may seek his protection and spend your time happily. You can perform the holy rituals, meditate and think of Shri Rama. In that alone lies your well-being.

A Disconsolate Sita Mourns Her Fate

Listening to Lakshmana's unwelcome words, Sita fell unconscious. She lay like that, weeping inconsolably. Later, coming to her senses, speaking humbly to Lakshmana, Janaki said,

'Lakshmana, it seems that the Creator has given me birth only to make me suffer. That is why, today I face a mountain of sorrows.

'What sin had I committed in an earlier birth, or whom did I seduce away from his wife that the king has deserted me even after I proved my devotion to him in a fire ordeal?

'Saumitra, earlier I preferred to live in a forest with all its inconvenience and discomfort so that I could stay with Shri Rama. How shall I spend my time alone in an ashrama away from those whom I love? With whom shall I share my suffering?

'What fault of mine shall I tell the munis if they ask me the reason why Shri Rama has banished me?

'Saumitra, I would have drowned myself in the Ganga at this very moment. However, I cannot do so because that will bring to an end my husband's dynasty.

'Saumitra, you have to obey the king's orders. Let me be here to suffer alone.

'When you return, on my behalf, bow at the feet of all my mothers and the king's feet and enquire after their well-being. Kindly convey my greetings to all the venerable women in the palace. To each one including the king, you will carry the following message:

'Raghava, you are aware that Sita is chaste and that she always thinks of you and you alone. You know that she loves you immensely and is devoted to you.

'O warrior, I consider it to be my duty as well to ward off the calumny because of which you have given me up. I am the root cause of these insulting comments, of this misinformation. My salvation ultimately lies in you.

'Lakshmana, tell the maharaja that he must follow his dharma and stay alert of his enemies. He must treat his praja as affectionately as he treats his brothers. That is his sacred and paramount duty and that alone will bring him name and fame.

'Rajan, the punya you will gather by doing your duty to your citizens, is your most desirable dharma, your most prized possession and a source of your glory. As for me, I am least concerned about my bodily comforts.

'Raghunandan, lead a life where you can avoid this kind of calumny. For a woman, her husband is her devata, the closest of relations, and a guru. That is why, in particular, she must do what is good for him even if she has to lay down her life.

'Lakshmana, please convey these words to Raghunath. And before you depart, learn that I hold in me your king's progeny; I bear his seed.'

An unhappy Lakshmana could hardly utter a word. He bowed to her and weeping, he went around her in parikrama. He bowed to Vaidehi and getting into the boat he ordered the boatman to row him to the other side. Reaching the northern banks of Ganga, Lakshmana still in a stupor, ascended his chariot. Repeatedly, he turned back to look at the weeping Sita who was rolling on the ground like an orphan.

Looking at Lakshmana and his chariot receding into the distance, Sita was upset. Intense grief enveloped her as soon as she lost sight of the chariot. She could not see anyone who could protect her. The venerable queen who was pregnant with a king's child, crushed by a mountain of sorrow, sat weeping loudly in the forest resounding with the cries of peacocks.

Lakshmana Consoles Rama

Returning home, Lakshmana approached Rama who sat on his throne with eyes full of tears. Lakshmana fell at his brother's feet and said,

'Maharaja, following your command, I have returned to serve you after leaving Janaka's chaste and venerable daughter close to the Valmiki Ashrama on the banks of the Ganga.

'O lion among men, do not sorrow. It was destined to be so. Wise and high-minded men like you do not grieve over such happenings.

'In this world, all attainments are ultimately lost. Whatever rises, comes down in the end. Every union ends in separation and life in death.

'As separation is unavoidable, we must never be attached to a wife, son, friend or wealth.

'Great men like you do not lose their equilibrium under any such circumstance. My master, be firm and courageous, calm and strong; control your thoughts and do not grieve.'

Rama smiled as a token of gratitude for his brother's words and said,

'Saumya, listening to you I am relieved of my sorrow. Your thoughtful words have restored my peace of mind.'

5

Valmiki Takes Charge of Vaidehi

Some children playing nearby noticed the weeping Sita. They ran into the ashrama and apprised Maharshi Valmiki of her presence. They said,

'Bhagwan, on the banks of the Ganga sits a woman who looks like Lakshmi incarnate. She appears to be wife of some noble king. We have never seen her. She weeps because she is unable to understand what has befallen her. Her face is distorted while she weeps.

'Bhagwan, please come and judge for yourself. She appears to be a Devi who has descended from the skies. She is very good looking, but appears to be in deep sorrow. She sits alone, helpless and weeps bitterly like an orphan.

'It appears that she seeks your protection. That is why she has descended near the ashrama.'

Valmiki possessed divine vision. He saw through the situation and arrived at the site where Maithili sat weeping inconsolably. He was accompanied by some pupils. He carried a pretty arghya vessel to welcome the wife of Ramachandra.

The glorious Valmiki's presence made Sita comfortable and happy. Affectionately addressing her in sweet words, he said,

'Pativrate, you are the daughter-in-law of the maharaja Dashratha, beloved queen of the king Ramachandra and the daughter of the king Janaka of Mithila. I welcome you wholeheartedly. I became aware of your arrival while meditating. Further, I am aware of the circumstances of your departure from Ayodhya. I know why you have been banished by Rama. Through my divine insight I get to know of all the happenings in the three worlds.

'Vaidehi, I am certain of your chastity. Give up your grief and shed all worries. You are safe under my protection.

'A few tapasvinis live close to my ashrama, and are engaged in tapasya. They will look after you like a daughter.

'I offer you arghya and welcome you. You may forget your worries and let go of fear. Considering this ashrama to be your home, you must shed your grief.'

Listening to Valmiki's soothing words, Sita bowed her head to him and said,

'I shall do as you desire.'

6

Sita Gives Birth to Twins

It was midnight when Sita gave birth to twins. The ashrama children brought the good tidings to Valmiki. They said,

'Bhagwan, Ramachandra's wife has given birth to two sons. O glorious Maharshi, kindly take whatever action you have to, to make sure that the infants stay healthy.'

Valmiki went over to the cottage where the babies were born. The infants looked pretty as the new moon and glorious like the sons of the devatas. He chanted mantras to protect them from all negative omens. He gathered a bunch of kusha grass and sheaves of corn and asked the attending elderly women to purify the young ones. The child delivered first was to be sprinkled with the holy water from kusha leaves and to be named Kusha. The later born was to be purified with the holy water sprinkled with sheaves of corn and named Lava. He said,

'These boys will be known as Kusha and Lava and these names will be renowned in the world.'

By coincidence, Shatrughna, the youngest brother of Rama was camping in the same ashrama. He heard of the murmur in a cottage near his abode and the names of Rama and Sita being mentioned repeatedly. Learning of the birth of the twins, he entered Sita's cottage. He bowed to her and said,

'Mother, this is a great event and a sign of good fortune.'

Shatrughna sat talking to Sita at the birth of sons to the royal family.

Twelve Years Later

Under Rama's orders, Shatrughna had carved a new kingdom on the banks of the Ganga with a capital named Madhupuri. After a lapse of twelve years, he decided to visit his elder brother at Ayodhya and seek his blessings.

Travelling towards Ayodhya, Shatrughna spent a night at the Valmiki Ashrama. The latter welcomed him and offered the king hospitality befitting his status. Later in the evening, Valmiki told Shatrughna several tales of bravery and devotion.

After dinner, a recital of Rama Charitra had been arranged for the delight of the king and his entourage. It was a melodious recitation to the accompaniment of a veena. It was a poetic composition sung in mandra, madhyama and taar swaras that sprang from the heart, the throat and the crown. The poem had been written in Sanskrit with flawless grammar. Various styles of composition had been used while writing the verses. Every shloka was set to music in appropriate tala and raga.

It was a truthful rendition of Rama's life and a unique narrative in itself. Listening to this, Shatrughna shed tears and lost consciousness.

When the young king came to his senses, he took several deep breaths. In the words of the song, he had heard the story of the past happenings. His companions commented and said,

'Maharaja, we witnessed these events and now we are hearing their narration in this ashrama. It is incredible. Is it a dream? Why not ask Maharshi Valmiki about this amazing thing?'

However, after talking it over they decided not to make any enquiry of the Maharshi.

7

Kusha and Lava Recite the Ramayana in Rama's Court

Rama Performs the Ashwamedha Yagya

As befitted a mighty king, Rama on the advice and suggestion of his gurus and ministers, decided to perform the Ashwamedha Yagya. Under the protection of Lakshmana a black horse was sent to the territories not directly under Rama's control in order to establish Ayodhya's suzerainty. In the meantime, kings from several other territories descended on Ayodhya to pledge their loyalty to Rama. They were ceremoniously welcomed by Bharata and Shatrughna and were put up in luxurious tents. In due course Lakshmana returned with the Ashwamedha horse unchallenged.

Valmiki Arrives with Kusha and Lava; Asks Them to Recite the Ramayana

Muni Valmiki too arrived with his pupils to participate in the great yagya. Comfortable and pretty cottages made of leaves and grasses were erected for him and his companions near the residences of other rishis. Several carriages full of grain and other goods were stationed near his cottage. These were loaded with excellent fruit, roots and vegetables. Rama himself worshipped the Maharshi on his arrival and so did the other assembled sages.

Valmiki sent for his two healthy pupils, Kusha and Lava and asked them to joyously, with concentration, recite the Ramayana Kavya while wandering from place to place for the benefit of the assembled kings, sadhus and the public. He said,

'Recite the Kavya at the sacred land occupied by the rishis and the Brahmins. Sing it at the main roads and near the palaces where the kings have been lodged.

'In particular, recite the Ramayana in front of the palace of Ramachandra, standing in front of the massive gates where Brahmins are busy with the yagya rituals and where the priests are performing sacrifice.

'All along the roads grow the fruit trees bearing delicious fruit. Pluck a few and enjoy them when hungry. Taking these tasty and nourishing fruit, you will never get tired. Taking the fruit will not hurt your throat or the sweetness of the melody.

'Behave with humility if maharaja Rama sends for you to listen to your song. I have taught you the Ramayana chapters with different number of shlokas. You may sing twenty chapters at one go every day in your trained voice.

'Do not covet any wealth. Of what use is money to the ashrama inmates subsisting on fruit and vegetables?

'If the king asks you about your parentage, just tell him that you are the pupils of the Maharshi Valmiki.

'Both of you may sing to the accompaniment of veena and in tune with each other. Rest assured of your success.

'Start at the beginning. You must not say anything that insults the king at any point. According to dharma, a king is like a father to all his praja.

'You should start tomorrow morning, wholeheartedly and joyously.'

Kusha and Lava nodded in affirmation and spent the night in anticipation of seeing the king the next morning.

The Ramayana is Recited in Rama's Court

It was a court full of wise men and saints, including Vedic scholars and grammarians. Several neighbouring kings were present along with people in large numbers. Musicologists present at the court appreciated the content and delivery of the Ramayana.

The two pupils of Maharshi Valmiki sang a song and narrated a unique story. Their melody flowed non-stop and the subject matter entranced the listeners who eagerly waited for the recital next day.

The munis and kings gathered in the court experienced a current of joy as they looked at the two young tapasvis. Repeatedly they looked at their faces and noticed a resemblance with Rama. Exchanging notes, they said,

'These boys resemble the king; they are like his reflection. If not for the long hair and clothes made of bark, it would be difficult to distinguish between them and Shri Rama.'

Rama's Curiosity about the Author of the Poem

Having heard the recitation of the first twenty chapters, Rama asked Bharata to reward the young singers with eighteen thousand gold coins. He further desired that the young men be provided with whatever else they asked for.

Kusha and Lava, however, declined Bharata's gift of the gold coins. The young singers said,

'We are the denizens of a forest. We survive on wild fruit, root and vegetables. Carrying gold and silver into the forest is of no use to us.'

Their reply surprised Rama and everyone present in the court. It excited everyone's curiosity about their identity. Rama was keen to know about the author of the cantos that the boys had been singing. He said,

'How many shlokas does this epic consist of? Where does the poet, its great author reside? Where is he at the present moment?'

The young tapasvis replied,

'Maharaja, the epic poem that narrates the events of your life in totality, has been authored by Maharshi Valmiki and he is present in the yagyashala at present. The poem consists of twenty four thousand shlokas divided into six cantos and five hundred chapters. Our guru, Maharshi Valmiki is the sole author of the epic narrating the great events of your life. He has now added Uttarakanda narrating the events after you banished your queen.

'O great charioteer, O mighty king, in case you decide to listen to the entire epic, kindly spare some time after the yagya is over to listen to it in its entirety in the company of your brothers.'

Rama readily agreed to this suggestion.

8

Once Again Rama Wants Sita to Swear on Her Chastity

Daily, Rama, surrounded by the rishis, kings, vanaras and others listened to Kusha and Lava reciting the Ramayana. He learnt that Kusha and Lava, who narrated the story, were his sons, born as twins to Sita. At this he summoned a few wise messengers and sent a message to Maharshi Valmiki.

'If Sita is chaste, if she has not committed any wrong, she, with your permission, should come here and prove her chastity in the presence of the public.

'Find out how Maharshi Valmiki and Sita react to this suggestion. Inform me if she is willing to come here and prove her innocence.

'I want her to attend the morning court tomorrow and in the presence of the populace swear upon her chastity.'

The messengers approached the glorious Valmiki in his cottage and conveyed Rama's message. The sage replied,

'Sita will do as desired by Raghava. For a woman, her husband is a devata.'

Rama was pleased when he got Valmiki's affirmation. He asked the rishis, ministers and public to be present in the court next day to witness Sita swearing upon her chastity.

Valmiki Attests to Sita's Chastity

Next morning, Rama sat in his court surrounded by his praja and the rishis including Vasishtha, Jabali, Kashyapa, Durvasa, Markandeya, Bhargava, Bhardwaj, Narada and Agastya. The rakshasa and the vanara kings and courtiers were also present. Everyone wanted to witness Sita swearing by her chastity and sat silent and still like stones.

Soon after, Valmiki arrived with Sita in his footsteps. She walked with her head lowered, hands folded and eyes brimming with tears. Despite all that had happened in the past years, her mind was still full of Shri Ramachandra. She was overwhelmed with grief. Walking behind Valmiki, Sita looked like Shruti following Brahma. Everyone present showered blessings on her.

Addressing the king, Valmiki said,

'Dashrathanandana, Sita has always followed her dharma. She is steadfast in her resolve. Afraid of calumny, you made arrangements to abandon her near my ashrama.

'Sita will assure you of her chastity because you have been frightened by the praja talking against her. Please command her to do so.

'These two young boys, Kusha and Lava are twins born to her in my ashrama. They are your children and are brave like you. This alone is the truth.

'Raghunandan, I am the tenth son of Pracheta and never utter a lie. Truthfully, I assert and tell you that these boys are your sons.

'I have performed tapasya for thousands of years. If Maithili has ever committed any error, I forfeit the punya of my tapasya.

'I have never sinned in thoughts, actions or in speech. I pray that I get the punya for this blameless conduct only if Sita is chaste and pure.

'Raghunandan, I had given shelter to Sita after ascertaining the purity of her conduct through my inner vision and five senses. We had found her near a waterfall in the forest. She is blameless in deed and conduct. She worships her husband as her god. You are disturbed by the calumny heaped upon her by some members of the public; Maithili would prove them false and assure you of her purity.'

9

9

Sita Asserts Her Chastity and is Transported from this World by Prithvi

Rama Clarifies His Stand

Listening to Maharshi Valmiki, Rama looked at the beauteous Sita. Addressing the Maharshi with folded hands, he said,

'O great man, you understand dharma better than anyone else. Whatever you have said about Vaidehi is correct. I believe in your words and I accept that Janaki is chaste and unblemished.

'Even earlier, in the presence of the devatas, I had accepted that Sita was chaste. She had sworn by her purity and I had accepted her station in the palace.

'However, later a large number of my subjects raised grave doubts about her chastity and about my decision. Perforce, I had to abandon Maithili. O great Brahmin, even though convinced about the veracity of her statement, I banished her out of the fear of my subjects. I ask your forgiveness for what I did.

'I am aware that the twins, Kusha and Lava are my sons. However, I can accept Sita's return only if the public accepts the truth of her statement.'

Understanding Rama's intent a number of prominent devatas including Mahendra, Aditya, Vasu, and Rudra, led by Brahma arrived at the scene to witness Sita swearing by her chastity. Looking at them, Rama once again reiterated his stand. He said,

'O mighty devatas, although I believe in Maharshi Valmiki's words, I shall be pleased if Sita proves her innocence in the presence of the public.'

Sita Invokes Prithvi, Her Mother

What transpired now had never happened before. It was unthinkable and unprecedented.

Sita was dressed in ochre like a tapasvini. With head bent low, with hands folded, addressing the crowd, she said,

'I never think of any man other than Raghava. If it be true, may Devi Prithvi take me into her embrace!

'If I, indeed, in words and thought, worship Rama alone, may Devi Prithvi take me into her embrace!

'I have never known a man other than Shri Ramachandra. If it be true, may Devi Prithvi take me into her embrace!'

As Maithili swore her fidelity, the earth split and a unique throne appeared. It looked celestial and beautiful. It was supported by celestial nagas who had gems studded in their foreheads. Along with this throne arrived Prithvi, the goddess. She took Sita warmly into her arms and welcomed her to the divine throne.

The devatas could see that the throne was disappearing into the subterranean regions and shouted their blessings. They said,

'Sita, you are chaste and blessed. You are of a noble character and temperament.'

An amazing sight took all the assembled munis and the public by surprise. With mouths agape they looked at a disappearing Sita and the sorrowing king. People wept as Prithvi closed herself, and Sita disappeared forever.

Glossary and Notes

Abhishek: Coronation.

Aachaman: Rinsing the mouth. Sipping water before religious ceremonies from the palm of the hand.

Abhijit Nakshatra: Vega in the constellation, Lyra, a northern constellation. Vega, á Lyrae, is the fifth brightest star in the sky, a blue-white star, and 25 light years away. In November, it shines bright in the north-western sky. The constellation, Lyra, is fully visible between 90° N and 42° S. Valmiki's mention is astronomically correct.

Adharma: The absence of Dharma, of propriety, of a sense of duty.

Adikavya: The first epic.

Agastya: In the Rig Veda, Agastya and Vasishtha are said to be the sons of Mitra and Varuna whose seed was discharged at the sight of the lovely nymph, Urvashi, at a sacrificial site. A part of the seed fell into a jar and a part into water. From the former was born Agastya and from the latter Vasishtha. In the Ramayana, Agastya plays a distinguished role. He dwelt in a hermitage on the Mount Kunjara, to the south of the Vindhyas. In the course of their wanderings, Rama, Sita and Lakshmana arrived at the hermitage of Agastya who became Rama's friend, adviser and protector. For the dwellers of the earth, Agastya puts the sun at the highest pedestal of worship because our life depends on that star. [*Yuddhakandam*, 31] In astronomy, Agastya is the star Canopus, Alpha Carina, the second brightest star in the sky, a white super giant, 14,000 times more luminous than the sun. It lies 310 light years away from the earth and forms part of the Carina constellation.

Agnihotri: One who pours samidha, the fragrant offerings of milk, oil, sour gruel, wood splinters and herbs into the havana kunda. One who maintains the sacred fire for the yagya.

Ahuti: An offering to Agni during yagya.

Airavata: Indra's mount, an elephant; a symbol of majesty and power.

Akshara: A letter of the alphabet. A syllable. Imperishable. An epithet of the Supreme.

Amaresha: Literally, the god of gods. Rudra. Shiva.

Amla: Indian gooseberry. Its fruit, rich in vitamin C, is an ingredient of pickles and sherbets.

Amravati: Abode of the gods. Residence of Indra.

Amrita manthan: Churning of the ocean by the devatas and the asuras in order to obtain Amrita. It forms a fascinating tale in the Shrimadbhagavata Purana. (For a detailed account, see *Krishnaleela* by Rajendra Tandon, Rupa).

Ananda: Bliss.

Anarya: Conduct unworthy of an Arya, of a worthy person.

Andhakasura: An asura son of Kashyapa and Diti and killed by Shiva when he attempted to carry the Parijata tree from the Swargaloka. He is called Andhaka because he walked like a blind man although he could see very well.

Arghya: A respectful offering to a god or a venerable person. A ritual welcome to a guest often performed by offering a few drops of water.

Arjuna tree: A tree that grows on the banks of rivers in central and south India and bears fruits and flowers. The flowers are fragrant, a pale dust yellow and bloom from April to July. It is also known as jarul or the Pride of India.

Arundhati: The wife of Vasishtha. A morning star, part of the constellation Pleiades. She, like her husband, Vasishtha, was a guide and a counsellor of the Raghu kings and queens.

Asan: The name of a tree. *Peetashala*.

Asoka: One that does not grieve.

Ashwamedha yagya: Literally, the sacrifice or yagya of a horse. In Vedic times this sacrifice was made by kings desirous of begetting a son. Later it was performed to establish suzerainty over other kings. A horse under the protection of a limited force was let loose to wander in various principalities. Wherever it went, the ruler had either to submit or fight. If the animal returned successfully, its return was celebrated with great pomp and show. It was believed that a hundred such sacrifices would make the king replace Indra in the Swargaloka.

Ashwini Kumar: The twin sons of Ashwini, the sun's wife, a nymph represented as a mare. According to Vedic delineation, they are the harbingers of Ushas, or the Dawn. They are young, beautiful, bright and swift, and represent the transition from darkness to light. Mythically, they were physicians to the gods and were celebrated for their active benevolence and curative power which they demonstrated in restoring the youth and life of Chyavana who had grown old and decrepit.

Asoka tree: A herald of spring, this tree bears scarlet bunches of flowers in early March. The tree grows tall and stays evergreen.

Astra: A weapon.

Asura: A demon.

Atimukta: A creeper going around a mango tree and represented as its beloved. Mountain ebony.

Aurasa son: A son born out of wedlock or without physical relations between a particular couple but accepted as genuine: like Hanuman accepted as a son of Pavana.

Ayonija: Not born of a woman, such as Sita who had emerged out of Prithvi and not from the womb of Janaka's queen.

Baheda: A tree that grows tall and handsome. It has a massive crown, shaped like a dome. Its leaves are large and are clustered at the end of twigs. The new leaves emerge a striking crimson. Its fruit is used as a part of the combination known as triphala (harad, baheda and amla) in Ayurveda, and used as a medicine for cough and several other diseases.

Bakul: Maulashri. A majestic tree that grows all over India and Malaysia. It is lush and evergreen. Flowers are seen from March to July and are small, star-like and highly fragrant.

Bel: A middle-sized, thorny tree. Native to monsoon forests. Grown in temple compounds because its leaves and fruit are offered in the worship of Shiva. Flowers in late May. The bel fruit is like a mid-sized ball. Its pulp is used in Ayurveda for digestive problems such as dysentery and diarrhoea. The bel pulp has antibiotic and anti-inflammatory properties. The mucous of the unripe fruit is used by jewellers as cement and by masons in making mortar.

Bela: A variety of jasmine.

Bhadrapada: Name of the lunar month corresponding to August-September. A period of heavy rains in India.

Bhadre: O blessed woman!

Bhadra: Auspicious. Prosperous. Foremost. Kind. Gracious.

Bhamini: A charming young woman. A passionate woman. Used as a term of endearment. Lustrous. Splendid.

Bheri: A musical instrument played in festivities. A kettle-drum.

Bhrigu: A sage. One of the ten patriarchs created by Manu. Sent to determine the greatness of Brahma, Vishnu and Mahesh, he judged Vishnu to be greatest of the three because he wielded the mightiest of all weapons, viz. kindness and generosity.

Bilva: The wood-apple tree.

Bimba: a climber with bright red fruit often compared to the lips of a woman.

Brahmastra: A divine weapon blessed by Brahma.

Brihaspati: Jupiter, the preceptor of the devatas; lord of devotion; the god of wisdom and eloquence.

Chakravaka: The ruddy goose. Lives near water and resembles a swan. According to legend, the male and female geese are destined to separate every night. They stay together during the day but part company at night. In Sanskrit poetry these birds symbolize deep conjugal affection.

Chakva, chakvi: The domestic duck. A large brown duck with paler head and neck and sometimes a faint black collar at its base. Found at open tanks and on shingle river banks.

Champa: Champaka. Frangipani. The tree grows all over India, Myanmar, Thailand and Malaysia and flowers all the year around. Its flowers are white, yellow, pink or red and are deeply fragrant. The flowers have a two-tone colouring, a silky feel and five petals. Women love to use the champa flowers as ornaments for their beauty, feel and scent.

Chandan: The sandalwood tree. Its fragrant paste is used as a beauty unguent and for applying a tilaka on the forehead of the deity and of the worshipper. The sandalwood is used for carving as well.

Charana: The single line of a stanza. A quartet.

Chataka: Pied, crested cuckoo. *Papiha*. A handsome, crested black and white cuckoo. Its plaintive, metallic call has been used by poets as a call for a beloved in numerous lyrics.

Chaumasa: The four months of the rainy season.

Chaupala: A place for a social gathering in a village, usually under a tree where participants sit to discuss social matters.

Daitya: A demon.

Daiva: Fate, destiny, fortune, luck.

Darshana: Appearance by a deity, a holy man or a king to bless the devoted onlooker. The word is associated with good fortune, a privilege on being in the presence of a superior being.

Dashagreeva: (dasha=ten; greeva=necks) Ravana, the warrior with ten necks.

Dashanana: (dasha=ten, anana=face) Ravana, the warrior with ten faces.

Dashrathanandana: Son of Dashratha.

Devangana: A celestial damsel. An apsara.

Devata: a divine being. A deity. Followers and companions of Indra as against the rakshasas who were evil incarnate in their conduct.

Devakanya: A celestial damsel. A nymph.

Deveshwara: God of gods.

Dhanada: Kubera, the god of wealth and elder brother of Ravana.

Dharma: Duty as ordained by scriptures. Ethics. Religious or moral merit. Virtue. Righteousness. Good deeds. Justice, equity, impartiality.

Dharmagya: Knowledgeable in the principles of dharma.

Dharmatma: A virtuous soul.

Dhruva: The son of Uttanapada and his second wife Suniti, and grandson of Manu. Being a devotee of Vishnu, Dhruva was discarded by his father. He left the paternal palace, retired to the woods, meditated and was elevated by Vishnu to the highest place in the sky. The pole star personified as Dhruva. Immovable. Stable. Permanent. Everlasting. Eternal.

Divakara: The sun. The one who causes and illuminates the day.

Dundubhi: A large kettle-drum played to welcome or to make an announcement.

Durbuddhe: Literally, you evil minded person!

Eight types of wisdom: 1. Genuine desire to listen to another's point of view. 2. Patient listening. 3. To understand and adopt the other's point of view. 4. To act upon the said advice. 5. To logically argue one's point of view. 6. To understand the intent of an argument. 7. To acquire the knowledge of the essentials. 8. To understand the Niti Shastra.

Five senses: The external organs of vision, taste, hearing, smell, and touch, called *indriyas*. These are often compared to restive horses, which, if not controlled, will lead a human being astray.

Fourteen qualities of a leader: 1. To understand the importance of time and place in devising a policy. 2. Determination. 3. Stamina to undergo hardship. 4. An effort to learn several branches of knowledge. 5. Intelligence. 6. Enthusiasm. 7. Capability to maintain confidentiality. 8. Not to make contradictory statements. 9. Valour. 10. An appreciation of one's own and the enemy's strength. 11.Gratitude. 12. Protection to one who surrenders. 13. Conquest over anger. 14. A stable temperament.

Gandhamadana Mountain: A mythological mountain supposed to be near the lake Manasarover, next to Mount Kailas, renowned for its sensually fragrant forests.

Gandharva: A heavenly being. A celestial musician. A singer in general.

Garuda: King of birds. He is the son of Kashyapa by his wife Vinata. He is the chief of the feathered race, an implacable enemy of the serpents and older brother of Aruna, the charioteer of the sun. Garuda is represented as the mount of Vishnu. He has a white face, an aquiline nose, red wings and a golden body.

Gayatri mantra: An invocation to the sun recounting his might; his powerful rays to instil life in everything that matters in our universe and asking for the whetting of the supplicant's intelligence. It is a mantra recited during most rituals as a source of purification and intellectual uplift.

Girirajakumari: Parvati, the daughter of Himalaya.

Grihastha: A householder.

Gurukul: A residential school where the pupils lived and studied as a member of the teacher's family.

Havishya: Anything fit for an oblation, as an offering during yagya. It usually consists of ghee, sandalwood splinters, grain, and other fragrant substances.

Hiranyabha: Of the lustre of gold. The sun.

Hiranyakashipu: A son of Kashyapa and Diti and a celebrated king of the demons. He subjected his son Prahlad to untold cruelty because of the boy's devotion to Vishnu. Ultimately he was torn to pieces by Vishnu appearing as Nrisimha.

Hree: Modesty. Bashfulness.

Hrishikesha: a name of Vishnu, of Krishna.

Indragopika: Ladybird.

Indra's thousand eyes: Indra had seduced Ahalya, the first woman created by Brahma. She was the wife of the rishi Gautama. Indra came disguised as her husband when the rishi was away. A flattered Ahalya willingly cohabited with him. Discovering the truth, Gautama cursed Indra that his body will be covered by a thousand sores in the shape of vagina. Later these marks were changed into a thousand eyes. Ahalya was cursed to turn into a stone. She was restored to her human form by Rama. Indra came to be called Netra-yoni or Sahasraksha. (Refer chapter 12, Balakandam.)

Jamun: A dark purple, sweet fruit that grows in abundance on trees lining a lot of avenues in India. It has excellent medicinal properties. Rose apple or Java plum. Indian blackberry. Jambolan. The tree itself is large-canopied and pretty to look at.

Janakatmaja: Sita, the daughter of Janaka.

Janapada: A community, race, nation. An inhabited place.

Kadamba: A sacred tree with a short trunk that is irregular in shape. It has a cheerful and large crown. It's fragrant, round and pale yellow flowers are associated with Krishna who is described as playing his flute under this tree. Its fruit consists of tiny capsules, clustered in round heads, between 100 and 150 in each cluster. A hardy tree adapted to growing in sandy beds of seasonal streams. A dominant tree in the Vrindavan forests. Popular in Delhi. Also known as 'kaim'.

Kajal: Kohl.

Kala: Time as a continuous transition, all powerful and unavoidable.

Kalagni: The fire of destruction.

Kalpavriksha: A mythical tree that can yield what you need, desire or ask for. A tree in Indra's Swargaloka granting all that is asked for, all that is feasible.

Kama: Love, lust, sex. Amour. Passion. Kamadeva, the god of love.

Kamadhenu: A mythical cow that can grant any wish. Any source of power that can yield the result requested for.

Kamandalu: A small copper pot used by ascetics to carry water.

Kanera: A common flowering bush found in every garden in India. The flowers have no scent. Its flowers were popular with women in ancient India because these are easily grown, have lovely colours and shape, and can be threaded into decorative ornaments to embellish various parts of the body. Oleander, the yellow kanera is mildly scented.

Kansa: A tall grass used for making mats.

Kanta: Beloved. A lovely woman.

Kapishrestha: The best among the vanaras. Hanuman.

Kartal: Metallic discs held in separate hands and struck to make rhythmic sound.

Kathala: A fruit used in preparation of curries.

Kartik: The lunar month corresponding to October-November, in which the full moon is visible against the constellation Taurus. In north India, a mild winter sets in at this time.

Kaustubha: A celebrated gem obtained with thirteen others during Samudra manthan and worn by Vishnu on his chest.

Kavya: Poetry. Possessed of the qualities of a sage or a poet. Prophetic. Inspired. Poetical.

Keerti: Fame. Glory.

Ketaki: Kewra plant.

Kewra: A tree with fragrant, sword-shaped flowers. Its essence is used in food preparation and for ceremonial sprinkling to welcome guests.

Khair tree: Acacia catechu. A small deciduous tree with deeply cracked and flaking bark. Its tiny flowers are clustered on long spikes. Catechu obtained from the khair tree yields kattha used as a paste for betel leaves. Further purified, it is used in medicines. Huge forests of Khair are maintained and commercially exploited in Uttaranchal near Ramnagar and the Corbett Park.

Kheer: A pudding made with milk, sugar and rice. A well-known dessert.

Kinner: A mythical being with a human body and the head of a horse. Kinners played musical instruments and sang praise of the devatas along with the gandharvas.

Kopabhavana: A chamber where a beloved could retreat when angry. [*Kopa*: Anger.]

Kos: A measure of distance in ancient India.

Kovidar: Name of a tree.

Kraunch: A heron.

Krishnapaksha: The dark half of the lunar month, from full to a new moon.

Krittikas: Pleiades. A large, pretty, bright open star cluster, easy to see with the naked eye in the constellation Taurus [*Vrishabha*]. The cluster is over 400 light years away. With the naked eye we can see six stars. However, with a telescope, dozens are visible.

Krodha: Anger.

Kshama: Forgiveness.

Kubera: The god of wealth. Ravana's elder half-brother. He possessed the Pushpak Vimana in which Rama returned to Ayodhya after the war in Lanka. His abode is Kailas.

Kukubha: A kind of spirituous liquor.

Kunda: A tiny flower with six petals, pure white and used as an offering to Shiva. A variety of jasmine, also known as 'Makaranda'.

Kutaja: A small tree with white flowers.

Lodhra: A tree found throughout India. Its bark is used to tan leather. Its root is powdered to make a dye.

Lopamudra: A daughter of the king of Vidarbha and the wife of the sage Agastya. She is said to have been formed by the sage himself from the most beautiful parts of different animals and then secretly introduced into the king's palace where she grew up as a princess. She forced Agastya to acquire immense riches before she consented to marry him.

Lokanatha: Master of the universe.

Lokapala: A regent or a guardian of a part of the world.

Madhushala: A chamber where liquor is served.

Madhusudana: An epithet of Vishnu.

Madiralaya: A den of liquor.

Mahabaho: O brave man with long arms!

Mahabali: A warrior.

Mahakapi: A great vanara. Hanuman.

Mahatapasvi: A great ascetic.

Mahavira: A chivalrous person.

Mahua: Butter tree. A source of food and a popular intoxicant consumed by several tribes in central India. Sugar is extracted from its flowers. Its new leaves have a vivid red hue. Its oil is used in making soap and its wood for sports goods.

Malati: Clover-scented jasmine. Chandni.

Mallika: Jasmine.

Manda, madhyama, uchcha: The ascending scale of sound in music. The bass, the mid-range and the higher notes.

Mandarachala Mountain: the Mountain used as a churning stick during the Samudramanthan.

Mangala: The planet Mars. Auspicious, lucky, propitious. Fortunate. A good omen.

Maruta: Relating to or arising from the wind. The god of wind, the deity presiding over wind.

Maulashri: See 'Bakul'.

Milap: Union. Coming together as in Bharata Milap.

Mandapa: A pavilion.

Mridanga: A large-sized, oblong drum, beaten on two sides with fingers or palms and used in Carnatic music. It produces a sound of great resonance.

Mrigtrishna: Chasing a dream. Trying to find an oasis in a desert. An unrealistic desire.

Muhoorta: An auspicious moment for performing a task. Usually, determined astrologically.

Munishrestha: O superior among the sages!

Mayasura: A demon who could work magic, change form through 'maya' or illusion.

Nagakeshara: A tree with fragrant flowers. Indian rose chestnut. Ironwood. An elegant tree with a conical bushy crown. Its leaves emerge bright red, turn pink and then change to pale green and lastly dark green. Its flowers have large white petals and yellow stamens.

Nagapasha: Snake used as a rope to tie an enemy.

Nahusha: A king of the lunar race and father of Yayati. He was a powerful and wise king and occupied Indra's throne in his absence. Once there, he wanted to wed Indrani. The rishis cursed him to fall to the earth as a serpent to be resurrected by Yudhishthira long afterwards.

Nala-Damyanti: Nala was a celebrated king of the Nishadhas. He was noble-minded and virtuous. Damyanti chose him against opposition by devatas.

This angered Kali who too had vied for her hand. He decided to persecute Nala and entered his mind in such a way that the king lost everything to his younger brother while playing dice. Nala and Damyanti were banished from the kingdom. One day during his wanderings he deserted Damyanti, almost naked and went away. As a hunchback he secured a job with Rituparna, the king of Ayodhya, as a groom for the horses. He regained Damyanti with the king's help and lived happily ever after. He is the hero of the poem, *Naishadhacharita*.

Nandeeshwara: Literally, master/ god of Nandi, i.e. Shiva. Nandi, the bull, is Shiva's mount.

Naradhipa: A king.

Naraka: The netherworld. Hell.

Narayana: Vishnu.

Narayana measuring the sky in one step: Refer Vamana.

Nayika: The heroine of a narrative. The female character in a literary composition. Mistress. Wife.

Neel: Blue, dark blue. A sapphire.

Neem: Margosa. Indian lilac. Most parts of the tree have medicinal qualities. Its seeds yield yellow, bitter oil used to treat leprosy, skin diseases, ulcers, rheumatism and what not. It repels insects. Its wood is hard and durable.

Neewar: Rice growing wild or without cultivation.

Nidra: Sleep.

Nishachara: A denizen of the night. A demon.

Nishacharendra: The king of the demons.

Nishachari: A rakshasi.

Niti/ Aniti: Propriety and the reverse of it. A policy. A regulatory system for diplomacy and human conduct. Guidance. Management. Policy, prudence, wisdom. The science of morality, morals, ethics and moral philosophy. Political science.

Nitishastra: The rule book for proper conduct, for diplomacy and for running a kingdom.

Omkar: The sacred syllable 'OM' uttered at the beginning and end of a reading of the Vedas or prior to the commencement of a prayer or a sacred task. The word OM first appears in the Upanishads as a mystic monosyllable, and is regarded as the object of the most profound mediation. In the *Mandukya Upanishad*, it has been said that this syllable is all what has been, that which is, and is to be, that all is OM, only OM.

Padma: A lotus. A lotus like ornament.

Palash: Flame of the forest. Bright vermilion-red flowers appear in March-April. These are soaked in water to make brilliant colour for revelry during Holi, the Indian festival of colours. The trees when in bloom, present a spectacular sight. They grow all over India and Myanmar.

Papiha: Refer 'Chataka'.

Parnakutir: A cottage made with leaves.

Parantapa: One who can destroy his enemies.

Parikrama: Ritually going round a deity, a temple or a person.

Parmartha: The highest truth, spiritual knowledge, knowledge about Brahman or the Supreme Spirit.

Patala: The mythical underground world.

Pativrate: O chaste woman!

Pausha: The lunar month in winter, corresponding to December-January.

Pinaka: Shiva's bow later gifted to Sita's father, King Janaka of Mithila.

Pipal: Sacred fig. Boo tree. A deciduous large tree. Its trunk exudes milk. The leaves are large with long stalks. At the base, the leaves are heart shaped. It has several medicinal properties. Its juice is used to reduce toothache and strengthen weak gums. The leaves and young shoots are purgative. Its figs ripen around mid April and are a favourite with birds. Pipal is a holy tree, an object of worship all over India as the female of the banyan. A pipal leaf is an essential part of the Yagyopavit ceremony. Ladles made from the pipal wood are used to pour ghee into the havana kunda. Gautam Buddha is said to have achieved enlightenment under a pipal tree which came to be known as the 'Bodhi Tree' later.

Pitambar: A yellow covering used by hermits. A favourite of Krishna.

Poornima: The day of the full moon.

Prajapati: An epithet of the ten lords of creation first created by Brahma.

Pralaya: Apocalypse. The day when everything will cease to exist. Destruction, annihilation, dissolution.

Prana: The breath. The life force.

Prasad: A gift. Kindness. A part of food or flowers offered to a deity, distributed to the worshippers as the god's blessing.

Prithvinath: A king. Master of the earth.

Priyala: The name of a tree. A vine.

Priyangu: A creeper with fragrant root grown in western India, Singapore, Java and Malaysia. It bears sweet fruit.

Punarvasu: The stars, Castor and Pollux of the constellation, Gemini. Castor is a multiple star, blue and white in colour. Pollux is among the twenty brightest stars in the sky. It is an orange coloured star, thirty-two light years away. Both the stars are visible to the naked eye. The stars have been seen together for millions of years and are often compared by the poets to Rama and Lakshmana.

Punnag: A fragrant flower. Silky ash tree. It has serrated leaves and dense panicles of small, white flowers blooming in April.

Punya: The reward for good deeds, of meditation, devotion to god. Accumulated fruit of good deeds. Sacred. Pure.

Pushya Nakshatra: Cancer.

Purushottama: The best among men. An epithet used for Rama.

Pushparatha: A chariot bedecked with flowers.

Rajahansa: Greater flamingo.

Rajnichara: One who walks and works at night. Someone engaged in stealthy activities. A demon. An asura.

Rajyabhisheka: Coronation.

Rohini: The star, Aldebaran, part of the constellation Taurus. It is a red star, sixty-five light years away.

Rudra shooting Tripurasura: Shiva is said to have destroyed with one shot three cities of gold, silver and iron built in the sky for the demon Maya. Their ruler is referred to as Tripurasura, the demon of the three cities.

Sagara: A king of the Surya dynasty and therefore, an ancestor of Rama. Sixty thousand sons were born to him. These sons, while guarding an Ashwamedha horse, strayed into the ashrama of the rishi Kapila. The rishi reduced them to ashes with the fire of his anger. Later, Bhagiratha, a grandson of Sagara, performed penance and brought Ganga down to earth, to deliver his ancestors by washing away their ashes. Following Bhagiratha, the Hindus continue to scatter the ashes of their dead in Ganga to date. They believe that this immersion ensures deliverance from the results of any untoward deeds done in this world. Refer chapter 10, Balakandam.

Sahasraksha: Indra. See '*Indra's thousand eyes*'.

Sama and dana: Give and take.

Sama, Dana, Danda and Bheda: The four principles on which rajaneeti, that is, the policy of a State is based. *Sama*: Conciliation, pacification, negotiation. Gentle, mild treatment of subjects. *Dana*: To restore, reconcile, give up, yield, surrender, entice, extend a privilege, grant, bestow. To placate. *Danda*: Use of force. Punishment, retribution. To administer justice. The sceptre of a king, a symbol of his authority. *Bheda*: Splitting. Opening a chasm. To betray. Sowing dissension in the enemy camp in order to win over a faction.

Samidha: Sacrificial sticks for the sacred fire. Fire. Fuel.

Samudramanthan: Refer 11, Balakandam. A fascinating tale of Hindu mythology. During one of the periodic deluges after Creation, Amrita, the nectar of immortality was lost. The devatas and the asuras got together to churn the Ksheerasagara, the ocean of milk to retrieve Amrita. They used the Mount Mandarachala as a churning rod. The mountain began to sink because of its weight. Vishnu came to everyone's rescue and supported the mountain by taking birth as Kurma, a tortoise, in order to rest the mountain on his back as a pivot. Vasuki the serpent served as the churning rope. As the churning progressed, not only Amrita but several other precious objects emerged from the ocean. These included Lakshmi, the goddess of wealth and beauty; Dhanvantari, the physician; Sura, the wine goddess; Chandra (moon); a few apsaras; Uchchaisravas, a magnificent white horse; Parijata, a tree that could grant any wish; Kaustubha, a rare jewel; Surabhi, a plentiful cow; Airavata, a mighty elephant; Shankha, the conch of victory; a mighty bow called Dhanusha; and Visha, the poison vomited by Vasuki. There was quite a row for the possession of the pitcher of Amrita. Ultimately, the asuras were cheated of this prize.

Sanatana Dharma: (sanatana = ancient; dharma = code of conduct; duty towards self, society and mankind) Ancient principles of the Hindu religion, everlasting, durable, yet flexible, with belief in what is written in the Vedas, Upanishads, and later in the Puranas. The central core of the Sanatana Dharma is a belief in god as the Supreme Being. It is a philosophy with a place for every school of thought.

Sandhya: The evening prayers. Morning or evening twilight. Union.

Sankalpa: Determination.

Saptaparni: A common tree that that bears seven leaves in a cluster symmetrically engaged.

Saptarishi: The Ursa Major. The seven rishis who form the prominent stars of the constellation: Marichi, Atri, Angiras, Pulastya, Pulaha, Kratu and Vasishtha.

Sarika: A small talkative bird known as '*mynah*' or '*bulbul.*' The common babbler.

Sarkanda: A form of tall grass.

Sattva: The essence. Life. Spirit. Breath. Vitality. An embryo. Brahman, the supreme consciousness that permeates the entire universe.

Satyayuga: The first of the divisions of time according to the Hindu belief: The period in which truth alone prevailed. The four yugas are of the duration of 1,728,000, 1,296,000, 864,000 and 432,000 years respectively and are named Satya, Treta, Dwapara and Kali Yugas, respectively. It is believed that the descending length of the yugas represents a corresponding physical and moral deterioration of the people.

Satyavana/Savitri: Satyavana or Satyavata was the husband of Savitri. He was the king of Salva. Savitri's story is that of a chaste woman who could persuade even Yama to return her dead husband to life. She was the daughter of the king Avapati. She was so lovely that all the suitors who came to ask for her hand were put off by her superior lustre. Her father then asked her to go and find a suitable match for herself. She chose Satyavana son of Dyumatsena, king of Salva, who having been driven out of his kingdom was leading the life of a hermit. At that moment, Narada informed her that though Satyavana was in every aspect a suitable choice, he was destined to die within a year and in case Savitri married him, she would be a widow all her life. Savitri declared that her choice could not be altered. After the marriage, Savitri took off her jewels and started living a hermit's life. She was a devout wife and an obedient daughter-in-law to her husband's parents. Three days prior to the predicted time of Satyavana's death, Savitri started fasting to propitiate her gods. On the fourth day, when her husband was about to go to the woods to collect fuel for his yagya, Savitri insisted on accompanying him. Having collected the sticks, Satyavana fell asleep in her lap. Just then Yama descended and walked away with the prince's soul. Savitri chased Yamaraja and prayed him not to do so. As a chaste wife she pleaded her case in touching words. Yamaraja was moved. He granted her many boons except the life of her husband. However, Savitri did not give up. She did not care for any boons except her husband's life. Ultimately, moved by her eloquent appeal and her devotion to her husband, the god relented and restored her husband's spirit. Savitri returned delighted and found her husband as if just awakened from sleep. Savitri is regarded as a model of chastity and young brides are ritually blessed to be like Savitri and fearlessly protect their husbands.

Saumya: Charming, handsome and pleasant as the moon [Soma]. Gentle, soft, mild, placid. A gentleman.

Senapati: Head of the armed forces. Commander-in-chief.

Setu: A bridge.

Shachi: Wife of Indra.

Shakti, rishthi, pasha: Different weapons. Different types of swords and a snare.

Shala tree: A tall and stately timber tree. *Shorea Robusta*. It is one of the trees associated with the birth of the Buddha.

Shami: Jhand tree. Medium sized. Deciduous. A thorny desert tree. It has a deeply fissured bark, and feathery, grey-green foliage. It provides nutritious fodder. Its pods are cooked and eaten in Rajasthan. Its yellow or creamy flowers are a favourite of the bees. They bloom tiny, yellow and densely clustered on spikes.

Sharangadhanva: A bow carried by Vishnu.

Shataghni: A stone missile studded with iron spikes.

Shirish: Pink, white or greenish feathery flower of the fry-wood tree. It has an intoxicating scent. It looks like a jhoomar, a pendant for the forehead.

Shobhane: O charming woman! *Shobha*: Charm. Beauty. Splendour. Glory.

Shoka: Sorrow.

Shoola: A weapon that can pierce. A thorn. A pointed, sharp object. Pain.

Shrawan: A lunar month corresponding to July-August.

Shree: Wealth, riches, affluence, prosperity, plenty. Lakshmi, the goddess of wealth. Auspicious. Most commonly used honorific for addressing/ naming a person.

Shreeman: One who possesses *Shree*.

Shringara: Make up. Dressing up for a beloved. The essence of romance, of amour. The erotic sentiment.

Shringara bhava: The erotic sentiment in art, literature, drama.

Shrivatsa: An epithet of Vishnu. The mark of a curl of hair on Vishnu's chest.

Shubhadarshane: O good looking woman!

Shukra: Shukracharya, the guru to the asuras who, by means of his magic, restored to life the demons killed in the battle. The planet Venus. Bright, radiant, shining.

Siddhi: An accomplishment. Attainments. Successes. Superhuman powers or faculties.

Siddha: Semi-divine beings possessing eight super-human faculties, known as siddhis. Siddhas are said to be holy and beings of great character.

Sindoor: A powder for applying tilaka in the central parting of hair as the sign of a married woman. It is considered auspicious to apply sindoor in this fashion. Red lead.

Sindhuvar: A horse of a good breed, brought from Sind or Persia.

Somarasa: Wine. Liquor.

Stuti: Eulogy.

Sumukhi: One who has a charming face.

Sutanu: Having a beautiful body. Delicate. Slender.

Swaha: An oblation or offering made to gods. Wife of Agni.

Swayambhu: Brahman. The Supreme Being.

Tada tree: An evergreen tree from the Eastern Ghats.

Takkol: A smallish, deciduous tree. Pale grey bark.

Tala: Palmyra palm. Toddy palm. Fan leaved palm, evergreen. Large fruit up to 20 cm. in diameter. Its sap is fermented to make country liquor known as toddy. Native to coastal areas in India.

Tamala: A tree with a dark bark.

Tarakasura: The demon killed by Kartikeya. Brahma had blessed him that he would not be killed by anyone except a child seven days old. When he started harassing the Devatas, the latter asked Brahma for redress. They were told that only a child of Shiva could kill this demon. Later Kartikeya accomplished this deed.

Teertha: A place of pilgrimage.

Tejaswi: Glorious. Resplendent.

Tejasvini: A glorious woman.

Tendu: A tree grown and commercially exploited in central India. Its leaves are used to roll biris, the poor man's cigarette.

Tilaka: An auspicious coloured mark on the forehead.

Tinish: The name of a tree.

Tribhuvana: The three worlds. The universe.

Trinetra: Shiva who has three eyes.

Tripathagamini: The Ganga that traverses the three paths, that is, the sky, the earth and the patala.

Trishanku: A king of Ayodhya, father of Harishchandra. He was a wise, pious and a just king. However, he loved his person excessively. He was stopped mid-air by Vishwamitra while he was ascending heavenwards. The monarch remained suspended with his head downwards as a constellation in the southern hemisphere.

Trivikrama: Vishnu in the Vamana Avatar.

Utpal: A blue lotus.

Vairagya: Renunciation. Absence of worldly desire or passions. Indifference to the world. Asceticism.

Vajra: A thunderbolt. A weapon made of iron with spikes.

Vamana avatar: Literally, short in stature. Name of Vishnu in his fifth incarnation, when he was born as a dwarf to humble the asura king Bali. The latter was the grandson of Prahlad, Vishnu's devotee. The devatas, fed up with his misdeeds, prayed to Vishnu to get rid of him. Vishnu took birth as a dwarf, son of Kashyapa and Aditi. Dressed as a mendicant, he approached Bali for charity. The king asked him to take whatever he could cover in three steps. Vamana assumed a mighty form and covered the entire earth and the heavens in two steps. With permission, he placed the third step on Bali's head and sent him and his hordes to the Patalaloka where the latter still rules as an immortal. It is said that pleased with Bali's generosity, Vishnu guards his palace door forever.

Vansha: The dynasty.

Vanaprastha: A brahmin in the third stage of his religious life. A hermit.

Vanarakesari: The lion among the vanaras. Hanuman.

Varaha avatar: The third incarnation of Vishnu as boar who saved Prithvi from submerging into waters when pulled down by the demon Hiranyaksha. Varaha was forty miles wide and 4,000 miles tall. He had the bulk of a mountain. He is described as dusky. His roar is ear-shattering. He has sharp white tusks. His fiery eyes flash like lightning. He is glorious like the sun.

Vararohe: O woman with attractive buttocks.

Varadan: A blessing; a boon.

Vasava: Indra.

Vasudha: the earth.

Vasuki: The king of snakes used as a rope during Samudramanthan.

Vasus: The soul. The Supreme Being. The constellation, Punarvasu, that is, alpha, beta Gemini.

Vayunandana: son of Vayu: Hanuman.

Veena: A stringed musical instrument.

Videhanandini: Sita, the princess of Videha.

Vilambit, madhya and drut: The progression in a musical performance going from defining the melody at leisure to the middle to the crescendo.

Vilasini: A passionate woman.

Vimana: A vehicle. A chariot. A car. A balloon. A palace.

Virata roopa: Vishwa roopa Brahma; The Universe.

Vishakha: The constellation Libra.

Vishala lochane: O woman with large eyes!

Vishnu's attack on Bali: Refer 265 ante.

Vishwanath: Master of the universe.

Vritrasura: A demon of darkness killed by Indra.

Yagya kunda: The bowl in which yagya is performed by burning wood, ghee and other fragrant substances.

Yagyashala: The place where yagya is performed.

Yagyopavit: Sacred thread worn by brahmins, kshatriyas and the vaishyas, and even by other castes over the left shoulder and under the right arm. It signifies a vow to lead a religious and virtuous life.

Yajamana: The patron for whom a ritual is performed. A person who performs a sacrifice and pays for its expenses.

Yaksha: A class of demi-gods who are described as attendants of Kubera, the god of wealth.

Yakshini: A female demi-goddess, one of the attendants of Kubera, the god of wealth.

Yantras: Chariots. Wagons. Machines.

Yavana: Any foreigner or a barbarian as compared to an Aryan.

Yayati: A king of the solar dynasty who married Devayani, daughter of Shukra, the preceptor of the asuras. He later fell in love with Sharmistha, daughter of the asura king who had accompanied Devayani as a maid. An angry Shukracharya cursed him with impotence and old age. Later Shukra relented and allowed Yayati to exchange his infirmity with his son Puru. The rejuvenated king enjoyed life for 1000 years and yet was unsatisfied. Realizing his folly, he restored to Puru his youth and repaired to the woods to live a sanyasi's life.

Yogeshwara: The prime among the yogis. A self-realized person.

Yojana: A measure of distance equal to approximately eight miles.

Yupa: A sacrificial post to which the victim was fastened at the time immolation.